Fee

Feedback Control Theory
for Engineers

Second Edition

P. Atkinson

B.Sc. (Eng.), A.C.G.I., C.Eng., M.I.E.E, M.I.E.R.E.
Senior Lecturer in Applied Physical Sciences,
University of Reading

Heineman Educational Books
London

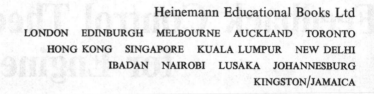

Heinemann Educational Books Ltd

LONDON   EDINBURGH   MELBOURNE   AUCKLAND   TORONTO
HONG KONG   SINGAPORE   KUALA LUMPUR   NEW DELHI
IBADAN   NAIROBI   LUSAKA   JOHANNESBURG
KINGSTON/JAMAICA

ISBN 0 435 71813 4
© P. Atkinson, 1968, 1972
First published 1968
Second edition 1972
Reprinted 1974, 1977

Published by
Heinemann Educational Books Ltd
48 Charles Street, London W1X 8AH

Printed and bound in Great Britain by
William Clowes & Sons, Limited
London, Beccles and Colchester

Preface to the Second Edition

There has been no revision of the majority of the text, but a number of printing errors and mistakes have been corrected. However an additional chapter on analog computation and simulation, which includes sections on digital simulation of control systems and hybrid computers, has been added. It is felt that although this is not strictly 'feedback control theory' many courses on this topic do embody analog computing and this extra chapter will thus add to the attraction of the book as a teaching text. Moreover the ideas of digital simulation are becoming progressively more important as the art of computer-aided design progresses.

1972   P.A.

Preface to the First Edition

Textbooks in the field of control engineering have, in the main, been written for electrical engineers and the standard of the mathematics used has been relatively high. The purpose of this work is to provide a course of study in elementary control theory which is *self-contained* and suitable for students of all branches of engineering and of applied physics. The book assumes that the student has a knowledge of mathematics of A-level or O-2 level standard only. All other necessary pure and applied mathematics is covered for reference purposes in chapters 2–6. As a students' textbook it contains many fully worked numerical examples and sets of examples are provided at the end of all chapters except the first. The answers to these examples are given at the end of the book.

The book covers the majority of the control theory likely to be encountered on H.N.C., H.N.D. and degree courses in electrical, mechanical, chemical and production engineering and in applied physics. It will also provide a primer in specialist courses in instrumentation and control engineering at undergraduate and postgraduate level. Furthermore, it covers much of the control theory encountered in the graduateship examinations of the professional institutions, for example I.E.E. Part III (*Advanced Electrical Engineering* and *Instrumentation and Control*), I.E.R.E. Part 5 (*Control Engineering*) and the new C.E.I. Part 2 (*Mechanics of Machines* and *Systems and Control Engineering*).

Whilst this book is meant mainly as a teaching textbook, the problems of design have not been neglected and practising engineers should find aspects of the last five chapters of use. Design in the frequency domain, with translation of specifications to the time domain using second-order correlations, has been given consideration and many examples, worked in complete detail, are included in the text.

vi

The background to the subject and the commonly encountered terms are introduced in the first chapter. Chapters 2–4 provide the necessary background in signal theory and pure mathematics, the use of the operator $j\omega$ and the operator D being given detailed treatment. Chapter 5 gives a survey of elementary definitions, laws and SI units in mechanics and electrodynamics. The book uses SI units exclusively throughout. Chapter 6 is concerned with the formulation, solution and interpretation of the differential equations governing the dynamics of some elementary mechanical and electrical arrangements. Chapter 7 contains a brief but general survey of physical components encountered in control systems. Whilst no single chapter of any book could ever cover components adequately, this chapter should help the student to obtain a practical feel for the subject.

Chapter 8 treats the problem of the torque-proportional-to-error servomechanism in detail, considering its specification in terms of its step and ramp responses. Methods of improving the performance of this system are discussed and its frequency response is derived. The correlations between frequency response and transient response are presented.

Chapter 9 deals with the definition, determination and physical interpretation of transfer functions of components and single loop and multiloop systems. The ideas of instability are introduced and the Routh-Hurwitz stability criterion is defined and used.

Chapter 10 introduces the determination and use of open-loop frequency response data. Representation of such data on the polar diagram is described and a simple version of the Nyquist stability criterion is presented. The concepts of absolute and relative stability are discussed together with the ideas of phase margin, gain margin and M-circles. Brown's construction is described and several examples are worked in the text. Chapter 11 is exclusively concerned with the use of frequency response methods using the Nyquist diagram in the design of series compensated systems. Detailed design methods are given and these are illustrated with worked examples. Chapter 12 introduces the use of inverse Nyquist diagrams for the design of parallel compensated systems and provides methods of designing systems with auxiliary velocity (rate) feedback, transient velocity feedback and acceleration feedback.

Chapter 13 contains a description of the method of construction of the Bode diagram together with its application in conjunction with Nichols charts for design of series compensated systems. A practical approximate version of Bode's theorem is quoted together with a description of its use in the stability analysis of systems. The use of the diagram for the determination of transfer functions from experimental data is also described. Each new concept is adequately supported by worked examples.

It is emphasized that this is not meant to be 'just another book on servomechanisms'. The general theory of linear continuous feedback control systems is treated in chapters 9–13, frequently using the servomechanism as a typical example of a feedback control system. The theory is however applied very specifically in chapter 14 to process control systems, the study of which is made more difficult by its own folk-lore and jargon. The accepted definitions of terms associated with this sphere of the subject are given and the dynamics of some physical processes are analysed. Some typical hardware, particularly the commonly used pneumatic devices, is described and its performances are analysed. The problem of transport delay or distance/velocity lag is introduced and the stability of systems containing such lags is discussed. The dynamics of controllers receives particular attention and the problem of setting up a three term controller to match the dynamics of a plant is considered in detail. Again the text is sprinkled with worked numerical examples. Although the Laplace transform is not used in the main text it is included as an Appendix as an aid to readers who wish to study some of the related literature in which the method has been used exclusively.

This book embodies my experience over some ten years of teaching this difficult subject. I make no pretence that it contains anything very new or anything advanced but I know from personal experience that reasonably intelligent students who receive an initial training based on material presented in this way have little difficulty in applying the methods to practical control problems or to passing quite difficult examinations in the subject. Furthermore the book should provide a good background for engineers specializing in this field and going on to study more advanced topics such as the Laplace transform, the root locus method, phase-plane and phase-space and describing function methods, random signal analysis, sampled-data systems, self-adaptive systems, etc.

P.A.

Acknowledgements

I wish to thank Mr. F. W. Kellaway, Principal of the College of Technology, Letchworth for originally suggesting that I write this book. I also wish to thank Professor P. B. Fellgett, Professor of Cybernetics and Instrument Physics at the University of Reading, and Dr. G. R. Whitfield, Lecturer in Applied Physical Sciences at the University of Reading for reading the manuscript and for making valuable suggestions.

My thanks are also due to Mr. R. C. Moore, Research Assistant in the Department of Applied Physical Sciences, University of Reading for detailed checking of the manuscript and for assistance in the preparation of the worked examples.

I am grateful to Mr. L. Tottman, Senior Lecturer in Mathematics at the College of Engineering Technology, Rugby for providing expert advice on presentation of the mathematics in chapters 3 and 4 and also for reading the proofs.

I am especially grateful to Mr. R. H. O. Stannett, Senior Technician in the Department of Applied Physical Sciences of the University of Reading, for spending a great deal of his spare time for eighteen months converting my rough sketches into such excellent diagrams. His efforts to provide suitable illustrations of the components described in chapter 7 are particularly appreciated.

Finally I render my gratitude to my wife, without whose great patience and diligence in typing the manuscript I could never have completed the work.

Contents

Chapter One

Introduction to Control Engineering

1.1 Introduction

Whenever energy is to be used purposefully, some form of control is necessary. In recent times there has been a considerable advance made in the art of automatic control. The art is, however, quite old, stemming back to about 1790 when James Watt invented the centrifugal governor[1,2] to control the speed of his steam engines. He found that whilst in many applications an engine speed independent of load torque was necessary, in practice when a load was applied the speed fell and when the load was removed the speed increased.

A simple centrifugal governor is shown in Fig. 1.1. In this system, variations in engine speed are detected and used to control the pressure of the steam entering the engine.

Under steady conditions the moment of the weight of the metal spheres balances that due to the centrifugal force and the steam valve opening is just sufficient to maintain the engine speed at the required level. When an extra load torque is applied to the engine, its speed will tend to fall, the centrifugal force will decrease and the metal spheres will tend to fall slightly. Their height controls the opening of the steam valve which now opens further to allow a greater steam pressure on the engine. The speed thus tends to rise, counteracting the original tendency for the speed to fall. If the extra load is removed, the reverse process takes place, the metal spheres tend to rise slightly, so tending to close the steam valve and counteracting any tendency for the speed to rise.

Typical responses of this system to load increase with and without the governor are shown in Fig. 1.2.

It is seen that without the governor the speed would fall considerably on load. However, in a correctly designed system with a governor the fall in speed would be very much less. An undesirable feature which

1

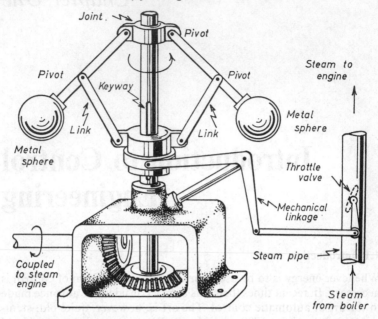

Fig. 1.1 *Simple centrifugal governor.*

accompanies a system which has been designed to be very sensitive to speed changes, is the tendency to 'hunt' or oscillate about the final speed. The real problem in the synthesis of all systems of this type is to prevent excessive oscillation but at the same time produce good

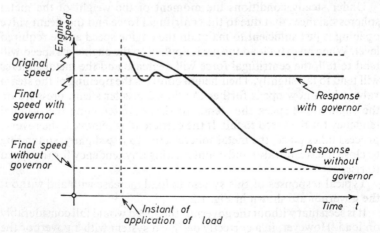

Fig. 1.2 *Response of steam engine to suddenly applied load torque.*

'regulation'. Regulation is defined as the percentage change in controlled quantity on load relative to the value of the controlled quantity under condition of zero load. Regulators form an important class of control system, their object generally being to keep some physical quantity constant (e.g. speed, voltage, liquid level, humidity, etc.) regardless of load variation. A good regulator has only very small regulation.

The 1914–1918 war caused military engineers to realize that to win wars it is necessary to position heavy masses (e.g. ships and guns) precisely and quickly. Classic work was performed by N. Minorsky in the U.S.A. in the early 1920's on the automatic steering of ships and the automatic positioning of guns on board ships.

In 1934 the word 'servomechanism' (derived from the Latin *servus*, meaning slave) was used in the literature for the first time by H. L. Hazen. He defined a servomechanism as 'a power amplifying device in which the amplifier element driving the output is actuated by the difference between the input to the servo and its output'. This definition can be applied to a wide variety of 'feedback control systems'. More recently it has been suggested that the term 'servomechanism' or 'servo' be restricted to a feedback control system in which the controlled variable is mechanical position.

The automatic control of various large-scale industrial processes, as encountered in the manufacture and treatment of chemicals, food and metals, has emerged during the last thirty years as an extremely important part of the general field of control engineering. In the initial stages of development it was scarcely realized that the theory of process control was intimately related to the theory of servomechanisms and regulators. Even nowadays complete academic design of process control systems is virtually impossible owing to our poor understanding of the dynamics of processes. In much of the theory introduced in this book, servomechanisms and regulators are used as examples to illustrate the methods of analysis. These methods are, however, often applicable to process control systems, which are themselves introduced separately in chapter 14.

1.2 Definitions

In general there are two types of control systems, open loop and closed loop.

1.2.1 Open-loop System

In an open-loop system an input signal or command, is applied, amplified in a 'controller' and a power output is obtained from an 'output element'.

3

The location of the output element is often remote from the input station. The input may be applied manually, as by turning a dial. The expected output is normally predetermined by calibration, and the input control may be accompanied by some sort of calibration chart. The actual output obtained depends on the validity of the calibration, and if components of the system are affected by time, temperature, humidity, lubrication, etc., the actual output may vary from the expected output. Such systems are also acutely affected by load variation.

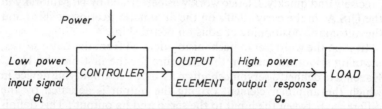

Fig. 1.3 *Open-loop system.*

A simple example of an open-loop control system is a steam engine *without* a governor. Such an arrangement is shown diagrammatically in Fig. 1.4.

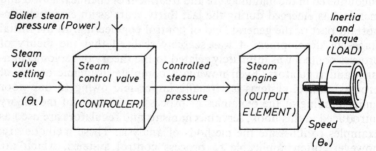

Fig. 1.4 *Schematic of steam engine without a governor.*

The speed is primarily affected by changes in load torque but will also be altered by changes in boiler steam pressure, the state of lubrication and wear in moving parts.

1.2.2 Closed-loop System

In a simple closed-loop system, the controller is no longer actuated by the input but by the 'error'. The error is defined as the difference between the system input and its output. Such a system contains the same basic elements as the open-loop system, plus two extra features —an 'error detector' and a feedback loop.

4

The error detector is a device which produces a signal proportional to the difference between input and output.

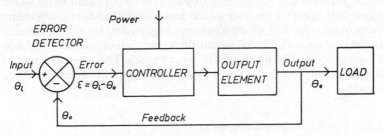

Fig. 1.5 *Simple closed-loop system.*

The open-loop system of Fig. 1.4 may be made 'manual closed loop' by means of an output speed indicator and a human operator. The human operator must watch the engine speed continuously and make suitable adjustments to the steam valve opening when variations occur, in an attempt to keep the speed constant. The reasons why in many instances automatic control systems are preferred to human operators are given in §1.6.

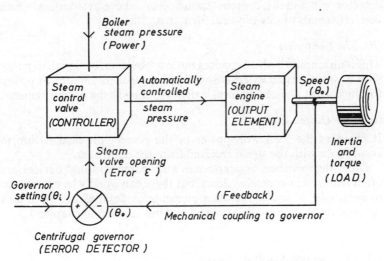

Fig. 1.6 *Schematic of steam engine with a governor.*

The steam-engine may be incorporated as part of a closed-loop speed control system as illustrated in Fig. 1.6.

It has already been explained in §1.1 how the governed steam engine regulates against speed changes due to alterations in load torque. Apart from this obvious advantage over the open-loop system, there is another more subtle advantage. The system possesses the ability to correct against its own defects. For instance, supposing the boiler steam pressure should decrease slightly. This would tend to make the speed fall; the error detector would sense this fall and cause the steam valve to open further, giving a corresponding increase in the controlled steam pressure. The speed would then tend to increase thus counteracting the original tendency for the speed to fall. The speed of response to changes in load is also very much faster than that of the open-loop system.

1.2.3 Control System Components

It is evident from the block schematic of the closed-loop system (Fig. 1.5) that three basic components are required:

(*i*) The Error Detector

This is a device which receives the low-power input signal and the output signal which may be of different physical natures, converts them to a common physical quantity for the purposes of subtraction, performs the subtraction, and gives out a low-power error signal of the correct physical nature to actuate the controller. The error detector will usually contain 'transducers'; these are devices which convert signals of one physical form to another.

(*ii*) The Controller

This is an amplifier which receives the low-power error signal, together with power from an external source. A controlled amount of power (of the correct physical nature) is then supplied to the output element.

(*iii*) The Output Element

It provides the load with power of the correct physical nature in accordance with the signal received from the controller.

Other devices such as gear-boxes and 'compensating' devices are often featured in control systems, but these can usually be considered to form part of one of the other elements. A detailed description of some of the devices used in control systems is given in chapter 7.

1.3 The Position-Control System

The regulator, whose object is to maintain the value of some physical quantity at a fixed level in spite of disturbances, is an important example of a closed-loop system. Equally important and certainly more challenging as an exercise in engineering design is the servomechanism whose object is to *follow* input commands. An example of such a device is the position-control servomechanism which must reproduce at some remote point the motion applied to a handwheel located at a local command station. The output motion might be used to drive a heavy object such as a missile launcher into a required position; power amplification of the command and accurate reproduction are thus necessary.

The signals can be transmitted by direct mechanical linkage or by hydraulic, pneumatic, or electric conduit. Apart from mechanical linkage the most rapid transmission may be achieved with electrical connection and this is often but not always used. Where it is used, the mechanical input and output signals are first converted into proportional electrical signals and then transmitted through wires to a subtracting device which produces a signal proportional to the error. A typical arrangement is shown in Fig. 1.7.

The low-power error signal is used to drive an amplifier which also receives power from an external source and delivers controlled power to the motor.

The combination of transducers and subtracting element form the *error detector*, the amplifier is the *controller* and the motor together with its gear box form the *output element*.

The amplifier may be purely electrical if the motor is electrical but must be either electro-hydraulic or electro-pneumatic if the motor is either hydraulic or pneumatic.

It is emphasized that the object of the system is to make the rotatable mass *copy* as nearly as possible the motion of the handwheel. Let us consider what will happen if the position of the handwheel is turned very rapidly through an angle θ_i, the mass being initially at rest.

Initially the mass has no velocity and the output position θ_o is zero, thus a signal $k\theta_i$ instantaneously appears at the terminals of the amplifier; power from the source is allowed to reach the motor which then begins to drive the mass so as to reduce the error. As θ_o approaches θ_i the error gets smaller and thus less power is allowed to reach the motor. Systems are usually designed so that the mass just overshoots the required position; since θ_o is then greater than θ_i, the error becomes negative and the motor forces the mass to stop and reverse direction. Some undershoots and further overshoots will then probably take place before the mass finally settles at the required position with θ_o equal to θ_i. Only when exact coincidence occurs does the amplifier receive zero signal and thus the motor is forced to move either one way or the other until all motion dies away. The motor can therefore only come to rest when the signal entering the amplifier is zero, i.e. when the output position is exactly equal to the command θ_i.

It becomes evident from the above discussion that unless very great care is taken in the design, it is quite possible that the oscillations about the desired position will build up instead of dying away quickly. A system in which oscillations build up is said to be *unstable* and much of the design work in control engineering is associated with producing

7

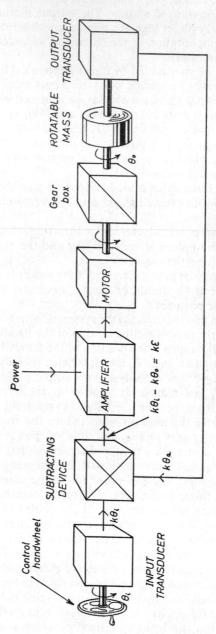

Fig. 1.7 *Position-control servomechanism.*

a stable system. Adequate stability is, of course, only one of several requirements. Another requirement is faithful reproduction of a variety of input signals, and it has already been seen that the system of Fig. 1.7 is unlikely to reproduce a sudden change in input position with any degree of fidelity. Another type of input command might consist of handwheel motion of constant angular velocity. The system would then respond with an oscillatory transient and the mass would finally settle down with a velocity equal to the command but with a position lagging the command by a small angle. The slight difference between input and output positions would represent a positive constant error which would be of such magnitude as to produce an output torque from the motor sufficient to drive the mass at the required velocity against frictional torques. The error could not be zero otherwise the motor would stop and the error would then build up.

It is thus apparent that whilst the output θ_o will automatically align itself with the command θ_i under *static conditions*, under dynamic conditions the output motion only approximates to that of the command. The closeness of the approximation can however usually be made as good as is necessary to overcome most physical problems; for example, in certain types of automatically controlled profile milling machines a tracking accuracy to 0·0001 inch has been achieved.

Another object of the position control system is that it must be capable of holding the output position equal to the command in the presence of severe load disturbances. For example, a launcher must remain pointing in the desired direction regardless of random gusts of wind. The position control system of Fig. 1.7, if correctly designed, would be able to achieve quite good regulation against load disturbances of this kind but a steady load disturbance would inevitably produce a small misalignment between output and command. In systems where such a misalignment would be intolerable, a more sophisticated type of controller must be used, having properties other than that of simple amplification. Design of a stable system is then correspondingly more difficult.

It should be appreciated that in a fully automatic system the 'handwheel' of Fig. 1.7 can be made to produce the necessary command signals without human aid. Indeed in many instances the handwheel may not even exist; the commands may be purely electrical in nature, having been derived directly from sensing elements. For example, in flight-control systems the control surfaces are normally actuated by servomechanisms which have command signals as directed by the pilot via the 'joy-stick'. However, in aeroplanes containing autopilots, the pilot may switch to 'automatic', whereupon the command signals are generated directly from sensing gyroscopes which automatically detect deviations from the required path. Similarly some automatically-controlled machine tools have servomechanisms which react directly to electrical signals received from a digital computer. The computer usually acts partly as a memory which is able to reproduce a variety of complicated commands in a certain sequence and partly as arithmetic device to perform subtraction and produce highly accurate error signals on reception of digitized measurements of the output positions of the various servomechanisms under its control.

The position control servomechanism has many applications amongst which are:

Machine-tool position-control systems
Gun directors and missile launchers
Tracking radar systems
Positioners for radio and optical telescopes
Constant-tension control of sheet rolls in paper mills
Control of sheet metal thickness in hot-rolling mills
Missile guidance systems
Automatic pilots for aircraft
Automatic ship steering
Roll stabilization of ships
Recording instruments and servo-multipliers
Inertial guidance systems
Automatic handling of materials
Assisted braking and steering devices in motor vehicles

1.4 Process-Control Systems

It should be understood that any division of control engineering into 'regulators', 'servomechanisms' and 'process-control systems' is very artificial and is really due to historic rather than logical reasons. A process-control system is often fundamentally a regulator. However, a complicated process-control system may possibly contain several devices which could be defined as servomechanisms when considered individually. However, the following are examples of control problems usually classified as process control:

Control of chemical concentration in liquids
Control of liquid level
Control of rate of flow of fluids
Electrolytic plating control
Distillation process control
Gas-blending control
Reaction controls in nuclear reactors
Boiler plant control
Control of furnace temperature
Heat exchange process control

The philosophy of the design of process-control systems is rather different from that of the design of servomechanisms. However, many of the analytical problems involved are similar and most of the techniques of analysis and synthesis and methods of test are common to all branches of control engineering. In the past the controllers and motoring elements used in process control have been mainly pneumatic; electro-pneumatic devices have become rather more popular recently and there is considerable evidence that this trend will continue and that in the future large plants will be controlled by means of electronic digital computers.

An example of a typical process control system will now be considered. A schematic diagram of the arrangement is shown in Fig. 1.8.

The object of the system is to maintain the rate of flow of fluid at a fixed value in accordance with a fixed command termed the 'set value', regardless of disturbances in supply pressure and back pressure. The actual rate of flow is detected by means of an orifice plate; the pressure difference across the plate is then a function of the rate of flow. A signal (termed the 'measured value') which is proportional to the pressure difference and hence to a function of the rate of flow of fluid is then transmitted by means of a 'differential pressure transmitter' to the recorder-controller. The method of transmission can be mechanical, electrical or pneumatic. The measured value is usually recorded continuously on a chart recorder which forms an integral part of the recorder-controller unit. The measured value is also compared with the set value in a 'comparing element' which generates the 'deviation' θ representing the difference between the measured value and the set value. The nature of the comparing element depends largely upon the method of transmission of the measured value and the nature of the controller; in a pneumatic system a simple differential mechanical linkage is often used to produce a mechanical signal proportional to the deviation. The controller which is either pneumatic or electro-pneumatic responds to the deviation by producing a pneumatic pressure which is a function of the deviation. This pressure is used to control a pneumatic motor which moves so as to actuate a control valve placed in the fluid supply pipe. The control valve will be moved automatically in such a way as to keep the deviation at a minimum level. The rate of flow of fluid is thus held reasonably constant in accordance with the set value.

It is usually possible to vary the set value in such a system by manual adjustment of a control knob or by means of an auxiliary automatic control system.

Whilst the nomenclature associated with process control (as recommended in B.S. 1523 Section 2: 1960) is somewhat different from that popularly used for the description of servomechanisms, both types of system are essentially closed loop; it is therefore of interest to

11

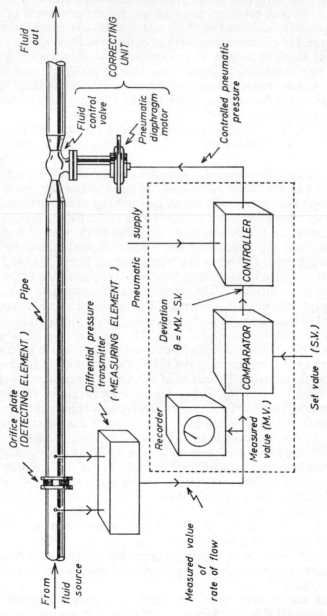

Fig. 1.8 *Process-control system for controlling rate of flow of fluid.*

compare the process-control system of Fig. 1.8 with the general block diagram for a simple closed-loop system shown in Fig. 1.5.

Process-Control Systems	*Simple Closed-loop Control System*
Measured value	Output θ_o
Set value	Input θ_i
Deviation	Minus error ($-\epsilon = \theta_o - \theta_i$)
Orifice plate ⎫	
Differential pressure transmitter ⎬	Error detector
Comparator ⎭	
Controller	Controller
Pneumatic motor ⎫	Output element
Control valve ⎭	
Process	Load

Definitions and symbols are always a source of disagreement and difficulty in a fast-moving field such as control engineering. As far as possible this book will adhere to the recommended symbols of the British Standards Institution but where these are liable to give rise to ambiguities, or they are not in popular use, exceptions will be made.

A particularly useful definition is that of a feedback control system as specified by the Institution of Radio Engineers (U.S.A.) in their *Standards on Terminology for Feedback Control Systems* (proceedings I.R.E. January 1956).

A feedback control system is a control system comprising one or more feedback control loops, which combines functions of the controlled signals with functions of the commands to tend to maintain prescribed relationships between the commands and the controlled signals .... A servomechanism is a feedback control system in which one or more of the system signals represent mechanical motion.

1.5 Autonomic Control Systems

The performance of a control system having a controller with *fixed parameters* will always depend to some extent on the parameters of the plant or system being controlled. Now the design of a controller having fixed parameters to produce optimum performance in a control system will depend on an accurate knowledge of the plant parameters and environmental conditions. In systems where the variation of plant parameters and environmental conditions is severe, the controller cannot be designed in such a way as to produce the desired performance at all times.

An autonomic or self-adaptive or self-optimizing system may,

13

however, be used to give the best possible performance. In this type of device, of which there are several classes, the parameters of the controller are *automatically adjusted* so that the system gives an optimum performance according to some inbuilt criterion of merit. Such systems are more complex then ordinary feedback control systems and require much additional equipment. The idea of autonomic control was conceived by Draper and Li and was first published[3] in 1951.

A wealth of theoretical work related to autonomic control systems now exists and a textbook[4] covering many aspects of the subject has now been published. Due to their considerable expense, autonomic control systems have only, as yet, found application in fields where conventional systems are grossly unsatisfactory. For instance in aircraft designed to fly at high speeds, the effectiveness of the control surfaces can vary greatly from low to high altitudes and from low to high speeds. The pilot can adapt his own behaviour at the controls to a certain extent to counteract this but a greatly improved performance has been shown to be possible with a self-adaptive control system.

1.6 Reasons why Control Systems are Preferred to Human Operators

Apart from the ideological issue that it is morally wrong to employ human beings to do laborious, soul-destroying, repetitive work which requires no judgement, and is far better done by machines, there are a number of very sound engineering reasons why automatic control systems are preferred to human operators, some of which are:

(i) The effect of human reaction time (0·3 sec) prevents manual control being used where high response speed is required (e.g. A.A. guns or radar sets which are required to engage high-speed targets).

(ii) Continuous operation over long periods causes boredom and fatigue in human operators with subsequent deterioration of performance. Also great stress or danger to operator causes a rapid falling off in efficiency.

(iii) It is impossible to standardize the behaviour of human operators unless very simple tasks are undertaken.

(iv) It is often uneconomical to use manual control.

(v) For many applications it is physically impossible for human operators to carry out an operation because of power and speed limitations, severe ambient conditions, the presence of harmful radiations, etc.

1.7 Concluding Remarks

The analysis and synthesis of practical control systems are not simple and they lean heavily on physical principles together with mathematical technique. The author rates the importance of these topics so highly that several chapters of this book are devoted exclusively to 'essential mathematics and physics'. Some readers may feel that their grasp of these subjects is already perfectly adequate and may wish to progress to topics directly related to control problems; it should be possible for them to merely scan through chapters 2, 3 and 5. The work introduced in chapters 4 and 6, is however, regarded as absolutely essential. The author wishes to emphasize that most courses in mathematics are often so totally unrelated to control engineering that a real barrier can exist to a full understanding of the problems of control unless symbols, units, definitions, and simple mathematical techniques are initially brought on to a common level which is completely suited to control requirements. The chapters on essential mathematics and physics have been designed with this object in mind; they are not in any way intended as a substitute for full courses in these subjects.

Graphical Representation of Signals

2.1 Introduction

Control engineering is mainly concerned with the control of large amounts of energy by means of 'signals' derived from a low-power source. A signal may be defined as a time-varying physical quantity carrying 'information' or 'intelligence'. In the testing of systems the signals may be very simple in form but in actual operation they may be very complicated and even entirely random; for instance, consider a tracking radar system whose object is simply to point an aerial at a randomly moving target. During tests, artificial targets which perform simple movements such as 'steps', 'ramps' and 'sinusoids' will often be used. However, when the system is attempting to follow a target which is taking evasive action, the command signal will be virtually random.

In control engineering we are frequently concerned with the graphical representation of time varying signals and it is the object of this chapter to present the graphs of certain important functions.

2.2 Steps, Ramps, Pulses and Impulses

2.2.1 The Step

In the testing of systems we often apply 'step' and 'ramp' inputs in order to judge whether the system is responding in the required manner.

A 'step' is a sudden change in the value of a physical quantity θ from one level (usually zero) to another value A in zero time. The value of time t at which this sudden change occurs may be zero for convenience or some other value t_1 as shown in Fig. 2.1 (a) and (b) respectively.

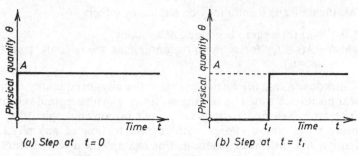

Fig. 2.1 *Graphical representation of a step.*

Three points which should be understood are:

(i) The physical quantity θ may be angular position, linear position, temperature, velocity, acceleration, etc.

(ii) The point in time $t = 0$ is an arbitrary zero taken at any instant to suit the problem and we interpret negative time simply as time occurring before this arbitrary zero. Physically $t = 0$ is usually taken to represent the instant we press the button to start the operation or process.

(iii) It is impossible, even electronically, to achieve a genuine step due to the inertia of physical systems. We can however, achieve rises which are very fast indeed compared with the response time of the system under test. It is also often possible to 'simulate' perfect steps artificially. Theoretically it is convenient to postulate an ideal step because the problems arising are mathematically simpler to solve than those which occur with 'practical steps' (Fig. 2.2) which possess a finite rise time.

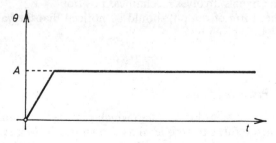

Fig. 2.2 *A 'practical step' with finite rise time.*

2.2.2 The Ramp

The ramp is a signal that starts at a value of zero and undergoes a linear increase with respect to time. It may begin at $t = 0$ or at $t = t_1$ as shown in Fig. 2.3 (*a*) and (*b*) respectively.

17

Mathematically θ and t may be related by either

(a) $\theta = kt$ for a ramp beginning at $t = 0$, or
(b) $\theta = k(t - t_1)$ for a ramp beginning at $t = t_1$ (only true for $t > t_1$).

Considering case (a) we notice that if the physical quantity θ were linear position, θ would be varying or 'moving' with constant velocity.

The term 'velocity' is frequently used in control engineering to represent the rate of change with respect to time of any physical quantity, not just linear position. For example, if a temperature is increasing at a constant rate of 10 degC per second then the quantity is said to have a velocity of this value.

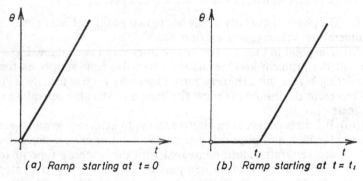

(a) Ramp starting at $t = 0$ (b) Ramp starting at $t = t_1$

Fig. 2.3 *Graphical representation of a ramp.*

This piece of jargon stems from a particular branch of control engineering, namely the study of servomechanisms in which one or more of the signals involves mechanical position.

For either form of ramp it should be noticed that the value of the velocity $d\theta/dt$ is given by

$$\frac{d\theta}{dt} = k$$

2.2.3 *The Pulse and Impulse*

A 'pulse' may be regarded as a step which persists for a limited duration and then returns to zero level as shown in Fig. 2.4. It may start at $t = 0$ or at an arbitrary time t_1. Its height A is quite arbitrary, as is the pulse 'width' T.

It should be understood that in practice the ideal pulse with zero rise and fall times cannot be achieved and a practical pulse will possess finite values of these quantities as shown in Fig. 2.5.

Normally the rise and fall times will be very small compared with the duration of the pulse. The impulse is a special type of pulse and is a popular test signal in control engineering. The perfect impulse occurs at $t = 0$ and has a width of zero and infinite height. The perfect impulse cannot be achieved in practice and a special type of impulse

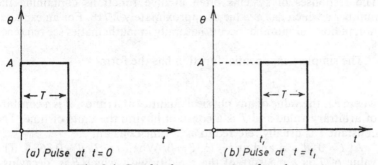

(a) Pulse at $t = 0$ (b) Pulse at $t = t_1$

Fig. 2.4 *Graphical representation of a pulse.*

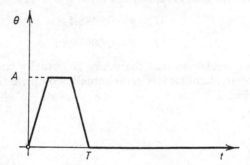

Fig. 2.5 *Practical pulse.*

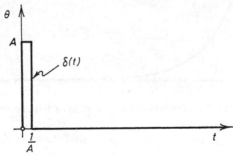

Fig. 2.6 *The Dirac delta function $\delta(t)$.*

is usually used for the theoretical and practical assessment of the response of a system. It is usually referred to as the Dirac delta function $\delta(t)$ and is defined as a pulse having a small width but unity area. A typical example of such a function is shown in Fig. 2.6.

The delta function is sometimes called the unit impulse.

19

2.3 Exponential Functions

2.3.1 The Exponential Decay

The responses of systems often involve functions containing the number e which has a value of approximately 2·718. For an explanation of how this number occurs naturally in mathematics see reference 5.

The simplest exponential function has the form

$$\theta = A\,e^{-t/T}$$

where θ is the value of any physical quantity at a time t, A is a constant of arbitrary value and T is a constant having the units of time. The constant T is usually referred to as a 'time constant'.

At $t = 0$, $\theta = A$ and at $t = \infty$, $\theta = 0$. When $t = T$, $\theta = 0·368A$. The value of T is a measure of the rapidity with which θ is 'decaying'. When T is small, θ decays rapidly but when T is large θ decays slowly.

When $\qquad\qquad\qquad t = 3T, \quad \theta = 0·0498A$

and when $\qquad\qquad\quad t = 5T, \quad \theta = 0·00674A$

It is usually reckoned that the decay is virtually complete after $t = 5T$, although of course it is never actually complete. The function is shown in Fig. 2.7.

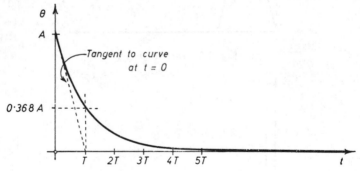

Fig. 2.7 *Graphical representation of* $\theta = A\,e^{-t/T}$.

An interesting feature of the exponential decay is the initial slope $d\theta/dt$ at $t = 0$.

Using differential calculus we see that in general

$$\frac{d\theta}{dt} = -\frac{A}{T}e^{-t/T}$$

Thus at $t = 0$, $\qquad\qquad d\theta/dt = -A/T$

i.e. the initial slope is $-A/T$.

20

It is sometimes more convenient to express the exponential decay in the form $\theta = A e^{-\alpha t}$ where $\alpha = 1/T$.

2.3.2 The Exponential Rise

Another important function is the exponential rise which may be expressed mathematically as

$$\theta = A(1 - e^{-t/T})$$

The height A is the final or maximum value of the rise and the curve is always 'aiming' towards this value but never quite reaches it. At time $t = T$ it has reached 63·2% of the final value and after $t = 5T$ it has achieved 99·3% of it, and the rise is considered to be virtually complete.

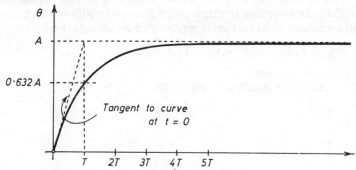

Fig. 2.8 *Graphical representation of* $\theta = A(1 - e^{-t/T})$.

An equally useful form is given by

$$\theta = A(1 - e^{-\alpha t})$$

where
$$\alpha = 1/T.$$

2.3.3 The Double Exponential Rise

We may sometimes encounter the double exponential rise given by

$$\theta = A \left\{ 1 - \frac{m_2 e^{m_1 t}}{m_2 - m_1} + \frac{m_1 e^{m_2 t}}{m_2 - m_1} \right\}$$

where m_1 and m_2 are both negative.

A is the final value because, since m_1 and m_2 are both negative, $e^{m_1 t}$ and $e^{m_2 t}$ disappear when t becomes large. The slope at $t = 0$ is zero. The graphical representation is shown in Fig. 2.9.

2.3.4 A Special Exponential Rise

In certain systems containing two energy transfer stages it is possible to arrange the constants so that the system is 'critically damped'. The

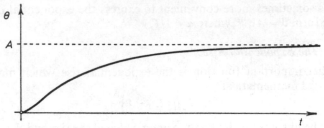

Fig. 2.9 *The double exponential rise*

$$\theta = A\left\{1 - \frac{m_2\,e^{m_1 t}}{m_2 - m_1} + \frac{m_1\,e^{m_2 t}}{m_2 - m_1}\right\}$$

response of such a system may be regarded as a double exponential with the fastest possible rise time to the final value without overshoot. Mathematically the function is represented by the equation

$$\theta = A\{1 - (1 + \alpha t)\,e^{-\alpha t}\}$$

where α is a constant.

The function is sketched in Fig. 2.10.

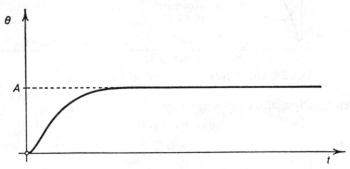

Fig. 2.10 '*Critical*' *double exponential rise* $\theta = A\{1 - (1 + \alpha t)\,e^{-\alpha t}\}$.

2.4 Sinusoidal Quantities

2.4.1 The Basic Sine Wave

An extremely important function is the sine wave which is conveniently expressed as

$$\theta = \hat{\theta}\sin \omega t$$

where $\hat{\theta}$ is the 'peak value' of the function, ω is a constant for a given wave called the 'angular frequency', and t is time.

The constant ω must possess the dimensions of radians per second so that ωt becomes radians. There are two ways in which the sine wave may be represented. In Fig. 2.11 (*a*) θ is plotted directly against time *t*; in Fig. 2.11 (*b*) θ is plotted against angle ωt which may be expressed in either radians or degrees.

The period *T* of the sine wave is the time for one complete cycle, i.e.

$$T = \frac{2\pi}{\omega}$$

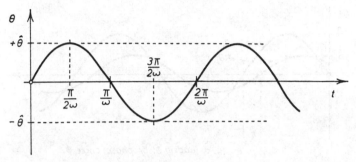

(a) To a base of time *t*

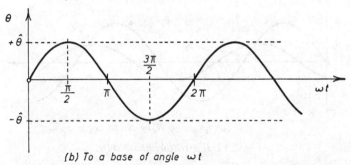

(b) To a base of angle ωt

Fig. 2.11 *Representation of the basic sine wave $\theta = \hat{\theta}\sin\omega t$.*

The frequency *f* of the sine wave is the number of times the complete cycle is executed in 1 second, i.e.

$$f = \frac{1}{T} = \frac{\omega}{2\pi}$$

or
$$2\pi f = \omega$$

2.4.2 Phase Angle

A sine wave $\theta_1 = \hat{\theta}_1 \sin(\omega t + \phi)$ is said to be 'phase displaced' from the basic sine wave $\theta_2 = \hat{\theta}_2 \sin\omega t$ by a 'leading phase angle' of ϕ.

A sine wave $\theta_3 = \hat{\theta}_3 \sin(\omega t - \psi)$ is phase displaced from the basic sine wave $\theta_2 = \hat{\theta}_2 \sin\omega t$ by a lagging phase angle of ψ. These possibilities are shown in Fig. 2.12 (*a*) and (*b*) respectively.

23

The cosine wave $\theta = \hat{\theta}\cos\omega t$ is better represented as a sine wave with phase lead of $\pi/2$ radians (i.e. 90°) because it may equally well be written as $\theta = \hat{\theta}\sin(\omega t + \pi/2)$. A thorough knowledge of the basic definitions associated with sine waves is vital for a full appreciation of the 'frequency response methods' which are so popular in the design and analysis of industrial control systems.

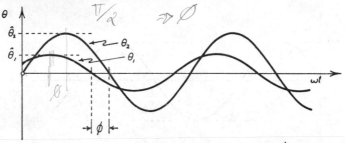

(a) θ_1 leading θ_2 by phase angle ϕ.

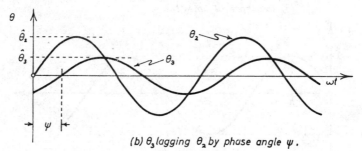

(b) θ_3 lagging θ_2 by phase angle ψ.

Fig. 2.12 *Illustrating phase shift.*

2.4.3 Mean and Root Mean Square Values

Mean Value of Sinusoidal Quantities

The mean value of a periodic function $f(t)$ with a period T is defined as the area enclosed by the curve during the interval T divided by the time T, i.e.

$$\text{mean value} = \frac{1}{T}\int_0^T f(t)\,\mathrm{d}t$$

For a sine wave, the positive area enclosed during the positive half-cycle is completely nullified by the negative area enclosed during the negative half-cycle. The true mean value is hence zero. However, it is convenient to define the mean value over half a cycle, i.e.

$$\text{half-cycle mean value} = \frac{2}{T}\int_0^{T/2} f(t)\,\mathrm{d}t$$

For a sine wave $f(t) = \theta = \hat{\theta}\sin\omega t$.

$\therefore$ half-cycle mean value $= \dfrac{2}{T}\displaystyle\int_0^{T/2} \hat{\theta}\sin\omega t\,\mathrm{d}t$

$$= -\frac{2\hat{\theta}}{\omega T}\Big[\cos\omega t\Big]_0^{T/2}$$

$$= -\frac{2\hat{\theta}}{\omega T}\Big[\cos\frac{\omega T}{2} - \cos 0\Big]$$

But from §2.4.1

$$\omega T = 2\pi$$

$\therefore$ half-cycle mean value $= -\dfrac{2\hat{\theta}}{2\pi}[\cos\pi - \cos 0]$

$$= \frac{2\hat{\theta}}{\pi}$$

$$= 0{\cdot}636\hat{\theta}$$

Root Mean Square Value of Sinusoidal Quantities

The root mean square value of a periodic function $f(t)$ with a period T is defined as the square root of the area enclosed by the square of the function during the time interval T when this area has been divided by the time T.

The root mean square (r.m.s.) value is of considerable importance in electrical engineering because we may use it to calculate the heating effect of alternating currents passing through resistive components. Most measurements of currents and voltages in electrical engineering and all alternating physical quantities in control engineering are expressed in r.m.s. values.

The r.m.s. value of the periodic function $f(t)$ is given by

$$\text{r.m.s. value} = \sqrt{\left\{\frac{1}{T}\int_0^T [f(t)]^2\,\mathrm{d}t\right\}}$$

If $f(t) = \theta = \hat{\theta}\sin\omega t$, then $[f(t)]^2$ becomes $\hat{\theta}^2\sin^2\omega t$; this function is illustrated in Fig. 2.13.

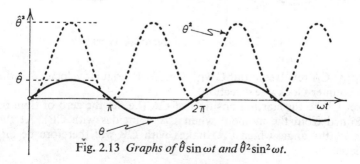

Fig. 2.13 *Graphs of $\hat{\theta}\sin\omega t$ and $\hat{\theta}^2\sin^2\omega t$.*

It is noticed that the areas under the square curve are positive for both half-cycles. The r.m.s. value for a sine wave may thus be calculated over a complete cycle, i.e.

$$\text{r.m.s. value of a sine wave} = \sqrt{\left\{\frac{1}{T}\int_0^T \hat{\theta}^2 \sin^2 \omega t \, dt\right\}}$$

$$= \sqrt{\left\{\frac{\hat{\theta}^2}{2T}\int_0^T (1 - \cos 2\omega t) \, dt\right\}}$$

$$= \sqrt{\left\{\frac{\hat{\theta}^2}{2T}\left[t - \frac{\sin 2\omega t}{2\omega}\right]_0^T\right\}}$$

$$= \sqrt{\left\{\frac{\hat{\theta}^2}{2T}\left(T - \frac{\sin 2\omega T}{2\omega} - 0 + \frac{\sin 0}{2\omega}\right)\right\}}$$

But $\omega T = 2\pi$.

$$\therefore \quad \text{r.m.s. value of a sine wave} = \sqrt{\left\{\frac{\hat{\theta}^2}{2T}\left(T - \frac{\sin 4\pi}{2\omega}\right)\right\}}$$

$$= \sqrt{\left\{\frac{\hat{\theta}^2}{2}\right\}} = 0 \cdot 707 \hat{\theta}$$

2.4.4 Representation of Sine Waves by Vectors

The Rotating Vector Diagram

Suppose a circle be drawn as shown in Fig. 2.14 of radius CA representing to scale the maximum value $\hat{\theta}$ of the physical quantity, and

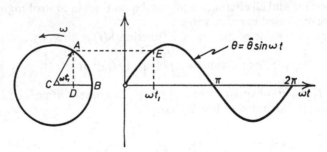

Fig. 2.14 *The rotating vector diagram.*

suppose CA revolves about C with a uniform angular velocity ω rad/s in a counter-clockwise direction.

Let CB be the starting position of CA (i.e. let the zero of time be reckoned from the moment when CA coincides with CB). At the time t_1, the angle which CA makes with CB will therefore be ωt_1 radians.

From A draw AD perpendicular to CB.

Then $$AD = CA \sin \omega t_1$$

$$= \hat{\theta} \sin \omega t_1$$

or AD represents the value at the time t_1 of the sinusoidal quantity θ of which the maximum value is $\hat{\theta}$.

Hence, if the values of t be plotted as abscissae, the corresponding projections of CA on the vertical will give the sine wave.

Thus the position and length of CA may be taken as representative of the sine wave at any instant. The line CA may be thought of as a VECTOR. In actual fact it is not a true vector in the sense that forces, velocity, etc. are vectors and it is more correct, academically to call it something else; the term ROTOR has sometimes been used. We will however conform with common usage and call it a vector. This vector representation of sine waves is extremely powerful because it allows us to combine sine waves by vector manipulation rather than by laborious analytical or point by point graphical techniques.

Vector Addition and Subtraction of Sine Waves

Suppose we have two sinusoidal quantities whose instantaneous values θ_1 and θ_2 are represented by the equations

$$\theta_1 = \hat{\theta}_1 \sin \omega t$$

and $$\theta_2 = \hat{\theta}_2 \sin (\omega t + \phi)$$

Let us assume we require $\theta_1 + \theta_2$. We may write down the analytical expression

$$\theta_1 + \theta_2 = \hat{\theta}_1 \sin \omega t + \hat{\theta}_2 \sin (\omega t + \phi)$$

$$= \hat{\theta}_1 \sin \omega t + \hat{\theta}_2 \sin \omega t \cos \phi + \hat{\theta}_2 \cos \omega t \sin \phi$$

$$= (\hat{\theta}_1 + \hat{\theta}_2 \cos \phi) \sin \omega t + \hat{\theta}_2 \sin \phi \cos \omega t$$

$$= \sqrt{\{(\hat{\theta}_1 + \hat{\theta}_2 \cos \phi)^2 + \hat{\theta}_2^2 \sin^2 \phi\}} \sin (\omega t + \psi) \qquad (1)$$

where $$\psi = \tan^{-1} \frac{\hat{\theta}_2 \sin \phi}{\hat{\theta}_1 + \hat{\theta}_2 \cos \phi}.$$

This rather lengthy analysis may be simplified by the use of vectors. We draw the vector representing θ_1 (written $\bar{\theta}_1$) as our reference (OA) and $\bar{\theta}_2$ is drawn leading $\bar{\theta}_1$ by the phase angle ϕ (AB). The resultant is OB, found using the triangle rule for vector addition, as shown in Fig. 2.15. Usually, scale drawings are not made, but the diagram is used as an aid to simplify the trigonometrical calculations. Extra lines AC and BC may be drawn as shown.

OA has a length representing $\hat{\theta}_1$ and AB a length representing $\hat{\theta}_2$.

Now $\qquad AC = \hat{\theta}_2 \cos \phi$

$\therefore \qquad OC = \hat{\theta}_1 + \hat{\theta}_2 \cos \phi$

Also $\qquad CB = \hat{\theta}_2 \sin \phi$

Thus $\qquad AC = \sqrt{\{(\hat{\theta}_1 + \hat{\theta}_2 \cos \phi)^2 + \hat{\theta}_2^2 \sin^2 \phi\}}$

Also $\qquad \psi = \tan^{-1} \dfrac{CB}{OC} = \tan^{-1} \dfrac{\hat{\theta}_2 \sin \phi}{\hat{\theta}_1 + \hat{\theta}_2 \cos \phi}$

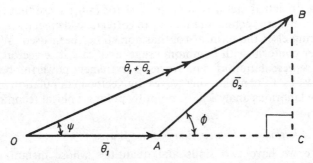

Fig. 2.15 *Vector addition of two sine waves.*

Thus the instantaneous value of the resultant may be written as

$$\theta_1 + \theta_2 = \sqrt{\{(\hat{\theta}_1 + \hat{\theta}_2 \cos \phi)^2 + \hat{\theta}_2^2 \sin^2 \phi\}} \sin(\omega t + \psi) \qquad (2)$$

We see that equations (1) and (2) are identical; it is thus evident that the vector approach produces the same result as the analytical approach but with rather simpler mathematics.

Vector subtraction of two sine waves may be performed by reversing the direction of the second vector as shown in Fig. 2.16.

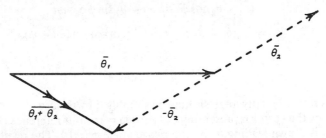

Fig. 2.16 *Vector subtratcion of two sine waves.*

When there are a large number of sine waves to be added and possibly subtracted the polygon rule may be used and a scale diagram

drawn. Scale diagrams have limited accuracy, however, and a
nique using 'quadrature' and 'reference' components is recommended.

Consider a sine wave $\theta = \hat{\theta}\sin(\omega t + \phi)$. This is drawn on a diagram
containing 'quadrature' and 'reference' axes in Fig. 2.17.

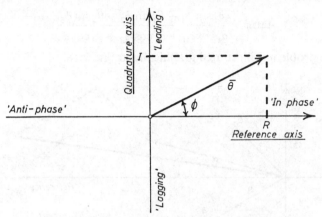

Fig. 2.17 *Representation of vectors.*

The vector $\bar{\theta}$ has two components, one along the 'in phase' reference
axis R and one along the 'leading' quadrature axis I.

We see that $\qquad\qquad R = \hat{\theta}\cos\phi$

and $\qquad\qquad\qquad\quad I = \hat{\theta}\sin\phi$

The resultant of R and I must of course give $\bar{\theta}$.

This technique of resolving into components simplifies the addition,
subtraction and measurement of sinusoidal quantities.

Supposing it is required to add the following

$$\theta_1 = \hat{\theta}_1\sin(\omega t + \phi_1)$$

$$\theta_2 = \hat{\theta}_2\sin(\omega t - \phi_2)$$

$$\theta_3 = \hat{\theta}_3\sin(\omega t + \phi_3)$$

We resolve each vector into its reference and quadrature components and then proceed to sum the two sets arithmetically with due
respect to sign. The problem may be best set down in tabular form.

	Reference Component	Quadrature Component
$\bar{\theta}_1$	$\theta_1\cos\phi_1$	$\theta_1\sin\phi_1$
$\bar{\theta}_2$	$\theta_2\cos\phi_2$	$-\theta_2\sin\phi_2$
$\bar{\theta}_3$	$\theta_3\cos\phi_3$	$\theta_3\sin\phi_3$
Resultant $\bar{\theta}$	$\theta_1\cos\phi_1 + \theta_2\cos\phi_2 + \theta_3\cos\phi_3$	$\theta_1\sin\phi - \theta_2\sin\phi_2 + \theta_3\sin\phi_3$

29

The peak magnitude of the resultant $\hat{\theta}$ is thus given by

$$\hat{\theta} = \sqrt{\{(\hat{\theta}_1 \cos\phi_1 + \hat{\theta}_2 \cos\phi_2 + \hat{\theta}_3 \cos\phi_3)^2}$$
$$+(\hat{\theta}_1 \sin\phi_1 - \hat{\theta}_2 \sin\phi_2 + \hat{\theta}_3 \sin\phi_3)^2\}$$

The phase angle ϕ of the resultant is given by

$$\tan\phi = \frac{\hat{\theta}_1 \sin\phi_1 - \hat{\theta}_2 \sin\phi_2 + \hat{\theta}_3 \sin\phi_3}{\hat{\theta}_1 \cos\phi_1 + \hat{\theta}_2 \cos\phi_2 + \hat{\theta}_3 \cos\phi_3}$$

The problem is illustrated graphically in Fig. 2.18.

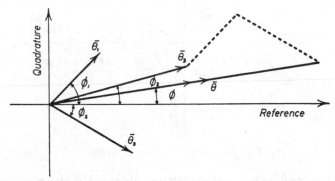

Fig. 2.18 *Addition of several vectors by resolving into components.*

2.5 Exponentially Damped Sinusoids

In control engineering we are often confronted by systems which respond to certain stimuli with exponentially decaying or increasing oscillatory responses. Typical of such patterns is the response given by

$$\theta = \hat{\theta} e^{\alpha t} \sin\omega t$$

where θ is the instantaneous value of a physical quantity, $\hat{\theta}$ is a positive constant, α is a constant which may be positive or negative, ω is a constant and t is time. The two types of graph resulting for α positive and negative are shown in Fig. 2.19.

In these patterns the frequency of oscillation f is given by $f = \omega/2\pi$ and the speed of decay or rise of the envelope is controlled by the value of α. If α is large the rate of decay or rise is great and conversely if α is small the rate of decay or rise is small.

In §§2.3.3 and 2.3.4 the 'double exponential' rise has been illustrated. These functions are representative of the responses of certain types of control system when step inputs are applied. An even more important type of response is that given by the equation

$$\theta = A\{1 - Be^{-\alpha t} \sin(\omega t + \phi)\}$$

where θ is the instantaneous value of a physical quantity, α, ω and A are positive constants, t is time and

$$B = \sqrt{\left\{1 + \left(\frac{\alpha}{\omega}\right)^2\right\}}$$

and

$$\phi = \tan^{-1}\frac{\omega}{\alpha}$$

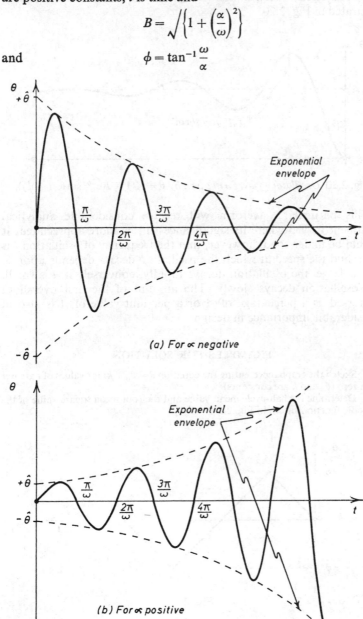

(a) For α negative

(b) For α positive

Fig. 2.19 *Oscillatory wave patterns given by* $\theta = \hat{\theta}\,e^{\alpha t}\sin\omega t$.

This type of response is given by second order servomechanisms when subjected to step inputs (see §8.3). The resultant waveform is illustrated in Fig. 2.20.

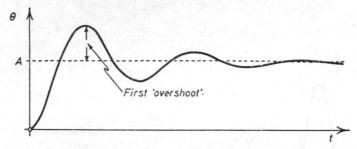

Fig. 2.20 *Oscillatory waveform given by* $\theta = A\{1 - Be^{-\alpha t}\sin(\omega t + \phi)\}$.

This particular waveform will receive considerable analytical treatment in §8.3 where its significance will be more appreciated. It should be understood, however, that the frequency of oscillation f is $\omega/2\pi$ and the speed at which the oscillation decays depends upon α. If α is large, the oscillation decays rapidly, conversely if α is small, the oscillation decays slowly. The amount of the first overshoot expressed as a percentage of A or a per unit value of A is also of considerable importance in design.

EXAMPLES FOR SOLUTION

1. Sketch the graph representing the equation $\theta = \theta_o + kt$ for values of t greater than zero (θ_o and k are constants).

2. Determine the half-cycle mean value and the root mean square value of the periodic function shown in Fig. 2.21.

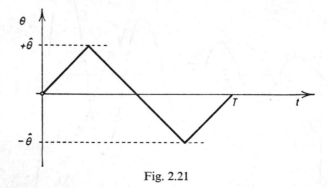

Fig. 2.21

3. The exponential rise illustrated in Fig. 2.22 has a time constant of value T. Determine an equation for this function.

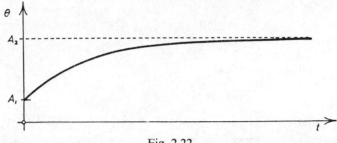

Fig. 2.22

4. An alternating quantity varying sinusoidally with a frequency of 100 c/s has an r.m.s. value of 10 units. Write down the equation for the instantaneous value and find this value (a) 0·00125 sec and (b) 0·000625 sec, after passing through the positive maximum value.

5. Use vector addition to find the sum of the following sinusoidal quantities:

$$\theta_1 = 5\sin\left(\omega t + \frac{\pi}{4}\right)$$

$$\theta_2 = 8\cos\left(\omega t + \frac{\pi}{4}\right)$$

$$\theta_3 = 10\sin\left(\omega t - \frac{\pi}{2}\right)$$

$$\theta_4 = 7\sin\left(\omega t + \frac{\pi}{3}\right)$$

Express the resultant in a similar form. Determine the r.m.s. value of the resultant.

6. Find the resultant of $8\sin\left(\omega t + \frac{\pi}{3}\right)$ subtracted from $5\cos\omega t$ by a vector method.

7. Sketch the waveforms representing the equation $\theta = A e^{\alpha t}\cos\omega t$ where A and ω are positive constants, t is time and α is a constant which may be (a) negative, and (b) positive.

Chapter Three

The Use of Complex Numbers in the Solution of Vector Problems

3.1 Introduction

In §2.4.4 the idea of representing sinusoidally varying quantities by means of vectors is introduced. In very simple problems vectors may be combined without undue difficulty. As the problems become more difficult however the algebra and triogonometry become exessively tedious and a simplifying technique is thus necessary. In this chapter the operator j will be introduced and it will be shown how apparently lengthy problems may be solved more simply.

The idea of *number* was originally confined to the positive whole numbers and its first extension was to positive fractions. It was later realized that certain numbers could not be expressed as the ratio of two positive whole numbers; for example the ratio of a diagonal of a square to its side ($\sqrt{2}$). Such numbers are called irrational. The use of the Arabic notation for numbers, in which the value of a digit is indicated by its position, led to the use of zero as the limit to which small numbers tend. A logical extension of the idea of large numbers to indefinite limits gives infinity (∞).

The operation of subtraction led to the idea of negative numbers because no positive number could represent the answer to such problems as 5 minus 8. The ideas of negative fractions, incommensurable numbers and $-\infty$ then follow.

All numbers between $-\infty$ and $+\infty$ so far considered are 'real' numbers.

3.2 Imaginary Numbers

Even in elementary problems it is found that the answer cannot always be expressed as a real number. For example, consider the problem

$$x^2 = -9$$

No real number can be found such that when multiplied by itself, the answer is −9. However, let us attempt some form of solution:

$$x = \sqrt{-9} = \sqrt{\{9 \times -1\}} = \sqrt{9} \times \sqrt{-1} = \pm 3\sqrt{-1}$$

since

$$\sqrt{9} = \pm 3$$

The problem of giving a meaning to the square root of any negative number thus reduces to that of finding a meaning for $\sqrt{-1}$. It is conventional in engineering to represent this quantity by the symbol j. Hence

$$\sqrt{-9} = \pm j3$$

Numbers like j3 are called 'imaginary' numbers, i.e. any real multiple of j whether positive or negative is an imaginary number. The term 'imaginary number' is a technical mathematical name as is 'real number'. Imaginary numbers may be added, multiplied, etc. in the same way as real numbers.

Several simple properties of j are of interest; since $j = \sqrt{-1}$, then $j^2 = -1$ and $j^3 = -j$, $j^4 = +1$, $1/j = j/j^2 = -j$, and so on.

3.3 Complex Numbers

These are numbers which contain both real and imaginary parts, e.g. $5 - j7$; $-8 + j3$; etc.

Any complex number may be put into the form $a + jb$ where a and b are real numbers.

3.4 Graphical Representation of Numbers

Real numbers may be represented as points on an infinitely long straight line, as shown in Fig. 3.1.

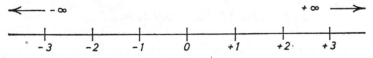

Fig. 3.1 *Representation of real numbers.*

The number zero is taken at an arbitrary point on the line; positive real numbers extend on the right of zero and negative real numbers on the left. Now since there are places on this line only for real numbers it follows that we must investigate other means of logically representing imaginary numbers.

If we define j as an *operator* this becomes possible. Considering, for example, the operation of multiplying 1 by j and then by j again, we obtain $1 \times j \times j$ or $1 \times j^2$, i.e. −1.

Hence by operating on $+1$ by j^2 we have obtained -1. Referring again to Fig. 3.1 we may interpret this operation graphically. If we regard the line 01 as representing the real number 1, it will be seen that we may arrive at the point -1 by revolving the line 01 about 0 through 180° either clockwise or counter-clockwise.

Hence the multiplication by j may be interpreted as the operation which performed twice in succession gives rotation through 180°. It

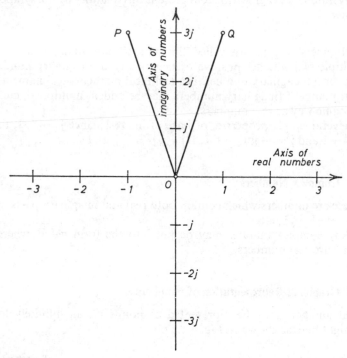

Fig. 3.2 *The Argand diagram.*

follows that multiplication by j may be given the meaning of a rotation through 180°/2, i.e. 90°. Conventionally we consider that:

(*a*) counter-clockwise rotation through 90° is taken as the operation of multiplying a number by $+j$;

(*b*) clockwise rotation through 90° is taken as the operation of multiplying a number by $-j$.

Imaginary numbers may thus be represented graphically by drawing a line through the point 0 at right angles to the line representing real numbers. Hence both real and imaginary numbers may be represented as shown in Fig. 3.2. It is called an *Argand diagram*.

A complex number may be represented on the Argand diagram by a combination of real and imaginary numbers. Consider for example the complex number $-1 + j3$. The operations to be performed are:

(1) To traverse a distance of 1 unit to the left of 0 along the axis of negative real numbers. This brings us to the point -1.

(2) Having arrived at the point -1, to turn through 90° counter-clockwise and traverse 3 units in the new direction. We thus arrive at the point P on the Argand diagram of Fig. 3.2. This point represents the number $-1 + j3$.

The complex number $-1 + j3$ may be considered to be represented either by the point P or the line OP.

It will be seen that to specify OP completely, not only its length must be given but also its direction with respect to one of the axes. The line OQ, for instance, on Fig. 3.2 has the same length as OP but a different direction and represents the complex number $+1 + j3$.

At this juncture we should notice the considerable similarity between Fig. 3.2 and Fig. 2.17. In Fig. 2.17 we drew a vector which represented a sinusoidally varying quantity on a diagram containing reference and quadrature axes. If we were to draw that vector on the Argand diagram of Fig. 3.2 it would enable us to specify the vector completely as a complex number.

Hence complex numbers are equivalent to vectors on the Argand diagram. This allows us to manipulate vectors as complex numbers with greater ease.

3.5 Addition and Subtraction of Vectors Represented by Complex Numbers

Suppose we have two vectors represented by the complex numbers $a + jb$ and $c + jd$ respectively. Vector $a + jb$ is represented by OA on Fig. 3.3 and vector $c + jd$ by OB.

Addition by the ordinary rules of algebra gives their sum as

$$a + jb + c + jd = (a + c) + j(b + d)$$

i.e. their sum is another complex number.

By the parallelogram rule for vector addition we see the resultant is OC. It is easily seen from Fig. 3.3 that OC, the diagonal of the parallelogram, represents the number $(a + c) + j(b + d)$.

Thus to find the sum of two vectors we may use ordinary algebra to add the complex numbers representing those vectors and so find the resultant as a complex number.

Vectors may also be subtracted by a similar process.

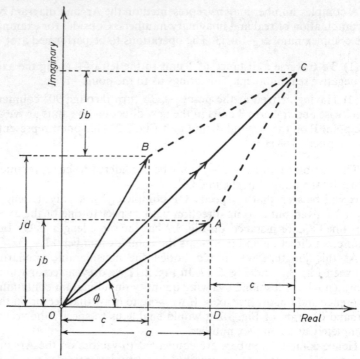

Fig. 3.3 *Vector addition on the Argand diagram.*

3.6 Polar Form of Complex Numbers

Considering the vector OA in Fig. 3.3, it is seen that whilst it is completely described by the complex number $a + jb$, it is also possible to describe it in terms of its length or MODULUS r and its phase angle or ARGUMENT ϕ. In fact on many occasions a vector is written as $r \angle \phi$ instead of $a + jb$.

In $\triangle$ OAD,

$$a = r \cos \phi$$

and

$$b = r \sin \phi$$

Thus

$$a + jb = r \cos \phi + jr \sin \phi$$

and

$$\phi = \tan^{-1} \frac{b}{a}$$

Note ϕ is *not* $\tan^{-1} \frac{jb}{a}$; it is a real angle and its tangent is a real number!

Also, the modulus r is given by

$$r = \sqrt{\{a^2 + b^2\}}$$

(Again r is a real length and the operator j does not
calculation.)

3.7 Exponential Form of Complex Numbers

The following relationships have been proved in Chapter   ..ne
book mentioned in reference 5, for real values of ϕ:

$$e^\phi = 1 + \phi + \frac{\phi^2}{2!} + \frac{\phi^3}{3!} + \cdots \tag{1}$$

$$\cos\phi = 1 - \frac{\phi^2}{2!} + \frac{\phi^4}{4!} - \cdots \tag{2}$$

$$\sin\phi = \phi - \frac{\phi^3}{3!} + \frac{\phi^5}{5!} - \cdots \tag{3}$$

From (1),

$$e^{j\phi} = 1 + j\phi + j^2\frac{\phi^2}{2!} + j^3\frac{\phi^3}{3!} + j^4\frac{\phi^4}{4!} + \cdots$$

$$= 1 + j\phi - \frac{\phi^2}{2!} - j\frac{\phi^3}{3!} + \frac{\phi^4}{4!} + \cdots$$

$$= \left(1 - \frac{\phi^2}{2!} + \frac{\phi^4}{4!} - \cdots\right) + j\left(\phi - \frac{\phi^3}{3!} + \frac{\phi^5}{5!} - \cdots\right)$$

Whence using (2) and (3)

$$e^{j\phi} = \cos\phi + j\sin\phi$$

Hence $\qquad r e^{j\phi} = r\cos\phi + jr\sin\phi$

or using the relations developed in §3.6

$$r e^{j\phi} = a + jb$$

Thus the exponential expression $r e^{j\phi}$ also represents the vector
OA on Fig. 3.3.

A useful extension of this theorem is found by writing $-\phi$ in place
of ϕ when we obtain

$$r e^{-j\phi} = r\cos\phi - jr\sin\phi$$

3.8 Representation of Sinusoidal Quantities by Complex Numbers

It is of interest at this point to determine exactly what we are doing
when we represent sinusoidal quantities by complex numbers. It was

39

.wn in chapter 2 how we could represent a sine wave by a 'rotating vector'.

If we have a sinusoidally varying quantity given by $\theta = \hat{\theta}\sin(\omega t + \phi)$ we may represent it on the Argand diagram as shown in Fig. 3.4.

We see that $a = \hat{\theta}\cos(\omega t + \phi)$ and $b = \hat{\theta}\sin(\omega t + \phi)$ hence the vector $\bar{\theta}$ may be written as the complex number

$$\bar{\theta} = \hat{\theta}\cos(\omega t + \phi) + j\hat{\theta}\sin(\omega t + \phi)$$

We notice that the instantaneous value of the sinusoidal quantity is in fact given by the imaginary part of $\bar{\theta}$. We may also express $\bar{\theta}$ exponentially thus,

$$\bar{\theta} = \hat{\theta}\,e^{j(\omega t + \phi)}$$

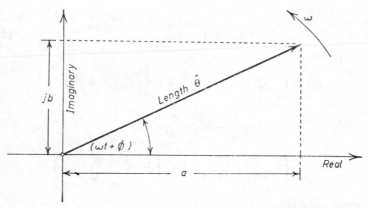

Fig. 3.4 *Representation of sinusoidal quantities on Argand diagram.*

It is important to realize that the vector representation is an abstract mathematical concept. We use it as an interim measure only in order to simplify the amount of computation necessary; the physical solution is then deduced from the vectorial result.

The problem of vector addition of two sine waves which was dealt with in §2.4.4 will now be attempted using the complex notation.

Suppose we are to add

$$\theta_1 = \hat{\theta}_1\sin\omega t \text{ to } \theta_2 = \hat{\theta}_2\sin(\omega t + \phi).$$

Written exponentially

$$\bar{\theta}_1 = \hat{\theta}_1\,e^{j\omega t} \quad \text{and} \quad \bar{\theta}_2 = \hat{\theta}_2\,e^{j(\omega t + \phi)}$$

$$\therefore \qquad \bar{\theta}_1 + \bar{\theta}_2 = \hat{\theta}_1\,e^{j\omega t} + \hat{\theta}_2\,e^{j(\omega t + \phi)}$$

$$= e^{j\omega t}(\hat{\theta}_1 + \hat{\theta}_2\,e^{j\phi})$$

But $$e^{j\phi} = \cos\phi + j\sin\phi$$

$$\therefore \qquad \bar{\theta}_1 + \bar{\theta}_2 = e^{j\omega t}(\hat{\theta}_1 + \hat{\theta}_2\cos\phi + j\hat{\theta}_2\sin\phi)$$

$$= e^{j\omega t}\, r\, e^{j\psi}$$

where $$r = \sqrt{\{(\hat{\theta}_1 + \hat{\theta}_2\cos\phi)^2 + \hat{\theta}_2^2\sin^2\phi\}}$$

and $$\psi = \tan^{-1}\frac{\hat{\theta}_2\sin\phi}{\hat{\theta}_1 + \hat{\theta}_2\cos\phi}$$

Hence $$\bar{\theta}_1 + \bar{\theta}_2 = r\, e^{j(\omega t + \psi)}$$

This is the vector solution and from it we deduce the instantaneous solution, i.e.

$$\theta_1 + \theta_2 = r\sin(\omega t + \psi)$$

The above simple example serves as an introduction to the operator approach.

3.9 Multiplication and Division of Complex Numbers

3.9.1 Multiplication

Many problems in control engineering involve the multiplication and/or division of vectors (representing sinusoidally varying quantities) by 'complex operators'. Such complex operators are used to represent certain physical quantities which are independent of time and hence do not rotate but nevertheless produce phase-shifting and magnitude-modifying effects on sinusoidal quantities.

Multiplication may proceed by either of the two following methods:

(1) If a vector $a + jb$ is to be multiplied by an operator $c + jd$, then using the ordinary rules of algebra we have

$$(a + jb)(c + jd) = ac + j^2bd + jad + jbc$$

$$= (ac - bd) + j(ad + bc)$$

(2) However, if the vectors are expressed in exponential form we have a vector $r_1 e^{j\phi_1}$ to be multiplied by $r_2 e^{j\phi_2}$.

Thus we have $r_1 e^{j\phi_1} \times r_2 e^{j\phi_2} = r_1 r_2 e^{j(\phi_1 + \phi_2)}$.

Example

A sinusoidal quantity $\theta = 20\sin(30t + 0.5)$ is operated on by a complex vector $(3 + j4)$. Determine an expression for the resultant.

Solution

In exponential form $\bar{\theta} = 20 e^{j(30t + 0.5)}$.

Operating complex vector $= 3 + j4 = \sqrt{\{3^2 + 4^2\}}\, e^{j\phi}$

where $\phi = \tan^{-1} 4/3 = 0.927$ radians.

$\therefore$ Operating complex vector $= 5\,e^{j0\cdot927}$

$\therefore$ resultant $= 5\,e^{j0\cdot927} \times 20\,e^{j(30t+0\cdot5)}$

$$= 100\,e^{j(30t+1\cdot427)}$$

Expressed as a sine wave the resultant becomes $100 \sin(30t + 1\cdot427)$.

3.9.2 Division

Division may again proceed by either of two methods:

(1) Suppose we are to divide a vector $a + jb$ by an operator $c + jd$, then the problem is to express $\dfrac{a + jb}{c + jd}$ as an ordinary complex number.

The method of doing this is to multiply both numerator and denominator by the complex number $c - jd$, which is called the *conjugate* of $c + jd$. The fraction is unchanged in value by this operation which is equivalent to multiplying by unity, but the denominator now becomes real number, viz.

$$(c + jd)(c - jd) = c^2 + d^2$$

The whole operation is as follows:

$$\frac{a + jb}{c + jd} = \frac{a + jb}{c + jd} \times \frac{c - jd}{c - jd} = \frac{ac + bd + j(bc - ad)}{c^2 + d^2}$$

$$= \frac{ac + bd}{c^2 + d^2} + j\,\frac{bc - ad}{c^2 + d^2}$$

which is in the form of an ordinary complex number. It is the method here which is important rather than the result.

(2) Suppose we are to divide a vector $r_1\,e^{j\phi_1}$ by an operator $r_2\,e^{j\phi_2}$, then

$$r_1\,e^{j\phi_1} \div r_2\,e^{j\phi_2} = \frac{r_1}{r_2}\,e^{j(\phi_1 - \phi_2)}$$

This procedure is so simple that where the final answer is most useful in the exponential form, it is probably worth converting from the co-ordinate form before dividing. Conversion to the exponential form is also useful when determining the nth power or the nth root of a complex number.

EXAMPLES FOR SOLUTION

1. Simplify the following: ¦(i) $(-7 + j3) - (2 + j8)$, (ii) $(8 - j5) + (3 + j2)$, (iii) $(-3 - j5) + (7 + j8)$, (iv) $(-9 - j4) - (8 + j3)$, (v) $5e^{j1\cdot2} - 7e^{j0\cdot3}$.

2. Simplify the following: (i) $(8 - j3)(3 - j)$, (ii) $(-8 + j3)(-3 + j)$, (iii) $(6 - j2)(-9 + j2)$, (iv) $\dfrac{8 - j6}{3 + j7}$, (v) $\dfrac{7 + j5}{4 - j2}$, (vi) $\dfrac{-2 + j}{-5 + j8}$, (vii) $\dfrac{-3 - j2}{-6 - j6}$, (viii) $5e^{j\pi/2} \times 6e^{j\pi}$ (express the answer in coordinate form), (ix) $\dfrac{7 - j2}{3\,e^{j1\cdot1}}$ (express the answer in exponential form), (x) $\dfrac{-3 + j2}{(3 + j)(-2 + j)}$.

3. Express £j^j in pence!

4. Express $\theta_1 = 8\sin(\omega t + \pi/4)$ and $\theta_2 = 3\sin(\omega t - \pi/8)$ as complex numbers and hence find their vector sum (*a*) as a complex number, (*b*) in exponential form, and (*c*) expressed as a sine wave.

5. The sinusoidal quantity $\theta = 7\sin(\omega t + \pi/8)$ is to be multiplied by a complex operator $(3 + j5)$; convert θ to a complex number and find the result of multiplication (*a*) as a complex number and (*b*) expressed as a sine wave.

6. Simplify (i) $\sqrt{\{(3 + j6)(-2 - j3)\}}$, (ii) $\sqrt{\left\{\dfrac{2 - j3}{-6 - j7}\right\}}$, (iii) $\dfrac{(2 + j)^2}{\sqrt{\{-3 - j2\}}}$.

Chapter Four

The Principles of Mechanics and Simple Electrodynamics Using SI Units

4.1 Introduction

Mechanical engineers in Britain have, in the past, tended to prefer to use the F.P.S. system of units when handling problems in mechanics. When one is dealing with hybrid subjects, such as control engineering, where problems in mechanics form only part of the subject, there are many disadvantages associated with the use of this system. For many years engineers throughout the world have used the rationalized M.K.S. system of units to specify electrical quantities. Thus, when the electrical parts of problems in control engineering are always expressed in M.K.S. units, it becomes tedious and prone to error to be continuously converting to F.P.S. in order to solve the mechanical section. Apart from this, the M.K.S. system has real advantages for the mechanical engineer in his own field. In this system the units of force and mass are different and the confusion normally arising between the lb force and the lb mass does not exist. Furthermore the use of absolute units in the M.K.S. system does not bring about a unit of force which is too small for practical purposes (M.K.S. unit of force, i.e. the newton, is about a quarter of a pound force). Engineers never favoured the F.P.S. absolute unit of force, the poundal, because it was too small.

The real beauty of the M.K.S. system is that it is capable of becoming, and will inevitably become, an international language used by all technologists and scientists throughout the world. Translation and conversion of systems of units will become redundant, with an attendant increase in efficiency and understanding. In fact at the time of preparation of the second edition of this book (1972) the International System of Units (SI) provides a coherent system comprising the metre, the kilogramme, the second, the ampere, the degree Kelvin, the candela, the radian and the steradian. This system has been adopted by the International Standards Organization and by the International Electrotechnical Commission and is expected to become the generally-accepted metric unit system throughout the world.

The main purpose of this chapter is to define and summarize the quantities which normally occur in such subjects as applied mechanics and principles of electricity but which are particularly applicable to the study of control engineering. The SI system will be used exclusively. The work will be covered in three sections dealing respectively with translational mechanics, rotational mechanics, and simple electrodynamics. The student should in no way regard this chapter as a substitute for complete courses in applied mechanics or principles of electricity. It is designed to summarize the information which should be particularly appreciated when approaching the subject of control engineering.

4.2 Translational Mechanics

4.2.1 Position

The position x of a point moving in a straight line is defined as its distance from an arbitrary reference. The SI unit of position is the metre (abbreviation m).

4.2.2 Velocity

The velocity v of a moving point at any time is the rate of change of its position with respect to time. Using the calculus notation

$$v = \frac{dx}{dt}$$

The units of velocity are metres per second (abbreviation m/s).

Example

The motion of a point along a straight line is described by the equation

$$x = 10t + 25t^2$$

Determine its velocity at $t = 3$ sec.

Solution

Differentiating we have

$$\frac{dx}{dt} = 10 + 50t$$

$\therefore$ at $t = 3$ sec the velocity $\dfrac{dx}{dt} = 10 + 150 = 160$ m/s.

45

4.2.3 *Acceleration*

The acceleration of a moving point at any time is the rate of change of its velocity with respect to time. Using the calculus notation

$$a = \frac{\mathrm{d}v}{\mathrm{d}t} = \frac{\mathrm{d}^2 x}{\mathrm{d}t^2}$$

The units of acceleration are metres per second per second (abbreviation m/s^2).

4.2.4 *Mass*

The mass m of a body is the quantity of matter in the body. The unit of mass is the kilogram (abbreviation kg).

4.2.5 *Force*

Force F is any cause which produces or tends to produce a change in the existing state of rest of a body, or its uniform motion in a straight line. The unit of force is the newton (abbreviation N). A force of 1 N is defined as that force which will give a mass of 1 kg an acceleration of 1 m/s^2.

Newton's second law relating force, mass and acceleration is:

$$F \text{ (newtons)} = m \text{ (kg)} \times a \text{ (m/s}^2)$$

Note, the 'weight' of a mass of 1 kg, i.e. its force downwards, is 9·81 N; the kilogram should *never* be used as a unit of force.

4.2.6 *Work*

When a force moves its point of application it is said to do work, and the measure of the work is the product of the force and the distance through which the point of application moves in the direction of the force.

If a force F newtons acts for a distance of x metres in its own direction,

$$\text{work done } W = F \text{ (newtons)} \times x \text{ (metres)}$$

$$= Fx \text{ (metre-newtons)}$$

A metre-newton of work is called a joule (abbreviation J).

Example

The slide of a machine tool moves in a straight line for 100 mm against a constant resisting force of 500 N. What is the total work done?

Solution

$$W = Fx$$

$$x = 100 \text{ mm} = 10^{-1} \text{ m} \left.\begin{array}{c} \\ \\ \end{array}\right\} \quad \therefore \quad \begin{array}{l} W = 500 \times 10^{-1} \text{ J} \\ = 50 \text{ J} \end{array}$$
$$F = 500 \text{ N}$$

4.2.7 Power

Power is defined as the rate of doing work. If P is the instantaneous power developed, then, using the calculus notation, we have

$$P = \frac{dW}{dt}$$

but the incremental work done dW when a force F moves its point of application through an incremental distance dx is given by

$$dW = F dx$$

$$\therefore \qquad P = F\frac{dx}{dt}$$

$$= \text{Force} \times \text{velocity}$$

The instantaneous power is rarely used in engineering work, the average power in a given period of time being regarded as a more practically useful measure.

The unit of power is the watt (abbreviation W) which is equal to a rate of working of 1 J/s.

4.2.8 Energy

The energy of a body is its capacity for doing work. Since the energy of a body is measured by the work it can do, the units of energy will be the same as those of work, i.e. joules.

In dynamics there are two forms of energy, *kinetic* and *potential*.

Kinetic energy of a body is the energy it possesses by virtue of its motion and is given by kinetic energy $U = \frac{1}{2}mv^2$ where $m = $ mass of body, and $v = $ velocity of body.

The potential energy of a body is the work it can do in moving from its actual position to some reference position.

For a more detailed treatment of energy and general elementary translational mechanics, the literature[6] should be consulted.

4.2.9 Elasticity

Certain materials and devices (such as springs) extend when a force is applied to them. So long as the force is not excessive the extension x is proportional to the applied force F.

The graph of Fig. 4.1 illustrates this law, which may be formulated as

$$F = kx$$

where k is a constant called the 'stiffness' having units of newtons per metre. The reciprocal of stiffness is termed the 'compliance'.

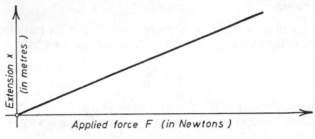

Fig. 4.1 *Illustrating elasticity.*

4.2.10 Friction

When mechanical surfaces are operated in sliding contact, there exist at least three types of retarding forces which are called friction:

  (i) Coulomb friction is a constant opposing force (independent of velocity).

  (ii) Stiction is the force required to initiate relative motion when the surfaces are at rest. In general, surfaces at rest appear to

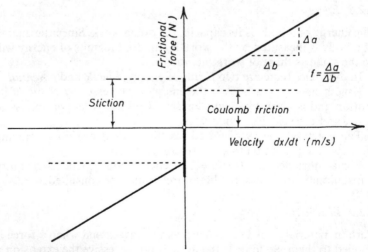

Fig. 4.2 *A graph illustrating the three types of friction.*

48

stick, and the force required to initiate motion is greater than the force required to maintain motion.

(iii) Viscous friction (which often predominates in control problems) is a force proportional to the relative velocity between the surfaces. In mathematical terms:

$$\text{Viscous friction force} \propto \text{velocity}, \mathrm{d}x/\mathrm{d}t$$

$$\therefore \qquad \text{Viscous frictional force} = f\frac{\mathrm{d}x}{\mathrm{d}t}$$

where f = viscous frictional constant in newtons per m/s.

The three types of frictional force may be represented graphically as shown in Fig. 4.2.

4.3 Rotational Mechanics

The summary of formulae given in this paragraph applies only to systems whose axis of rotation is *fixed*.

4.3.1 Angular Position

The angular position of a point P moving in a circle centre O is defined as the angle θ made between the line OP and a reference direction OA (see Fig. 4.3).

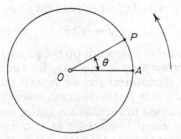

Fig. 4.3 *Angular position of a point moving in a circle.*

The unit of angular position is the radian (abbreviation rad).

4.3.2 Angular Velocity

The angular velocity ω of a point moving in a circle at any time is the rate of change of its angular position with respect to time. Using the calculus notation

$$\omega = \frac{\mathrm{d}\theta}{\mathrm{d}t}$$

The units of angular velocity are radians per second (abbreviation rad/s). Often, angular velocity is quoted in revolutions per minute or per second and it is then necessary to convert into the correct units before substituting into any formula.

4.3.3 Angular Acceleration

The angular acceleration α of a point moving in a circle at any time is its rate of change of angular velocity with respect to time. Using the calculus notation

$$\alpha = \frac{d\omega}{dt} = \frac{d^2\theta}{dt^2}$$

The units of angular acceleration are radians per second per second (abbreviation rad/s^2).

4.3.4 Moment of Inertia

If the mass of every element of a body be multiplied by the square of its distance from an axis, the sum of the products is called the *moment of inertia* of the body about that axis. Thus, if m represents the mass of an element and r denotes its distance from the axis, the moment of inertia is $\sum mr^2$.

If M represents the whole mass then we may define a quantity called the radius of gyration k such that

$$Mk^2 = \sum mr^2$$

The moment of inertia J of a body is thus given by

$$J = Mk^2$$

The radius of gyration k depends on the geometry of the body and its theoretical determination is only easy for simple shapes. A comprehensive analytical treatment and a reference table giving values of k^2 for various bodies may be found in reference 7.

The student is advised to regard moment of inertia as being equivalent to 'angular mass'; equations in rotational mechanics are generally analogous to those in translational mechanics. Wherever an equation occurs in translational mechanics involving mass m, there is an equivalent equation in rotational mechanics involving moment of inertia J.

The units of moment of inertia are kilogram metres^2 (abbreviation $kg\ m^2$).

4.3.5 Torque

Torque is the rotational equivalent of force. It is that which produces or tends to produce angular acceleration. If a force of F newtons is acting at right angles to a radius of d metres from a point

$$\text{torque } T = Fd \text{ newton metres}$$

The newton-metre is abbreviated N m or Nm.

The total torque T N m acting on a body of moment of inertia J kg m^2 may be related to the angular acceleration α that it produces, by an adaptation of Newton's second law. In mathematical form

$$T = J\alpha$$

This equation is of considerable importance in the solution of problems on torsional vibrations (chapter 6) and on the dynamics of control systems (chapters 8 and 9).

4.3.6 Work, Power and Energy in Rotational Systems

When torque T N m rotates through an angle θ rad, work W is done where

$$W = T\theta \text{ joules}$$

Power P is the rate of doing work and is given by

$$P = \frac{dW}{dt} = T\frac{d\theta}{dt}$$

But

$$d\theta/dt = \omega,$$

thus

$$P = T\omega$$

where ω = angular velocity.

Kinetic energy of a rotating body $= \frac{1}{2}J\omega^2$.

4.3.7 Torsional Elasticity

When an elastic material or device (such as a torsional spring) has a torque T applied to it, it twists through an angle θ. So long as the torque is not excessive the angle of twist is proportional to the applied torque.

In mathematical terms

$$T = K\theta$$

where K is a constant called the 'torsional stiffness' (or just stiffness). The units of K are N m/rad.

4.3.8 Friction in Rotational Systems

In §4.2.10, it was explained how, when mechanical surfaces are operating in sliding contact, various types of retarding forces exist. These frictional forces give rise to frictional torques in rotational systems. Thus we have the three basic types of frictional torque, namely coulomb frictional torque, stiction torque and viscous frictional torque as shown in Fig. 4.4.

51

The viscous component of frictional torque often predominates in control systems and this may be described by the relationship

$$\text{Frictional torque} = F\frac{d\theta}{dt}$$

where F is the viscous frictional torque constant having units of N m per rad/s.

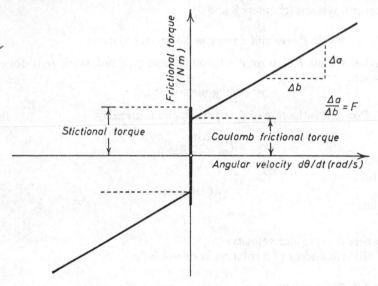

Fig. 4.4 *Frictional torques.*

4.4 Simple Electrodynamics

4.4.1 Electric Charge

Electric charge is the quantity of electricity. The smallest quantity of electricity which can exist on its own is the charge on an electron. It is so small that for practical purposes it has been found necessary to invent a unit of charge called the coulomb (abbreviation C). The charge on an electron is approximately 1.6×10^{-19} coulomb. Electric charge is designated by the symbol Q (steady value) or q (instantaneous value).

4.4.2 Electric Current

Electric current is defined as the rate of transfer of charge. The symbol i is used to indicate the instantaneous value of current and

I to indicate the steady value. Mathematically *i* and *q* are related by the equations

$$i = \frac{dq}{dt}$$

or

$$q = \int i \, dt$$

The unit of current is the ampere (abbreviation A) which is defined as a rate of transfer of electric charge equal to 1 coulomb per second.

These equations could be used to define the unit of current but it is more normal nowadays to define the ampere as that current which, when flowing in each of two infinitely long parallel conductors in a vacuum, separated by 1 metre between centres causes each conductor to have a force acting upon it of 2×10^{-7} newtons per metre length of the conductor.

The coulomb is then defined as the quantity of electricity which flows past a given point of a circuit when a current of 1 A is maintained for 1 sec.

4.4.3 Electromotive Force (e.m.f.)

An electromotive force is best regarded as that which impels electricity through a conductor. In general, energy is dissipated when electricity passes through a conductor and this energy has in fact been transferred from the source of e.m.f. to the conductor.

The amount of energy which a source imparts to a load when charge passes through it can be regarded as a measure of the effectiveness of the source. The e.m.f. *E* of a source is defined as the ratio of the energy imparted *U*, to the charge *Q* passing through the source.

Mathematically

$$E = \frac{U}{Q}$$

Whilst this definition of e.m.f. is fundamental, it is often more convenient to relate the e.m.f. to the rate at which energy is imparted (i.e. the power *P*) and the rate at which charge is flowing (i.e. the current *I*).

If a steady current *I* is flowing for a time *t*, delivering total energy *U*, then

$$Q = It$$

and

$$U = Pt$$

∴

$$E = \frac{Pt}{It} = \frac{P}{I}$$

An e.m.f. can be produced in a number of different ways:

(*a*) Chemically by means of a battery.
(*b*) Electromagnetically by means of a generator.

(*c*) Thermoelectrically by the effect of heat applied to the junction of two dissimilar metals.

(*d*) Electrostatically by means of special machines such as the Wimshurst.

(*e*) By the action of light on certain substances.

Methods (*a*) and (*b*) are of considerable practical importance as sources of electrical power. Method (*c*) is used as a method of measuring temperature electrically and finds application in temperature-control systems. Method (*e*) is useful as a detecting device in certain systems, e.g. burglar alarms, fire alarms, etc. Method (*d*) is of little practical importance.

Batteries and generators are represented symbolically in circuit diagrams as shown in Fig. 4.5.

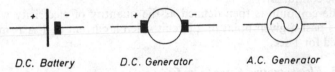

D.C. Battery   D.C. Generator   A.C. Generator

Fig. 4.5 *Symbolic representation of sources of e.m.f.*

The unit of e.m.f. is the volt (abbreviation V). A source is said to have an e.m.f. of 1 V if it imparts 1 joule of energy for each coulomb of charge transferred.

It will be noted that the d.c. sources symbolized in Fig. 4.5 are labelled with plus and minus signs. These indicate the polarity of the terminals. A source of e.m.f. attempts to force current to flow from the positive to the negative terminal, through the external circuit.

4.4.4 *Potential Difference*

When a simple circuit is fed from a source of e.m.f., energy is extracted from the source and delivered to the circuit. The potential difference (p.d.) between any two points in the circuit is the energy abstracted from the current between the points, per unit of the charge transferred. There is evidently a considerable similarity between e.m.f. and p.d. The unit of p.d. is exactly the same as the unit of e.m.f., namely the volt; the difference between e.m.f. and p.d. is best judged from the following equations:

(*a*) For a source:

Power supplied = e.m.f. × current
Energy supplied = e.m.f. × charge transferred

(*b*) For a circuit element:

Power consumed = p.d. × current
Energy consumed = p.d. × charge transferred

The symbol used to represent potential difference is V.

4.4.5 Resistance

Ohm's Law

When an e.m.f. E is applied across a conductor the current I which flows through it is proportional to the e.m.f. This is known as Ohm's law. In actual fact few conductors obey this law; a metallic conductor which is held at constant temperature does but one which is allowed to become hot does not. Conductors which do obey Ohm's law are termed 'linear', those which do not are 'non-linear'. It should, however, be understood that temperature variation is only one of several causes of non-linearities in conductors.

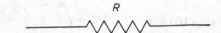

Fig. 4.6 *The circuit symbol for a resistor of resistance R.*

Ohm's law may be expressed mathematically as

$$I \propto E$$
or
$$E \propto I$$
∴
$$E = RI$$

where R is a constant for the particular conductor called its 'resistance'. The unit of resistance is the ohm (abbreviation Ω). A conductor has a resistance of 1 Ω if a current of 1 A will flow through it when an e.m.f. of 1 V is applied across it. The circuit symbol for a resistor is shown in Fig. 4.6.

Power Dissipated in Resistors

When current flows through a resistor energy is dissipated in the form of heat. Consider the circuit of Fig. 4.7.

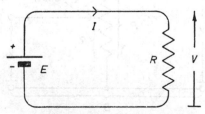

Fig. 4.7 *Simple circuit.*

55

The battery drives a current I through the resistor, thus using Ohm's law

$$E = RI \qquad (1)$$

Power supplied by source $= E \times I$. All this power is dissipated in the resistor in the form of heat. It will be noted that if we multiply both sides of equation (1) by I we obtain

$$E \times I = RI^2$$

Thus RI^2 is also an expression for the power dissipated.

Example

Find the current taken by a 100-W lamp when connected to a 250-V supply.

Solution

$$\text{Power} = 100 = E \times I = 250 \times I$$

$$\therefore \qquad I = 100/250 = 0\cdot4 \text{ A}$$

The P.D. Across a Resistor

If a current I flows through a resistor of resistance R then a p.d. V volts exists across it where

$$V = RI$$

The polarity of the p.d. is as shown in Fig. 4.7. Current flows through the resistor from the end of positive polarity towards the end of negative polarity.

The Principle of the Potentiometer

If fine resistance wire is wound evenly around a card and the ends brought out to a pair of terminals, a slider may be made to make electrical contact at points along the wire lying between the two terminals. Such an arrangement is symbolized in Fig. 4.8.

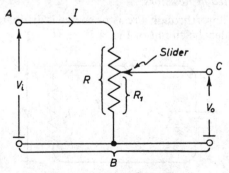

Fig. 4.8 *The potentiometer.*

The total resistance R between the terminals A and B will remain constant (so long as no external circuitry is connected between C and B). The resistance R_1 will vary as a direct function of the mechanical position of the slider. If no current is being drawn from the slider:

$$V_i = IR$$

and

$$V_o = IR_1$$

hence, combining, we obtain

$$\frac{V_o}{V_i} = \frac{R_1}{R}$$

This relationship finds practical application in control engineering in which the device is used as a component in one form of positional error detector.

Internal Resistance of a Source

It should be realized that all sources of e.m.f. have their own 'internal resistance'. It acts as though in series with the source. Thus if a d.c. source of 'open-circuit' e.m.f. E and internal resistance R_i is connected across a resistor of resistance R_x then the current I which will flow is given by

$$I = \frac{E}{R_i + R_x}$$

Often the internal resistance is very much smaller than the external resistance being connected. In such cases little error is introduced by assuming that the source resistance is zero.

Example

A source of internal resistance 0·1 Ω and e.m.f. 20 V is connected across a resistor whose resistance is 10 Ω. Determine the current which will flow (*a*) taking into account the effect of source resistance, and (*b*) neglecting source resistance.

Solution

(*a*)

$$I = \frac{E}{R_x + R_i} = \frac{20}{10 + 0·1} = 1·98 \text{ A}$$

(*b*)

$$I = \frac{E}{R_x} = \frac{20}{10} = 2·0 \text{ A}$$

Variation of Resistance with Temperature

The resistance of metallic conductors usually increases with increase in temperature. The resistance of a copper wire, for example, increases by about 20 % as its temperature rises from 15°C to 65°C.

The resistance R of a conductor at temperature $t°C$ is related to its resistance R_o at $0°C$ by the formula

$$R = R_o(1 + \alpha t)$$

where α is termed the 'temperature coefficient of resistance'. Whilst α is positive for most metals it is negative for carbon.

The variation of resistance with temperature is a nuisance in some engineering applications but the phenomenon is used in certain control devices as a means of detecting temperature changes.

4.4.6 Basic Electromagnetism

When a current of I amperes passes through a coil of wire of N turns a 'magnetic flux' Φ is set up. The existence of the magnetic flux may readily be proved by bringing a magnetic compass near to the coil. The magnitude of the flux may be determined by means of various measuring instruments (a fluxmeter for instance). It has been found experimentally that for *air-cored* coils the magnitude of the flux Φ is dependent upon the product NI which is called the magnetomotive force (m.m.f.), i.e.

$$\Phi \propto NI$$

or

$$NI \propto \Phi$$

or

$$NI = S\Phi$$

where S is a constant for a particular arrangement and is called the 'reluctance'.

For iron-cored coils S is not a constant.

The amount of flux passing normally through unit area (i.e. 1 m^2) is called the flux density B, i.e.

$$B = \frac{\Phi}{A}$$

where $A =$ area in square metres.

The unit of magnetic flux Φ is the weber (abbreviated Wb). This unit will be defined later. The unit of flux density is the weber per square metre (Wb/m^2) or the tesla T. The unit of m.m.f. is the ampere-turn (At).

The m.m.f. gradient H is defined as the m.m.f. per unit length of a magnetic circuit, i.e.

$$H = \frac{NI}{l} \text{ ampere-turns per metre}$$

where $l =$ mean length of magnetic circuit in metres.

The m.m.f. gradient is often also termed the 'magnetizing force', or 'magnetic field strength'.

4.4.7 Electromagnetic Induction

The Flux-cutting Rule

The conductor shown in Fig. 4.9 has a length *l* metres and it is placed at right angles to a magnetic field of flux density *B* Wb/m². It is then moved with a velocity of *v* m/s in a direction which is at right angles to both the conductor and the magnetic field.

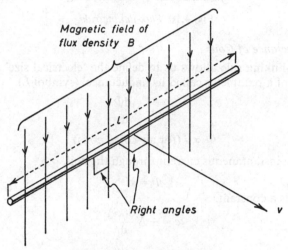

Fig. 4.9 *Flux-cutting rule.*

It may be shown that an e.m.f. of *E* volts is induced across the ends of the conductor where *E* is given by

$$E = Blv$$

Flux-linking Rule

When a coil of *N* turns is linking with a changing flux Φ an e.m.f. *e* appears across the ends of the coil given by

$$e = -N\frac{\mathrm{d}\Phi}{\mathrm{d}t} \text{ volts}$$

The negative sign indicates that the polarity of the induced e.m.f. is such that any current which may flow due to its existence will produce an m.m.f. which will oppose the initiating flux Φ.

This rule allows us to define the unit of magnetic flux. A flux is said to have a strength of one weber if when falling to zero at a uniform rate in one second it induces an e.m.f. of one volt per turn in a coil with which it links.

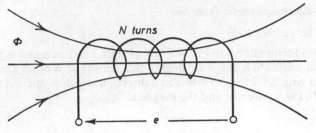

Fig. 4.10 *Flux-linking rule.*

Self Inductance of Coils

The flux-linking rule allows us to define the 'electrical size' of a coil in terms of a parameter called its 'inductance' (symbol L).

Now
$$e = -N\frac{d\Phi}{dt}$$

but $\Phi \propto i$ (for air-cored coils)

where $i =$ instantaneous current through the coil.

∴ $$\Phi = ki$$

where k is a constant.

∴
$$e = -N\frac{d(ki)}{dt}$$

$$= -Nk\frac{di}{dt}$$

The quantity Nk or $N\Phi/i$ is a constant for a particular coil called its self inductance L, i.e.

$$e = -L\frac{di}{dt}$$

The existence of the negative sign often leads to confusion when setting up the dynamic equations of physical systems, and the equation

$$v = +L\frac{di}{dt}$$

where $v =$ the potential difference across the coil, is often found to be less confusing.

The unit of inductance is the henry (abbreviation H). A coil is said to have an inductance of 1 H if, when a current flowing through it is changing at a rate of 1 A/sec, an e.m.f. of 1 V is induced across its ends.

The circuit symbol for a pure inductor of inductance L is shown in Fig. 4.11 (*a*). Real coils possess resistance R as well as inductance L and are represented as shown in Fig. 4.11 (*b*).

Energy U is stored in the magnetic field of an inductor where U is given by

$$U = \tfrac{1}{2}Li^2$$

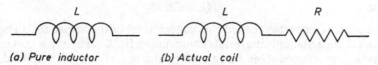

(a) Pure inductor   (b) Actual coil

Fig. 4.11 *Circuit symbols for inductors.*

4.4.8 Electromagnetic Production of Mechanical Force (The Motor Rule)

The conductor shown in Fig. 4.12 has a length l metres and is placed at right angles to a magnetic field of flux density B Wb/m². A steady current I is made to flow through the conductor.

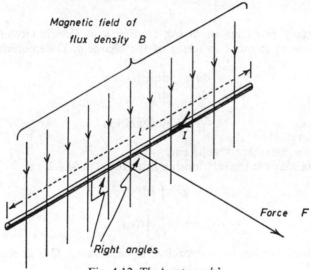

Fig. 4.12 *The 'motor rule'.*

It may be shown that a force of F newtons in the direction shown will exist, where F is given by

$$F = BIl$$

4.4.9 Capacitance

When two conductors are in close proximity to each other they possess the ability to store electric charge if an e.m.f. be applied

61

across them. The amount of charge Q stored in a given system is dependent on the e.m.f. E applied, i.e.

$$Q \propto E$$

or $$Q = CE$$

where C is a constant called the 'capacitance' of the 'capacitor'. The unit of capacitance is the farad (abbreviation F). A capacitor is said to have a capacitance of one farad if, when an e.m.f. of one volt is applied, a charge of one coulomb is stored.

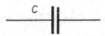

Fig. 4.13 *The symbol representing a capacitor.*

The instantaneous potential difference v across a capacitor containing an instantaneous charge q is related by a similar equation

$$q = Cv$$

In many problems involving transients in electric circuits it is inconvenient to work in terms of the charge q. Differentiating we obtain

$$\frac{dq}{dt} = C\frac{dv}{dt}$$

but $$\frac{dq}{dt} = i \text{ by definition}$$

where i = instantaneous current.

Or we may use the relationship introduced in §4.4.2, i.e.

$$q = \int i\,dt$$

thus $$v = \frac{1}{C}\int i\,dt$$

The circuit symbol for a capacitor of capacitance C is as shown in Fig. 4.13.

A capacitor stores energy U in its electric field where U is given by

$$U = \tfrac{1}{2}Cv^2 \text{ joules}$$

4.4.10 Kirchhoff's Laws

The Mesh Law

The mesh law states that in a closed electric circuit the algebraic sum of the e.m.f.'s acting round that circuit is equal to the algebraic sum of the p.d.'s round the same circuit.

To illustrate how this law may be applied in general to an electric network, consider the circuit of Fig. 4.14 which is fairly complicated.

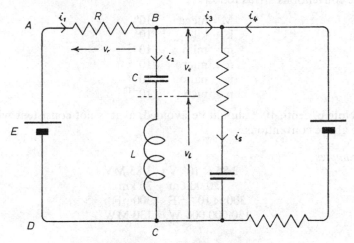

Fig. 4.14 *Electric network.*

A typical closed circuit is ABCD. The only e.m.f. acting round the path is E. There are p.d.'s across R, C and L given by

$$v_r = i_1 R$$

$$v_c = \frac{1}{C} \int i_2 \, dt$$

$$v_1 = L \frac{di_2}{dt}$$

Thus
$$E = v_r + v_c + v_1$$

$$= i_1 R + \frac{1}{C} \int i_2 \, dt + L \frac{di_2}{dt}$$

The Junction Law

The junction law states that the algebraic sum of the currents entering a junction in an electric network is zero.

For example, in Fig. 4.14 point B is a junction. Taking currents towards the junction as conventionally positive and away as negative we have

$$i_1 - i_2 - i_3 = 0$$

4.5 Abbreviations for Multiples and Sub-multiples

It is frequently found in practice, that the basic unit of a given quantity is very much too large or too small for its associated magnitude to be written shortly. To avoid writing large numbers and numbers with factors of ten attached, we prefix the abbreviated unit by a symbol. The conventions are as follows:

M	mega	10^6
k	kilo	10^3
m	milli	10^{-3}
μ	micro	10^{-6}
n	nano	10^{-9}
p	pico	10^{-12}

Note c, centi, 10^{-2} should be avoided, as it is not consistent with the above conventions.

Examples

$$3{\cdot}85 \times 10^6 \text{ V} = 3{\cdot}85 \text{ MV}$$
$$20,000 \text{ m} = 20 \text{ km}$$
$$300 \times 10^{-12} \text{ F} = 300 \text{ pF}$$
$$130,000,000 \text{ W} = 130 \text{ MW}$$

EXAMPLES FOR SOLUTION

1. The position x of a particle moving in a straight line is given by the equation

$$x = (7t + 8t^2) \text{ metres}$$

Determine (i) the velocity at $t = 2$ sec, and (ii) the acceleration at $t = 5$ sec.

2. The acceleration of a particle moving in a straight line is given by the equation

$$\frac{d^2 x}{dt^2} = (3 + 2t) \text{ m/s}^2$$

Find (i) the velocity at $t = 3$ sec assuming the velocity at $t = 0$ is 2 m/s, and (ii) the position at $t = 2$ sec assuming both the velocity and the position are zero at $t = 0$.

3. A force of 120 N acts on a mass of 10 kg. Determine the acceleration of the mass.

4. What force will give a mass of 50 kg an acceleration of 100 m/s²?

5. The position x of a particle moving in a straight line is given by

$$x = 20 \sin 20t \text{ metres}$$

Determine (i) the maximum velocity, and (ii) the maximum acceleration of the particle.

6. A rocket in free space exerts a constant motive force of 10^4 N. The rocket at the instant of firing the motor has a mass of 2000 kg but as the fuel burns it loses mass at a rate of 0·5 kg/s. Assuming the rocket has zero initial velocity and acceleration and that there are no retarding forces, determine expressions for the velocity and acceleration at time t from the instant of firing ($t \ll 4000$ sec). Calculate the values of each of these quantities at $t = 10$ sec.

7. A car weighing 2500 kg is accelerating at 0·5 m/s² up an incline of 1 in 50, the frictional resistance being 0·12 N per kg.

Find the kW power exerted when the speed is 10 m/s.

8. A destroyer is propelled at a speed of 20 m/s by means of engines whose effective power is 20 MW. Calculate the resistance to the motion of the ship, and

assuming that the resistance varies as the square of the speed, what power would be required for a speed of 22 m/s.

9. A flywheel of mass of 1000 kg and radius of gyration 1 m is rotating once every second. What is its kinetic energy and how long will it take to come to rest under the influence of a coulomb frictional torque of 40 N m?

10. A flywheel of mass 5000 kg is rotating at an angular velocity of 10 rad/s. It is found experimentally that its velocity falls by a factor of a quarter in 300 sec when the flywheel is subjected to a retarding viscous frictional torque of 100 N m per rad/s.

Determine the radius of gyration of the flywheel and the speed to which it would fall if the retarding torque is maintained for a further 300 sec.

11. An electric motor produces a constant torque of 20 N m when running at a steady speed of 1500 rev/min. Determine its output power rating in kW.

12. An electric motor takes 37 A at 250 V. Neglecting all losses, calculate the output power of the motor in kW and the number of joules of work which can be obtained from the motor in 5 min.

13. The energy absorbed in 6 min by a piece of electrical equipment of resistance 6·16 kΩ is 2×10^5 joules. Calculate (a) the current taken by it, (b) the quantity of electricity in coulombs taken in 2 min.

14. Determine the running resistance of a 100-W lamp designed to operate on a 250-V supply.

15. How many coulombs will flow in 5 hours if an e.m.f. of 2 mV is applied across the ends of a resistor of resistance 1 $\mu\Omega$?

16. A battery of internal resistance 0·5 Ω and open-circuit e.m.f. 10 V is connected across a resistor of resistance 5 Ω. Determine (i) the current which will flow, and (ii) the p.d. which will appear across the 5-Ω resistor.

17. When a resistor of 1 kΩ resistance is connected across a 100 V d.c. source, a current of 40 mA flows. Determine (i) the internal resistance of the source, (ii) the power dissipated in the 1-kΩ resistor, and (iii) the p.d. which appears across the 1-kΩ resistor.

18. The flux density inside a coil is 0·05 Wb/m², and the cross-sectional area of the coil is 2×10^{-3} m², calculate the value of the total flux in μWb.

19. An all-metal aircraft having a wing-span of 30 m is flying horizontally at a speed of 150 m/s. Calculate the e.m.f. generated between wing-tips, assuming the vertical component of the earth's field to be 40 μWb/m².

20. Calculate the inductance of a coil in which 25 V is induced when the current varies at a rate of 150 A/s.

21. At what rate is the current varying in a coil having an inductance of 500 μH if the induced e.m.f. is 10 V?

22. A coil having an inductance of 2 H and a resistance of 5 Ω is switched across a 100-V d.c. source of negligible internal resistance. Using Kirchhoff's mesh law, set up the differential equation relating the instantaneous current i which will flow to the time t.

23. A moving coil galvanometer has a square coil of 20 mm side with 120 turns; the coil can turn about a vertical axis, the restoring torque of the suspension being 1·5 × 10⁻⁶ N m per degree. The vertical sides of the coil move in a magnetic field of flux density 0·15 Wb/m², the field being directed radially relative to the axis of rotation. Find the sensitivity of the galvanometer in degrees deflection per mA.

24. A p.d. of 100 V exists across a 10-μF capacitor. Calculate the charge.

25. A d.c. source of negligible internal resistance and e.m.f. 100 V is switched across a 10-μF capacitor in series with a 1-MΩ resistor. Deduce a differential equation relating the instantaneous current i which will flow to the time t.

Chapter Five

The Solution of Linear Differential Equations with Constant Coefficients

5.1 Introduction

The dynamic behaviour of certain physical systems including linear, continuous control systems may be phrased in terms of linear differential equations containing constant coefficients. These equations are formulated using basic laws such as Newton's second law and Kirchhoff's laws. Consider for example an extremely simple problem involving an elastic, inertialess shaft connected to an inertialess, viscous damping paddle at the far end. The near end is being driven so that it moves with sinusoidal, angular oscillations of constant angular frequency ω and constant peak angular amplitude $\hat{\theta}_i$, so that the motion of the near end θ_i is described by

$$\theta_i = \hat{\theta}_i \sin \omega t$$

This arrangement is represented diagrammatically in Fig. 5.1.

The object is to set up an equation relating the motion of the paddle (θ_o) to the input motion (θ_i).

Let $\theta =$ angle of twist in the shaft, thus

$$\theta = \theta_i - \theta_o$$

Now torque transmitted through shaft to paddle is $K\theta$ and this must be balanced by the retarding torque due to the damping paddle $F d\theta_o/dt$, i.e.

$$F\frac{d\theta_o}{dt} = K\theta$$

$\therefore$
$$F\frac{d\theta_o}{dt} = K(\theta_i - \theta_o)$$

66

hence
$$F\frac{d\theta_o}{dt} + K\theta_o = K\theta_i$$

But
$$\theta_i = \hat{\theta}_i \sin \omega t$$

$\therefore$
$$F\frac{d\theta_o}{dt} + K\theta_o = K\hat{\theta}_i \sin \omega t$$

This is the differential equation describing the output motion of the system. The left-hand side of the equation is a description of the physical response of the system and the right-hand side represents the 'driving function', which is responsible for motion. The term driving function will be used henceforth to mean the right-hand side of the differential equation.

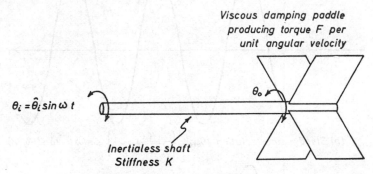

Fig. 5.1 *Simple mechanical system.*

The differential equation may be solved by using certain rules and its solution (which is called the 'response of the system') will be made up of two distinct parts:

(i) The **transient response** θ_{ot} (which mathematicians[8] call the complementary function); this part of the response occurs near to $t = 0$ and subsequently decays.

(ii) The **steady-state response** $\theta_{o\,ss}$ (which mathematicians[8] call the particular integral); this part of the response is continuously present from $t = 0$ to $t = \infty$, but at $t = \infty$, it is in fact the complete solution. The driving function is entirely responsible for the existence and nature of $\theta_{o\,ss}$.

The complete response θ_o is the sum of the transient and steady-state solutions, i.e.

$$\theta_o = \theta_{ot} + \theta_{o\,ss}$$

By means of rules which will be described later we may deduce that for the example which was considered:

$$\theta_{ot} = A\,e^{-Kt/F}$$

67

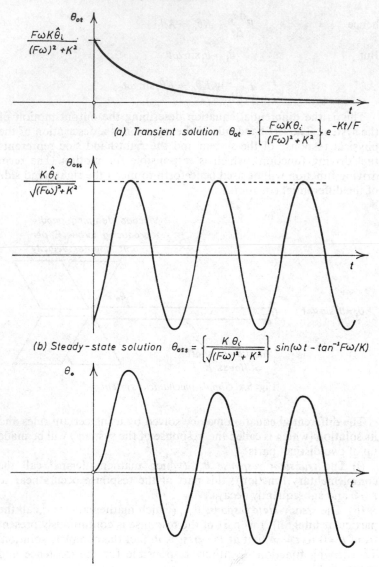

(a) Transient solution $\theta_{ot} = \left\{\dfrac{F\omega K\hat{\theta}_i}{(F\omega)^2 + K^2}\right\} e^{-Kt/F}$

(b) Steady-state solution $\theta_{oss} = \left\{\dfrac{K\theta_i}{\sqrt{(F\omega)^2 + K^2}}\right\} \sin(\omega t - \tan^{-1} F\omega/K)$

(c) Complete particular solution $\theta_o = \theta_{ot} + \theta_{oss}$

Fig. 5.2 *Response of simple system*

where A is an arbitrary constant,

and $\qquad \theta_{o\,ss} = \dfrac{K\hat{\theta}_i}{\sqrt{\{(F\omega)^2 + K^2\}}} \sin(\omega t - \tan^{-1} F\omega/K)$

68

The complete *general* solution is thus

$$\theta_o = A\,e^{-Kt/F} + \frac{K\hat{\theta}_i}{\sqrt{\{(F\omega)^2 + K^2\}}} \sin(\omega t - \tan^{-1} F\omega/K)$$

The arbitrary constant may only be found if the value of θ_o at the constant $t = 0$ is specified. This value is termed an 'initial condition'. In the present problem let us specify that at $t = 0$, $\theta_o = 0$, then the *particular* complete solution becomes

$$\theta_o = \frac{F\omega K\hat{\theta}_i}{\{(F\omega)^2 + K^2\}}\,e^{-Kt/F} + \frac{K\hat{\theta}_i}{\sqrt{\{(F\omega)^2 + K^2\}}} \sin(\omega t - \tan^{-1} F\omega/K)$$

The student should verify that this solution is correct by differentiation and substitution in the original differential equation. The transient, steady-state and complete particular responses of the system are represented graphically in Fig. 5.2.

It should be noted in Fig. 5.2 (*c*) how the transient response decays leaving only the steady-state response.

The equations to be discussed in this chapter are of the form

$$a_n \frac{d^n\theta}{dt^n} + a_{n-1}\frac{d^{n-1}\theta}{dt^{n-1}} + \ldots + a_1 \frac{d\theta}{dt} + a_o\theta = f(t)$$

where $f(t)$ is a function of time t, the driving function, θ is a physical quantity, the a's are constants and n is a positive integer. The solution to such a differential equation represents the response of a physical system and as in the example previously discussed this response is composed of a transient component θ_t and a steady-state component θ_{ss}.

There is a routine technique for finding θ_t which involves the solution of an ordinary equation of nth degree. For values of n equal to or less than 2, this may be solved algebraically. When n is greater than 2, unless the equation factorizes, it may only be solved approximately using arithmetic methods. There is no routine analytical method for finding θ_{ss} (unless the *Laplace transform*[9, 10] is used—see the Appendix), and a different technique is necessary for every different type of driving function. However, there are only a few types of driving function that occur in system design and analysis and it will be possible to give in this chapter suitable procedures for solving equations which feature them. For verification of the methods the literature[8] should be consulted.

5.2 Determination of the Transient Response θ_t

To find θ_t from the differential equation

$$a_n \frac{d^n\theta}{dt^n} + \ldots + a_1 \frac{d\theta}{dt} + a_o\theta = f(t)$$

the following procedure is used:

(i) The *auxiliary equation* in m is constructed. This is the algebraic equation formed by replacing $d^n\theta/dt^n$ by m^n, $d^{n-1}\theta/d^{n-1}t$ by m^{n-1} and so on down to $d\theta/dt$ by m and θ by 1 and taking the right-hand side as zero, i.e.

$$a_n m^n + \ldots a_1 m + a_o = 0$$

(ii) This equation is solved. In cases where $n \leqslant 2$ this is easy; for $n > 2$ a simple solution is only possible when the equation factorizes. However, the solution can always be obtained to some specified degree of accuracy and the values of m (roots of the equation) will fall into one of the following categories:

(a) different real roots, e.g.

$$4m^2 + 9m + 5 = 0$$

has roots $m = -\frac{5}{4}$ or -1

(b) complex conjugate roots, e.g.

$$4m^2 + 12m + 13 = 0$$

has roots $m = \dfrac{-3 \pm 2j}{2}$

(c) repeated roots, e.g.

$$4m^2 + 9m + \tfrac{81}{16} = 0$$

has the root $m = -1\frac{1}{8}$ repeated twice; this is because the equation factorizes into $(2m + \frac{9}{4})^2 = 0$ and each bracket gives $m = -1\frac{1}{8}$.

Notice that an equation of degree higher than 2 may have roots in all these categories, for instance the equation formed by multiplying the three examples together, i.e.

$$(4m^2 + 9m + 5)(4m^2 + 9m + 13)(4m^2 + 9m + \tfrac{81}{16}) = 0$$

has the six roots, two in each category.

(iii) Form θ_t as the sum of a number of terms as follows:

(a) for each different real root $m = \alpha$, a term of the form $A e^{\alpha t}$.

(b) for each pair of conjugate complex roots, $m = \alpha \pm j\omega$, a term of the form

$$e^{\alpha t}(A \cos \omega t + B \sin \omega t)$$

(c) for any number (p say) of repeated roots $m = \alpha$, a term of the form

$$(A_1 + A_2 t + \ldots + A_p t^{p-1}) e^{\alpha t}$$

Here A, B, A_1, A_2, etc. are arbitrary constants of integration. The actual value of these constants may be found by using the initial conditions. These are the values of $d^{n-1}\theta/dt^{n-1}$, $d^{n-2}\theta/dt^{n-2}$, ... θ

when $t = 0$. If the arbitrary constants are to be determined the initial conditions must be known. The method of determining the arbitrary constants is explained in §5.4. In general if the equation is nth order, there must be n arbitrary constants.

Examples

(1) Find the transient solution of the differential equation

$$5\frac{d\theta}{dt} + 2\theta = 3 \sin \omega t$$

Auxiliary equation is

$$5m + 2 = 0$$

$$\therefore \qquad m = -\tfrac{2}{5}$$

$$\therefore \qquad \theta_t = A e^{-2t/5}$$

(2) Find the transient solution of the equation

$$\frac{d^2 \theta}{dt^2} + 3\frac{d\theta}{dt} + 2\theta = 5t$$

Auxiliary equation is

$$(m + 2)(m + 1) = 0$$

Solutions are

$$m = -2 \quad \text{and} \quad m = -1$$

$$\therefore \qquad \theta_t = A e^{-2t} + B e^{-t}$$

(3) Find the transient solution of the equation

$$5\frac{d^2 \theta}{dt^2} + 3\frac{d\theta}{dt} + \theta = t e^{-3t}$$

Auxiliary equation is

$$5m^2 + 3m + 1 = 0$$

Solution is

$$m = \frac{-3 \pm \sqrt{(9 - 20)}}{10}$$

$$= -0.3 \pm j 0.332$$

Thus

$$\theta_t = e^{-0.3t}(A \cos 0.332t + B \sin 0.332t)$$

(4) Find the transient solution of the equation

$$\frac{d^2 \theta}{dt^2} + 4\frac{d\theta}{dt} + 4\theta = 5 e^{-3t} \sin 30t$$

Auxiliary equation is

$$m^2 + 4m + 4 = 0 \quad \text{or} \quad (m + 2)^2 = 0$$

$$\therefore \qquad m = -2$$

Thus

$$\theta_t = (A + Bt) e^{-2t}$$

71

(5) Find the transient solution of the equation

$$4\frac{d^2\theta}{dt^2} + \theta = 3$$

Auxiliary equation is

$$4m^2 + 1 = 0$$

∴

$$m = 0 \pm j0.5$$

Thus

$$\theta_t = e^{ot}(A\cos 0{\cdot}5t + B\sin 0{\cdot}5t)$$

$$= A\cos 0{\cdot}5t + B\sin 0{\cdot}5t$$

(6) Find the transient solution of the equation

$$\frac{d^2\theta}{dt^2} + 3\frac{d\theta}{dt} = 0$$

Auxiliary equation is

$$m^2 + 3m = 0,$$

∴

$$m(m + 3) = 0$$

∴

$$m = 0 \quad \text{or} \quad m = -3$$

Thus

$$\theta_t = A e^{ot} + B e^{-3t}$$

$$= A + B e^{-3t}$$

5.3 Determination of the Steady-state Response θ_{ss}

5.3.1 *The Operator D*

The method of determining the steady-state solution θ_{ss} depends largely on the type of driving function $f(t)$. In control engineering there are a number of important types which are frequently encountered:

   (i) Zero driving function ($f(t) = 0$ for $t > 0$).
   (ii) A step driving function ($f(t) = k$ for $t > 0$).
   (iii) A ramp driving function ($f(t) = kt$ for $t > 0$).
   (iv) A constant acceleration driving function ($f(t) = kt^2$ for $t > 0$).
   (v) An exponential driving function ($f(t) = ke^{\alpha t}$ for $t > 0$).
   (vi) A sinusoidal driving function ($f(t) = k\sin\omega t$ for $t > 0$).

Here k is a constant. The graphical representation of these driving functions has been discussed previously in chapter 2.

In the determination of the steady-state solution we shall use the operator D which stands for $\frac{d}{dt}$, D^2 will be used for $\frac{d^2}{dt^2}$, D^3 for $\frac{d^3}{dt^3}$, and so on.

The expression

$$2\frac{d^2\theta}{dt^2} + 5\frac{d\theta}{dt} + 2\theta$$

may be written as $2D^2\theta + 5D\theta + 2\theta$.

Taking out a common factor θ this becomes $(2D^2 + 5D + 2)\theta$. This may be factorized and written as $(2D + 1)(D + 2)\theta$. It is thus intended to manipulate D as if it were an algebraic quantity. This approach is justified in the literature.[8] The operation $1/D$ will be defined as the reverse of the process of differentiation, that is integration. It is, however, only integration in form and the arbitrary constant may always be omitted.

5.3.2 *Determination of* θ_{ss} *when the Driving Function is Zero or Constant*

The Normal Approach

The differential equation

$$a_n\frac{d^n\theta}{dt^n} + a_{n-1}\frac{d^{n-1}\theta}{dt^{n-1}} + \ldots + a_1\frac{d\theta}{dt} + a_0\theta = k$$

becomes, using the D-operator,

$$(a_n D^n + a_{n-1}D^{n-1} + \ldots + a_1 D + a_0)\theta = k$$

To find θ_{ss}, D is equated to zero, the value of θ remaining is then θ_{ss}, i.e.

$$(a_n \times 0 + a_{n-1} \times 0 + \ldots a_1 \times 0 + a_0)\theta_{ss} = k$$

or

$$\theta_{ss} = k/a_0$$

This method is still applicable when $k = 0$, giving $\theta_{ss} = 0$.

The Failing Case

There is a failing case which gives an indeterminate form; this occurs when there is no term $a_0\theta$ and the equation takes the form

$$(a_n D^n + a_{n-1}D^{n-1} + \ldots a_1 D)\theta = k$$

Here we may take out a factor D,

$$(a_n D^{n-1} + a_{n-1}D^{n-2} + \ldots + a_1)D\theta = k$$

or

$$(a_n D^{n-1} + a_{n-1}D^{n-2} + \ldots + a_1)\theta = \frac{1}{D}k$$

Put $D = 0$ on left-hand side only

$$a_1\theta_{ss} = \frac{1}{D}k$$

In putting $\dfrac{1}{D}$ as the process of integration we have

$$a_1 \theta_{ss} = kt + A$$

where A is an arbitrary constant of integration. The value of A can only be determined if the complete solution is found and the initial conditions known (see §5.4).

$$\therefore \qquad \theta_{ss} = \frac{kt}{a_1} + \frac{A}{a_1}$$

5.3.3 Determination of θ_{ss} when the Driving Function is a Ramp or Constant Acceleration Function

It was mentioned in chapter 2 that a ramp function could be represented by the equation

$$f(t) = kt$$

A function having constant acceleration may be represented by the equation

$$f(t) = kt^2$$

Both these functions are special cases of the general equation

$$f(t) = kt^p$$

where p is an integer.

A differential equation of form

$$(a_n D^n + a_{n-1} D^{n-1} + \ldots + a_1 D + a_0)\, \theta = kt^p$$

may be written more briefly as

$$\{F(D)\}\, \theta = kt^p$$

and the steady-state solution is given (formally) by dividing by $F(D)$, i.e.

$$\theta_{ss} = \frac{1}{F(D)} kt^p$$

The form of θ_{ss} is now obtained by expanding $\dfrac{1}{F(D)}$ in a series of ascending powers of D; the method is illustrated in the following examples.

Examples

(1) Find the steady-state solution of the equation

$$\left(\frac{d^2 \theta}{dt^2} + 4\theta\right) = 3t$$

74

In D-form

$$(D^2 + 4)\theta = 3t$$

$$\therefore \quad \theta_{ss} = \frac{1}{D^2 + 4}3t$$

$$= \frac{1}{4\left(1 + \dfrac{D^2}{4}\right)}3t$$

$$= \tfrac{1}{4}\left(1 + \frac{D^2}{4}\right)^{-1}3t$$

Then, using the binomial expansion,

$$\theta_{ss} = \tfrac{1}{4}\left(1 - \frac{D^2}{4} + \frac{D^4}{16}\dots\right)3t$$

now

$$D.3t = \frac{d(3t)}{dt} = 3$$

and

$$D^2.3t = \frac{d^2(3t)}{dt^2} = 0$$

also higher powers of D acting on $3t$ all disappear.

$$\therefore \quad \theta_{ss} = \frac{3t}{4}$$

(2) Determine the steady-state solution of the the equation

$$\frac{d^2\theta}{dt^2} - 4\frac{d\theta}{dt} + 3\theta = 5t^2$$

In D-form the equation becomes

$$(D^2 - 4D + 3)\theta = 5t^2$$

thus

$$\theta_{ss} = \frac{1}{D^2 - 4D + 3}5t^2$$

$$= \frac{1}{3\{1 + \tfrac{1}{3}(-4D + D^2)\}}5t^2$$

$$= \tfrac{1}{3}\{1 + \tfrac{1}{3}(-4D + D^2)\}^{-1}\{5t^2\}$$

$$= \tfrac{1}{3}\{1 - \tfrac{1}{3}(-4D + D^2) + \tfrac{1}{9}(-4D + D^2)^2 + \dots\}\{5t^2\}$$

$$= \tfrac{1}{3}\{5t^2 - \tfrac{1}{3}(-40t + 10) + \tfrac{1}{9}(160)\}$$

$$= \frac{5t^2}{3} + \frac{40t}{9} + \frac{130}{27}$$

5.3.4 *Determination of the Steady-state Solution when the Driving Function is Exponential*

The Substitution Rule

A differential equation

$$a_n \frac{d^n \theta}{dt^n} + a_{n-1} \frac{d^{n-1} \theta}{dt^{n-1}} + \ldots + a_1 \frac{d\theta}{dt} + a_0 \theta = k\, e^{\alpha t}$$

may be written

$$\{F(\mathrm{D})\}\, \theta = k\, e^{\alpha t}$$

The steady-state solution is obtained by dividing by $F(\mathrm{D})$, i.e.

$$\theta_{ss} = \frac{1}{F(\mathrm{D})} \cdot \{k\, e^{\alpha t}\}$$

The form of θ_{ss} is now obtained by substituting α, the coefficient of the exponent, for D, i.e.

$$\theta_{ss} = \frac{1}{F(\alpha)} \times k\, e^{\alpha t}$$

If, however, $F(\alpha)$ is zero this result is without meaning and the shift rule must be used.

The Shift Rule

The shift rule is used when $F(\alpha)$ (as defined above) is zero.
   We have

$$\theta_{ss} = \frac{1}{F(\mathrm{D})} \{k\, e^{\alpha t}\}$$

$$= e^{\alpha t} \times \frac{1}{F(\mathrm{D} + \alpha)} \{k\}$$

It is then necessary to convert $1/F(\mathrm{D} + \alpha)$ into a series in ascending powers of D.

Example

Find the steady-state solution of the equation

$$\frac{d\theta}{dt} + 2\theta = 2\, e^{-2t}$$

In D-form the equation becomes

$$(\mathrm{D} + 2)\, \theta = 2\, e^{-2t}$$

$\therefore$
$$\theta_{ss} = \frac{1}{\mathrm{D} + 2} \{2\, e^{-2t}\}$$

We cannot use the substitution rule because $F(D)$ would disappear. Hence using the shift rule we have

$$\theta_{ss} = e^{-2t} \frac{1}{D - 2 + 2} \{2\}$$

$$= e^{-2t} \frac{1}{D} \{2\}$$

$$= 2t \, e^{-2t}$$

Note: the shift rule as quoted here is not the most general case. If $V(t)$ is any function of time t, then the most general statement of the shift rule is

$$\{F(D)\} \{e^{\alpha t} V(t)\} = e^{\alpha t} \{F(D + \alpha)\} \{V(t)\}$$

5.3.5 Determination of the Steady-state Solution for a Sinusoidal Driving Function

A differential equation

$$a_n \frac{d^n \theta}{dt^n} + a_{n-1} \frac{d^{n-1} \theta}{dt^{n-1}} + \ldots + a_1 \frac{d\theta}{dt} + a_0 \theta = k \sin \omega t$$

in D-form becomes

$$\{F(D)\} \theta = k \sin \omega t$$

Thus

$$\theta_{ss} = \frac{1}{F(D)} \{k \sin \omega t\}$$

The steady-state solution will take the form

$$\theta_{ss} = \frac{k}{Z} \sin (\omega t - \phi)$$

and a method of finding Z and ϕ is required. The quickest method is to use a technique involving complex numbers (see chapter 3) in which the driving function and the steady-state solution are represented as complex numbers.

Now the driving function $k \sin \omega t$ is a vector which may be represented by the complex number $k e^{j\omega t}$. Hence the complex number representing the steady-state solution $\bar{\theta}_{ss}$ is given by

$$\bar{\theta}_{ss} = \left\{ \frac{1}{F(D)} \right\} k e^{j\omega t}$$

The substitution rule (§5.3.4) is now used, i.e. we substitute $j\omega$ for D, thus

$$\bar{\theta}_{ss} = \frac{k e^{j\omega t}}{F(j\omega)}$$

77

Let $F(j\omega)$ have a modulus Z and an argument ϕ then

$$\bar{\theta}_{ss} = \frac{k}{Z} e^{j(\omega t - \phi)}$$

$\therefore$ the instantaneous value of the steady-state solution is given by

$$\theta_{ss} = \frac{k}{Z} \sin(\omega t - \phi)$$

Example

Find the steady-state solution of the equation

$$3\frac{d^2\theta}{dt^2} + 20\frac{d\theta}{dt} + 600\theta = 800\sin 20t$$

Solution

In D-form we have

$$(3D^2 + 20D + 600)\,\theta = 800\sin 20t$$

The driving function $800\sin 20t$ may be represented vectorially by $800\,e^{j20t}$. Thus, substituting j20 for D we obtain the vector equation

$$\bar{\theta}_{ss} = \left\{\frac{1}{3D^2 + 20D + 600}\right\} 800\,e^{j20t}$$

$\therefore \qquad \bar{\theta}_{ss} = \left\{\frac{1}{3(j20)^2 + 20(j20) + 600}\right\} 800\,e^{j20t}$

$\therefore \qquad \bar{\theta}_{ss} = \dfrac{800\,e^{j20t}}{-1200 + 600 + j400}$

$$= \frac{800\,e^{j20t}}{(-600 + j400)}$$

But $\qquad -600 + j400 = 100\sqrt{(6^2 + 4^2)}\,e^{j\psi} = 721\,e^{j\psi}$

Now this vector operator lies in the second quadrant, hence

$$\psi = \pi - \tan^{-1}(400/600)$$

$$= \pi - 0.588$$

$$= 2.55$$

$\therefore \qquad \bar{\theta}_{ss} = \dfrac{800\,e^{j20t}}{721\,e^{j2\cdot55}}$

From this vectorial result we extract the instantaneous value of the steady-state solution, i.e.

$$\theta_{ss} = 1.11\sin(20t - 2.55)$$

This method of solution is the best with the least arithmetic and the student is strongly recommended to utilize it. The substitution of $j\omega$ for D will be used throughout this book whenever the steady-state solutions of differential equations involving sinusoidal driving functions are required.

5.4 Determination of the Complete Solution

The complete solution of the differential equations that are being considered is the sum of the transient solution and the steady-state solution.

In general, the transient solution will contain n arbitrary constants of integration, where n is the order of the differential equation. In the example dealt with in §5.1 the differential equation is first order and thus n is 1. The complete solution is stated as

$$\theta_o = \underbrace{A\,e^{-Kt/F}}_{\theta_{o\,t}} + \underbrace{\frac{K\hat{\theta}_i}{\sqrt{\{(F\omega)^2 + K\}}}\sin(\omega t - \tan^{-1} F\omega/K)}_{\theta_{o\,ss}}$$

Here A is the single arbitrary constant. Now this solution is general and independent of the initial conditions. If the initial condition is specified and the value of A found for this specific condition the solution is then a particular solution. In the example the initial condition is specified as at $t = 0$, $\theta_o = 0$.

This means that

$$A = \frac{F\omega K\hat{\theta}_i}{\{(F\omega)^2 + K^2\}}$$

and the particular solution corresponding only to this specific initial condition becomes

$$\theta_o = \frac{F\omega K\hat{\theta}_i}{\{(F\omega)^2 + K^2\}}\,e^{-Kt/F} + \frac{K\hat{\theta}_i}{\sqrt{\{(F\omega)^2 + K^2\}}}\sin(\omega t - \tan^{-1} F\omega/K)$$

In general the procedure is to determine θ_t and θ_{ss}, and add them to give the general solution θ in terms of n arbitrary constants. When the initial conditions are specified (these are the values of $d^{n-1}\theta/dt^{n-1}$, $d^{n-2}\theta/dt^{n-2} \ldots \theta$ when $t = 0$) the particular solution may be found. To do this we substitute $t = 0$ and $\theta = \theta_1$ (the initial value of θ) into the general solution. This gives the first of n simultaneous equations involving the arbitrary constants as unknowns. The general solution is then differentiated successively $(n - 1)$ times and after each differentiation an initial condition is inserted. We thus form n simultaneous equations in the unknown arbitrary constants. These equations are solved simultaneously and hence the arbitrary constants

79

are found. Whilst this procedure may seem complicated when explained in general terms it does not normally involve much computation. Some examples will serve to show how we determine the general solutions and the particular solutions of differential equations.

Examples

(1) (i) Find the general solution of the differential equation

$$5\frac{d\theta}{dt} + 6\theta = 8$$

(ii) Find the particular solution for an initial condition $t = 0$, $\theta = 5/3$.

Solution

(i) The auxiliary equation is

$$(5m + 6) = 0$$

$$\therefore \qquad m = -\tfrac{6}{5}$$

Hence the transient solution is given by

$$\theta_t = A\,e^{-6t/5}$$

In D-form the equation becomes

$$(5D + 6)\,\theta = 8$$

Here the driving function is constant so we substitute zero for D (as in §5.3.2) giving

$$6\theta_{ss} = 8$$

$$\therefore \qquad \theta_{ss} = 8/6 = 4/3$$

General solution is thus

$$\theta = \theta_t + \theta_{ss}$$

$$= A\,e^{-6t/5} + \tfrac{4}{3}$$

(ii) But at $t = 0$, $\theta = 5/3$ (given initial condition)

Hence
$$\tfrac{5}{3} = A\,e^0 + \tfrac{4}{3}$$

But
$$e^0 = 1$$

$$\therefore \qquad A = \tfrac{1}{3}$$

Thus particular solution is given by

$$\theta = \frac{e^{-6t/5}}{3} + \tfrac{4}{3}$$

$$= \tfrac{1}{3}(e^{-6t/5} + 4)$$

(2) (i) Find the general solution of the differential equation

$$\frac{d^2\theta}{dt^2} + 6\frac{d\theta}{dt} + 13\theta = e^{-2t}$$

(ii) Find the particular solution assuming the initial conditions $t = 0$, $\theta = 0$, $d\theta/dt = 0$.

Solution

(i) The auxiliary equation is

$$m^2 + 6m + 13 = 0$$

$$\therefore \qquad m = \frac{-6 \pm \sqrt{(36-52)}}{2}$$

$$= -3 \pm j2$$

Hence $\qquad \theta_t = e^{-3t}(A\cos 2t + B\sin 2t)$

In D-form, the equation becomes

$$(D^2 + 6D + 13)\theta = e^{-2t}$$

The steady-state solution is given by

$$\theta_{ss} = \left\{\frac{1}{D^2 + 6D + 13}\right\}e^{-2t}$$

Using the substitution rule we have

$$\theta_{ss} = \frac{1}{(-2)^2 + 6(-2) + 13}e^{-2t}$$

$$= \frac{e^{-2t}}{5}$$

The general solution is thus

$$\theta = \theta_t + \theta_{ss}$$

$$= e^{-3t}(A\cos 2t + B\sin 2t) + \frac{e^{-2t}}{5}$$

(ii) Now at $t = 0$, $\theta = 0$

$$\therefore \qquad 0 = e^0(A.1 + B.0) + \frac{e^0}{5}$$

$$A = -\tfrac{1}{5}$$

$$\therefore \qquad \theta = e^{-3t}\left(-\frac{\cos 2t}{5} + B\sin 2t\right) + \frac{e^{-2t}}{5}$$

Differentiating,

$$\frac{d\theta}{dt} = -3e^{-3t}\left(-\frac{\cos 2t}{5} + B\sin 2t\right)$$

$$+ e^{-3t}\left(\frac{2\sin 2t}{5} + 2B\cos 2t\right) - \frac{2e^{-2t}}{5}$$

But at $t = 0$, $d\theta/dt = 0$

$$\therefore \qquad 0 = -3\,e^0\,(-\tfrac{1}{5} + B.0) + e^0\,(\tfrac{2}{5}.0 + 2B) - \tfrac{2}{5}$$

$$\therefore \qquad 0 = \tfrac{3}{5} + 2B - \tfrac{2}{5}$$

$$\therefore \qquad B = -\tfrac{3}{10}$$

Hence particular solution becomes

$$\theta = e^{-3t}\left(-\frac{\cos 2t}{5} - \frac{3\sin 2t}{10}\right) + \frac{e^{-2t}}{5}.$$

EXAMPLES FOR SOLUTION

1. Find the transient solutions of the following differential equations:

(i) $\dfrac{d^2\theta}{dt^2} - 6\dfrac{d\theta}{dt} + 13\theta = 3t^2$

(ii) $\dfrac{d^3\theta}{dt^3} - 6\dfrac{d^2\theta}{dt^2} + 11\dfrac{d\theta}{dt} - 6\theta = 7\,e^{-t}$

(iii) $2\dfrac{d^2\theta}{dt^2} + 5\dfrac{d\theta}{dt} + 2\theta = 0$

(iv) $\dfrac{d^2\theta}{dt^2} + 4\theta = 6\sin 3t$

(v) $\dfrac{d^2\theta}{dt^2} + 4\dfrac{d\theta}{dt} = 2t$

(vi) $\dfrac{d^2\theta}{dt^2} + 6\dfrac{d\theta}{dt} + 9\theta = 4$

2. Find the steady-state solutions of the following differential equations:

(i) $\dfrac{d^2\theta}{dt^2} + \dfrac{d\theta}{dt} + 3\theta = 0$

(ii) $\dfrac{d^2\theta}{dt^2} + 8\dfrac{d\theta}{dt} + 25\theta = 50$

(iii) $\dfrac{d^2\theta}{dt^2} + 5\dfrac{d\theta}{dt} = 10$

(iv) $\dfrac{d\theta}{dt} + 6\theta = 3$

(v) $\dfrac{d^2\theta}{dt^2} + 2\dfrac{d\theta}{dt} = 24t$

(vi) $\dfrac{d^2\theta}{dt^2} + 4\theta = 4t^2$

(vii) $\dfrac{d^2\theta}{dt^2} + 6\dfrac{d\theta}{dt} + 9\theta = 50\,e^{2t}$

(viii) $\dfrac{d^2\theta}{dt^2} - 4\dfrac{d\theta}{dt} + 4\theta = 50\,e^{2t}$

(ix) $\dfrac{d\theta}{dt} + \theta = 10\sin 2t$

(x) $2\dfrac{d^2\theta}{dt^2} - 5\dfrac{d\theta}{dt} + 12\theta = 200\sin 4t$

3. Find the complete particular solutions to the following equations

(i) $\dfrac{d^2\theta}{dt^2} + 5\dfrac{d\theta}{dt} + 4\theta = 0$, given $\theta = 0$, $\dfrac{d\theta}{dt} = 2$ at $t = 0$

(ii) $\dfrac{d^2\theta}{dt^2} + 9\theta = \sin 2t$, given $\theta = 1$, $\dfrac{d\theta}{dt} = -1$ at $t = 0$

(iii) $\dfrac{d\theta}{dt} + 3\theta = e^{-2t}$, given $\theta = 4$ at $t = 0$

(iv) $\dfrac{d^2\theta}{dt^2} + 4\theta = t$, given $\theta = 0$, $\dfrac{d\theta}{dt} = 1$ at $t = 0$

(v) $\dfrac{d^2\theta}{dt^2} + 5\dfrac{d\theta}{dt} + 6\theta = 2e^{-t}$, given $\theta = 1$, $\dfrac{d\theta}{dt} = 0$ at $t = 0$

(vi) $\dfrac{d^2\theta}{dt^2} + 6\dfrac{d\theta}{dt} + 5\theta = 10$, given $\theta = 0$, $\dfrac{d\theta}{dt} = 0$ at $t = 0$

Chapter Six

Equations of Physical Systems

6.1 Introduction

Where possible, control systems are designed and analysed on a mathematical basis, the reason being that in this way one may achieve the 'best' solution to the engineering problem in the least time. Even when much of the information provided is in a non-mathematical form (as is often the case in chemical process control) an intuitive mathematical understanding of the dynamic behaviour of systems is very valuable. Physically different systems may often be described by similar (or 'analogous') equations. Dynamic problems involving mechanical, electrical, thermal, pneumatic, hydraulic and electro-mechanical components may usually be phrased in mathematical form by using certain basic laws. For instance, problems on translational mechanics are usually formulated by using Newton's second law whilst problems on electric circuits can be analysed using Kirchhoff's laws.

The object of this chapter is to describe the method whereby the differential equations representing the dynamic behaviour of certain physical systems may be formulated. The methods of solution introduced in chapter 5 are then used to solve these equations. Owing to lack of space only a few mechanical and electrical systems can be considered. Students will find useful extensions of this work in the literature.[9,10,11]

6.2 Mechanical Systems

6.2.1 Simple Spring-mass Positional System without Damping

Consider a mass m lying on a smooth horizontal table attached to a light spring of stiffness k. The position of the mass is x_0. The other

84

end of the spring is to act as a command point, its instantaneous position being x_i. The basic arrangement is illustrated in Fig. 6.1.

The object of this system is to control the position of the mass x_o in accordance with the command or input signal x_i. Let x be the amount the spring be compressed at any instant, then

$$x = x_i - x_o$$

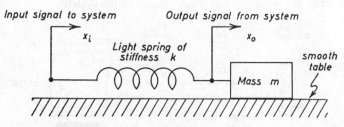

Input signal to system   Output signal from system

x_i x_o

Light spring of stiffness k

smooth table

Mass m

Fig. 6.1 *Simple spring-mass positional system.*

The instantaneous force F applied to the mass is kx. Defining a as the acceleration of the mass, Newton's second law gives

$$F = ma$$

but

$$F = kx$$

and

$$a = \frac{d^2 x_o}{dt^2}$$

Thus

$$kx = m \frac{d^2 x_o}{dt^2}$$

or

$$k(x_i - x_o) = m \frac{d^2 x_o}{dt^2}$$

$\therefore$

$$m \frac{d^2 x_o}{dt^2} + kx_o = kx_i$$

The detailed solution of this differential equation for a specific driving function will not be given because the next system to be considered gives an analogous differential equation. This equation is solved in detail and the results of the solution may readily be applied to the translational system considered here.

6.2.2 *Simple Angular Position Control System with no Damping*

Suppose it is required to control the angular position θ_o of a rotatable mass of moment of inertia J by means of an input signal θ_i applied to the light handwheel. The object of the system is to make θ_o and θ_i the

85

same. If neither torque nor power amplification is required, a simple method would be to connect the mass to the handwheel via a flexible shaft of stiffness K. Such an arrangement is shown in Fig. 6.2.

It is as well to remember the units of the various quantities. θ_i and θ_o are expressed in radians, J is in kg m^2 and K is in N m/rad.

We are going to make an assumption, which is not valid in practice, for the sake of academic argument. This assumption is that there are no frictional torques of any kind present in the system.

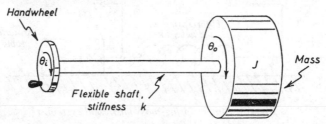

Fig. 6.2 *Angular positioning system.*

Some form of test input is necessary in order that we shall be able to judge the performance of the system. The most popular test is the input step-function. This implies that we suddenly, in zero time, displace the handwheel from zero to a position θ_i and hold it still in the new position. This is not practically possible, but a close approximation to it may be made. Alternatively, in practice, we can simulate the effect of a step-input by holding the handwheel fixed at a position θ_i and twisting the mass to zero position and finally releasing the mass at instant $t = 0$.

For any signal, if θ is the instantaneous angle of twist in the shaft, we have,

$$\theta = \theta_i - \theta_o$$

Now the instantaneous torque T tending to accelerate the mass due to the twist in the shaft is $K\theta$.

Also, Newton's second law applied to rotational systems states:

$$T = J\alpha$$

where α = angular acceleration of mass.

But in this system
$$\alpha = \frac{d^2 \theta_o}{dt^2}$$

$\therefore$
$$T = J\frac{d^2 \theta_o}{dt^2}$$

or
$$K\theta = J\frac{d^2 \theta_o}{dt^2}$$

or
$$K(\theta_i - \theta_o) = J\frac{d^2\theta_o}{dt^2}$$

Thus
$$J\frac{d^2\theta_o}{dt^2} + K\theta_o = K\theta_i$$

The auxiliary equation (see §5.2) is thus
$$(Jm^2 + K) = 0$$

giving
$$m = \pm j\sqrt{\frac{K}{J}}$$

Hence the transient response θ_{ot} is given by
$$\theta_{ot} = e^{ot}(A\sin\omega_r t + B\cos\omega_r t)$$
$$= A\sin\omega_r t + B\cos\omega_r t$$

where
$$\omega_r = \sqrt{\frac{K}{J}}$$

In D-form the differential equation becomes
$$(JD^2 + K)\theta_o = K\theta_i$$

The driving function is constant because θ_i is a step, hence using the method described in §5.3.2 we determine the steady-state response $\theta_{o\,ss}$ by equating D to zero, i.e.
$$K\theta_{o\,ss} = K\theta_i$$
$$\therefore \qquad \theta_{o\,ss} = \theta_i$$

The complete general solution is given by
$$\theta_o = \theta_{o\,ss} + \theta_{ot}$$
$$= \theta_i + A\sin\omega_r t + B\cos\omega_r t$$

Now we must insert the initial conditions. At $t = 0$, the mass will not have altered its position thus $\theta_o = 0$ at $t = 0$ whence
$$0 = \theta_i + 0 + B$$
$$\therefore \qquad B = -\theta_i$$
$$\therefore \qquad \theta_o = \theta_i + A\sin\omega_r t - \theta_i\cos\omega_r t$$

Also the mass cannot suddenly possess kinetic energy at $t = 0$, thus the angular velocity of the mass must be zero. Hence at $t = 0$, $d\theta_o/dt = 0$.

Now
$$\frac{d\theta_o}{dt} = 0 + A\omega_r\cos\omega_r t + \theta_i\omega_r\sin\omega_r t$$
$$\therefore \qquad 0 = 0 + A\omega_r$$
$$\therefore \qquad A = 0 \text{ since } \omega_r \neq 0$$

87

∴ complete particular solution is given by

$$\theta_o = \theta_i - \theta_i \cos \omega_r t$$
$$= \theta_i (1 - \cos \omega_r t)$$
$$= \theta_i \{1 - \sin(\omega_r t + 90°)\}$$

The response of the system is represented graphically in Fig. 6.3.

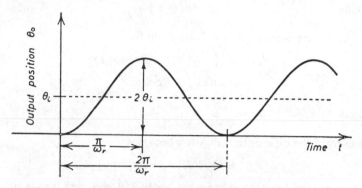

Fig. 6.3 *Response of angular positioning system to input step.*

The system thus executes continuous sinusoidal oscillations, and may be termed UNSTABLE. As a practical system it is thus useless and it is evident that some method of damping out the oscillation is necessary.

6.2.3 System Containing Viscous Frictional Damping

In order to damp out the oscillation we may employ either coulomb friction or viscous friction or a combination of the two. Coulomb friction has two basic disadvantages; the first is that it will cause a static error to exist between desired output position and actual output position—this represents a major practical disadvantage; the second is that it is difficult to solve the differential equation when a coulomb frictional term is introduced—this in itself could hardly be recognized as a practical disadvantage.

Viscous damping is the natural choice because it does not give rise to a static error (although it does, as will be shown, produce a dynamic error); it is also quite readily taken into account in the differential equation.

To achieve a viscous frictional damping torque, let us attach to the mass a light paddle rotating in a viscous fluid. The coupling shaft will be assumed to be perfectly rigid (see Fig. 6.4).

Let us assume that the paddle produces a retarding torque F N m per rad/s.

Now torque tending to accelerate mass $= K(\theta_i - \theta_o)$,

and torque tending to retard mass $= F d\theta_o/dt$

$\therefore$ resultant torque T, accelerating mass is given by

$$T = K(\theta_i - \theta_o) - F\frac{d\theta_o}{dt}$$

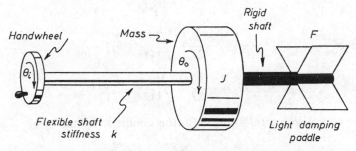

Fig. 6.4 *Angular positioning system with viscous damping.*

Now using Newton's second law applied to rotational systems

$$T = J\alpha$$

where $\alpha =$ angular acceleration of mass;

but
$$\alpha = \frac{d^2\theta_o}{dt^2}$$

$\therefore$
$$K(\theta_i - \theta_o) - F\frac{d\theta_o}{dt} = J\frac{d^2\theta_o}{dt^2}$$

$\therefore$
$$J\frac{d^2\theta_o}{dt^2} + F\frac{d\theta_o}{dt} + K\theta_o = K\theta_i$$

In D-form this becomes $(JD^2 + FD + K)\theta_o = K\theta_i$.

Now if the input signal is a step of magnitude θ_i, the steady-state solution is given by equating D to zero, i.e.

$$\theta_{o\,ss} = \theta_i$$

The transient response has three possible forms, depending on the roots of the auxiliary equation which is

$$(Jm^2 + Fm + K) = 0$$

The roots are given by

$$m = \frac{-F \pm \sqrt{(F^2 - 4JK)}}{2J}$$

$$= -\frac{F}{2J} \pm \sqrt{\left\{ \left(\frac{F^2}{4J^2} - \frac{K}{J} \right) \right\}}$$

Now the three possible forms depend on the value of F:

(i) The 'overdamped condition' where $F^2/4J^2 > K/J$, i.e. $F > 2\sqrt{(JK)}$, for which the transient solution θ_{ot} is given by

$$\theta_{ot} = A\,e^{m_1 t} + B\,e^{m_2 t}$$

where

$$m_1 = -\frac{F}{2J} + \sqrt{\left\{ \left(\frac{F^2}{4J^2} - \frac{K}{J} \right) \right\}}$$

and

$$m_2 = -\frac{F}{2J} - \sqrt{\left\{ \left(\frac{F^2}{4J^2} - \frac{K}{J} \right) \right\}}$$

The complete general solution for this condition is thus

$$\theta_o = \theta_i + A\,e^{m_1 t} + B\,e^{m_2 t}$$

Now at $t = 0$, $\theta_o = 0$ and $\dfrac{d\theta_o}{dt} = 0$ (as explained in §6.2.2).

Thus

$$0 = \theta_i + A + B \qquad (1)$$

and since

$$\frac{d\theta_o}{dt} = Am_1\,e^{m_1 t} + Bm_2\,e^{m_2 t}$$

$$0 = Am_1 + Bm_2 \qquad (2)$$

Thus from (2)

$$A = -\frac{m_2}{m_1} B$$

and substituting for A in (1) we have

$$0 = \theta_i - \frac{m_2}{m_1} B + B$$

$$\therefore \quad \left(\frac{m_2}{m_1} - 1 \right) B = \theta_i$$

$$\therefore \quad B = \frac{m_1 \theta_i}{m_2 - m_1}$$

Hence

$$A = -\frac{m_2 \theta_i}{m_2 - m_1}$$

90

Thus complete solution is given by:

$$\theta_{\mathrm{o}} = \theta_{\mathrm{i}} \left\{ 1 - \frac{m_2 \, \mathrm{e}^{m_1 t}}{m_2 - m_1} + \frac{m_1 \, \mathrm{e}^{m_2 t}}{m_2 - m_1} \right\}$$

The response is shown in Fig. 6.5.

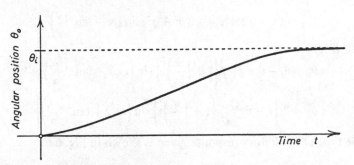

Fig. 6.5 *Response of overdamped system.*

(ii) The 'underdamped' condition where $F < 2\sqrt{(JK)}$, for which the transient solution $\theta_{\mathrm{o}\,t}$ is given by

$$\theta_{\mathrm{o}\,t} = \mathrm{e}^{-\alpha t} \{ A \sin \omega_{\mathrm{r}} t + B \cos \omega_{\mathrm{r}} t \}$$

where

$$\alpha = \frac{F}{2J}$$

and

$$\omega_{\mathrm{r}} = \sqrt{\left\{ \frac{K}{J} - \frac{F^2}{4J^2} \right\}}$$

Thus for this condition the complete solution is

$$\theta_{\mathrm{o}} = \theta_{\mathrm{i}} + \mathrm{e}^{-\alpha t} \{ A \sin \omega_{\mathrm{r}} t + B \cos \omega_{\mathrm{r}} t \}$$

The initial conditions are again at $t = 0$, $\theta_{\mathrm{o}} = 0$ and $\mathrm{d}\theta_{\mathrm{o}}/\mathrm{d}t = 0$

$$\therefore \qquad 0 = \theta_{\mathrm{i}} + 1(0 + B)$$

$$\therefore \qquad B = -\theta_{\mathrm{i}}$$

$$\therefore \qquad \theta_{\mathrm{o}} = \theta_{\mathrm{i}} + \mathrm{e}^{-\alpha t} \{ A \sin \omega_{\mathrm{r}} t - \theta_{\mathrm{i}} \cos \omega_{\mathrm{r}} t \}$$

Also,

$$\frac{\mathrm{d}\theta_{\mathrm{o}}}{\mathrm{d}t} = 0 - \alpha \, \mathrm{e}^{-\alpha t} \{ A \sin \omega_{\mathrm{r}} t - \theta_{\mathrm{i}} \cos \omega_{\mathrm{r}} t \}$$

$$+ \mathrm{e}^{-\alpha t} (A \omega_{\mathrm{r}} \cos \omega_{\mathrm{r}} t + \theta_{\mathrm{i}} \omega_{\mathrm{r}} \sin \omega_{\mathrm{r}} t)$$

Thus

$$0 = -\alpha(0 - \theta_{\mathrm{i}}) + (A \omega_{\mathrm{r}} + 0)$$

$$\therefore \qquad A = -\frac{\alpha \theta_{\mathrm{i}}}{\omega_{\mathrm{r}}}$$

∴ response is given by

$$\theta_o = \theta_i - \theta_i e^{-\alpha t}\left\{\frac{\alpha}{\omega_r}\sin\omega_r t + \cos\omega_r t\right\}$$

This form may be reduced if we use the trig. formula

$$p\sin x + q\cos x = \sqrt{(p^2 + q^2)}\sin\left(x + \tan^{-1}\frac{q}{p}\right)$$

This gives

$$\theta_o = \theta_i - \theta_i e^{-\alpha t}\sqrt{\left\{1 + \left(\frac{\alpha}{\omega_r}\right)^2\right\}}\sin\left(\omega_r t + \tan^{-1}\frac{\omega_r}{\alpha}\right)$$

or $\qquad\theta_o = \theta_i\left\{1 - e^{-\alpha t}\sqrt{\left\{1 + \left(\frac{\alpha}{\omega_r}\right)^2\right\}}\sin\left(\omega_r t + \tan^{-1}\frac{\omega_r}{\alpha}\right)\right\}$

The type of oscillatory response given is shown in Fig. 6.6.

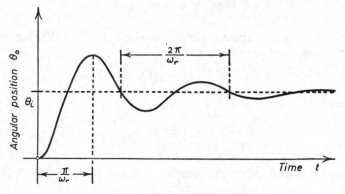

Fig. 6.6 *Oscillatory response of underdamped system.*

Considerable discussion will, in chapter 8, be devoted to this type of response which is, in practice, the most important.

(iii) The 'critically damped' condition where $F = 2\sqrt{(JK)}$, for which the transient solution θ_{ot} is given by

$$\theta_{ot} = (A + Bt)e^{-\alpha t}$$

where $\qquad\qquad\alpha = F/2J$

∴ $\qquad\qquad\theta_o = \theta_i + (A + Bt)e^{-\alpha t}$

A similar analysis may be performed to find A and B assuming that at $t = 0$, $\theta_o = 0$ and $d\theta_o/dt = 0$. This shows that the complete solution is given by

$$\theta_o = \theta_i\{1 - (1 + \alpha t)e^{-\alpha t}\}$$

This represents the fastest rise to the final value without any overshoot. Superficially it appears to be the most desirable form of response. In practice however a tolerance zone is usually given as part of the specification. This zone is usually a few per cent of the magnitude of the step-input. The specification will normally state that the system must 'settle' into this zone (never to come out again) in a particular time. It is, as will be shown in chapter 8, always possible to get the system to settle in the tolerance zone faster by using under-damping than critical damping. The optimum damping required for a given tolerance zone will be considered in chapter 8. It is sufficient to note at this stage that the rise time to the first peak depends on the value of ω_r. The larger the value of ω_r, the faster the rise. The time taken for the oscillation to decay is evidently dependent on α; the larger the value of α, the faster will be the decay. It should be noted, however, that since for underdamping $F < 2\sqrt{(JK)}$, then $F/2J < 2\sqrt{(JK)}/2J$, i.e.

$$\alpha < \frac{2\sqrt{(JK)}}{2J}$$

or
$$\alpha < \sqrt{\frac{K}{J}}$$

Thus there is a limit on the value of α.

6.2.4 The Response of the Angular Position Control System to a Constant Velocity Input

The response of the system to a 'ramp input' is of some importance because under operating conditions, constant velocity inputs are just as likely to occur as steps. The solution will be deduced by argument. When the ramp is first applied the output will respond with its normal transient, i.e. if it is an underdamped system the response will be oscillatory. After the transient, the mass will follow the handwheel— but it will lag it by a slight displacement (equal to the angle of twist θ in the shaft). The torque due to the twist in the shaft will be $K\theta$; under steady conditions, this torque will just counteract the viscous drag $F d\theta_o/dt$. Now if the handwheel is driven at a constant velocity given by $d\theta_i/dt = \omega_i$ then under steady conditions $d\theta_o/dt$ must also be given by $d\theta_o/dt = \omega_i$.

$\therefore$
$$F\frac{d\theta_o}{dt} = F\omega_i$$

and thus
$$K\theta = F\omega_i$$

or
$$\theta = \frac{F\omega_i}{K}$$

93

The response to a ramp is shown in Fig. 6.7. It is evident that the displacement between input signal θ_i and the output signal θ_o represents the 'error' between required output and actual output under

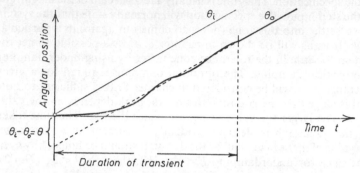

Fig. 6.7 *Response of underdamped system to a ramp input.*

dynamic conditions. In this case there is a constant positional error often called the 'velocity lag'. Usually it is desirable to keep this lag as small as possible, which involves making the stiffness K as large as possible, and F as small as possible consistent with adequate damping.

6.2.5 System Requiring Torque Magnification

When the mass to be moved is heavy, some form of torque magnification may be necessary. The simple answer to this problem is to employ a gear-box between the flexible shaft and the mass. It must be borne in mind that there is no power amplification involved in this system. A sketch of the system is shown in Fig. 6.8.

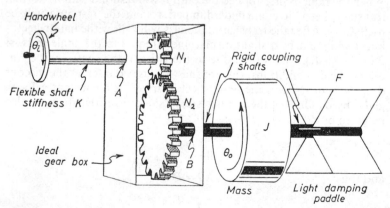

Fig. 6.8 *The gear-box used to obtain torque magnification.*

Suppose that the teeth ratio of the gear-box is $N_2:N_1$ and let $N_2/N_1 = N$. Note that for torque magnification N must be greater than unity. The inertia of the gears will be ignored (it is a simple matter to include their inertia as part of J). Now if point B moves through an angle θ_o then point A must move through an angle $N\theta_o$. Thus the angle of twist in the shaft θ becomes $\theta_i - N\theta_o$. Thus the torque available at point A is $K(\theta_i - N\theta_o)$. This is magnified by the gear-box and appears at point B as $NK(\theta_i - N\theta_o)$.

Hence torque tending to accelerate mass $= NK(\theta_i - N\theta_o)$; also torque tending to retard mass $= F\dfrac{d\theta_o}{dt}$; thus resultant torque T available to produce acceleration is given by:

$$T = NK(\theta_i - N\theta_o) - F\frac{d\theta_o}{dt}$$

Now Newton's second law applied to rotational systems gives

$$T = J\alpha$$

where α = angular acceleration of mass;

but
$$\alpha = \frac{d^2\theta_o}{dt^2}$$

Hence
$$NK(\theta_i - N\theta_o) - F\frac{d\theta_o}{dt} = J\frac{d^2\theta_o}{dt^2}$$

Thus
$$J\frac{d^2\theta_o}{dt^2} + F\frac{d\theta_o}{dt} + N^2 K\theta_o = NK\theta_i$$

In D-form this differential equation becomes:

$$(JD^2 + FD + N^2 K)\,\theta_o = NK\theta_i$$

For a step-input of magnitude θ_i, the steady-state solution $\theta_{o\,ss}$ is given by

$$N^2 K\theta_{o\,ss} = NK\theta_i$$

or
$$\theta_{o\,ss} = \frac{\theta_i}{N}$$

Physically we would expect the gear-box to step down the final position in this way.

The transient solution will be determined for the underdamped case only (for which $F < 2N\sqrt{(JK)}$).

Now by comparison with §6.2.3 where a solution was determined for the underdamped system without a gear-box we note that the differential equation is identical in form to the above, except that whereas previously the final term was $K\theta_o$ it is now $N^2 K\theta_o$. Thus for the same initial conditions, the solutions must be similar; we must

95

merely replace K by $N^2 K$ in the transient solution. Hence the solution is given by

$$\theta_o = \frac{\theta_i}{N}\left[1 - e^{-\alpha t}\sqrt{\left\{1 + \left(\frac{\alpha}{\omega_r'}\right)^2\right\}}\sin\left(\omega_r' t + \tan^{-1}\frac{\omega_r'}{\alpha}\right)\right]$$

where $\qquad\qquad \alpha = F/2J$

and $\qquad\qquad \omega_r' = \sqrt{\left\{\frac{N^2 K}{J} - \frac{F^2}{4J^2}\right\}}$

We note that α is unaffected but the resonant angular frequency ω_r' is higher. The responses of the underdamped systems with and without gear-box are compared in Fig. 6.9.

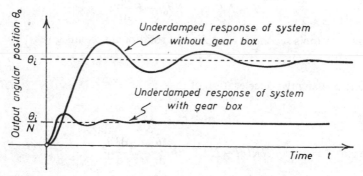

Fig. 6.9 *Responses of underdamped systems with and without gear-boxes.*

The basis on which the responses are drawn is that K and J are the same but F is adjusted in each case for the same degree of damping.

6.2.6 *Analysis of Rotational Systems Containing a Motor and Gear-box*

General

In many control systems the inertia load is driven by a motor through a gear-box as shown in Fig. 6.10. Both the motor and the load will possess inertia and probably viscous friction. The way in which the analysis should be approached is thus of some interest.

Simple Spur and Pinion Gear-box

The object of this analysis is to produce the equation of motion for this system in a simple form.

Let T = torque developed by motor, F_1 = viscous frictional torque on motor shaft per unit angular velocity of motor shaft, F_2 = viscous frictional torque on load shaft per unit angular velocity of load shaft,

J_1 = moment of inertia of motor plus pinion, J_2 = moment of inertia of load plus spur, $N_2/N_1 = N$ (the teeth ratio of the gear-box), T_p = resultant torque at pinion.

Angular velocity of motor shaft = $\mathrm{d}\theta_1/\mathrm{d}t$
Angular acceleration of motor shaft = $\mathrm{d}^2\theta_1/\mathrm{d}t^2$
Angular velocity of load shaft = $\mathrm{d}\theta_2/\mathrm{d}t$
Angular acceleration of load shaft = $\mathrm{d}^2\theta_2/\mathrm{d}t^2$

Now considering the motor shaft the resultant torque available to accelerate the motor is

$$T - F_1 \frac{\mathrm{d}\theta_1}{\mathrm{d}t} - T_p$$

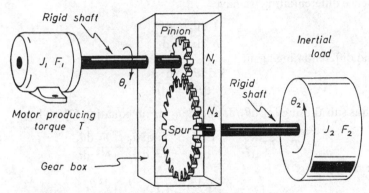

Fig. 6.10 *Geared rotational system.*

Thus using Newton's second law we have

$$T - T_p - F_1 \frac{\mathrm{d}\theta_1}{\mathrm{d}t} = J_1 \frac{\mathrm{d}^2\theta_1}{\mathrm{d}t^2}$$

$$\therefore \qquad T - F_1 \frac{\mathrm{d}\theta_1}{\mathrm{d}t} - J_1 \frac{\mathrm{d}^2\theta_1}{\mathrm{d}t^2} = T_p \qquad (1)$$

Now the torque available at the pinion is increased by a factor N in the gear-box. Hence torque available at the spur is NT_p.

Thus resultant torque available to accelerate the load is

$$NT_p - F_2 \frac{\mathrm{d}\theta_2}{\mathrm{d}t}$$

Thus, again using Newton's second law, we have

$$NT_p - F_2 \frac{\mathrm{d}\theta_2}{\mathrm{d}t} = J_2 \frac{\mathrm{d}^2\theta_2}{\mathrm{d}t^2}$$

$$\therefore \qquad T_p = \frac{J_2}{N} \frac{\mathrm{d}^2\theta_2}{\mathrm{d}t^2} + \frac{F_2}{N} \frac{\mathrm{d}\theta_2}{\mathrm{d}t} \qquad (2)$$

97

Thus eliminating T_p between (1) and (2) we have

$$T - F_1 \frac{d\theta_1}{dt} - J_1 \frac{d^2\theta_1}{dt^2} = \frac{J_2}{N} \frac{d^2\theta_2}{dt^2} + \frac{F_2}{N} \frac{d\theta_2}{dt} \tag{3}$$

Now a basic property of the gear-box is that

$$N_1\theta_1 = N_2\theta_2$$

$$\therefore \qquad \frac{N_1}{N_2}\theta_1 = \theta_2$$

$$\therefore \qquad \frac{\theta_1}{N} = \theta_2$$

Hence differentiating we have

$$\frac{1}{N}\frac{d\theta_1}{dt} = \frac{d\theta_2}{dt}$$

and differentiating again

$$\frac{1}{N}\frac{d^2\theta_1}{dt^2} = \frac{d^2\theta_2}{dt^2}$$

Thus substituting for $d\theta_2/dt$ and $d^2\theta_2/dt^2$ in equation (3) we have

$$T - F_1 \frac{d\theta_1}{dt} - J_1 \frac{d^2\theta_1}{dt^2} = \frac{J_2}{N^2} \frac{d^2\theta_1}{dt^2} + \frac{F_2}{N^2} \frac{d\theta_1}{dt}$$

or rearranging,

$$T - \left(F_1 + \frac{F_2}{N^2}\right)\frac{d\theta_1}{dt} = \left(J_1 + \frac{J_2}{N^2}\right)\frac{d^2\theta_1}{dt^2}$$

$$\therefore \qquad T - F_{r1}\frac{d\theta_1}{dt} = J_{r1}\frac{d^2\theta_1}{dt^2}$$

where

$$F_{r1} = F_1 + \frac{F_2}{N^2}$$

and

$$J_{r1} = J_1 + \frac{J_2}{N^2}$$

F_{r1} is the effective viscous frictional constant referred to the motor shaft and J_{r1} is the effective moment of inertia referred to the motor shaft.

When T is described in mathematical terms the differential equation in θ_1 may be solved. The motion of the load may always be found because

$$N_1\theta_1 = N_2\theta_2$$

Multiple-gear Train

Fig. 6.11 shows a multiple-gear train. The object is to produce the equation of motion of this system. Whilst a rigorous analysis of the

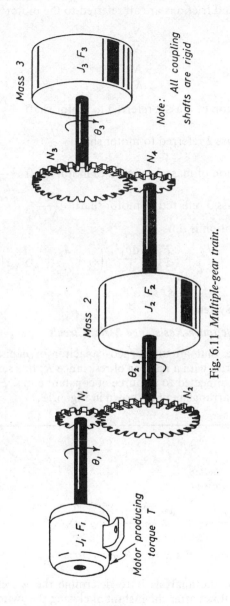

Fig. 6.11 *Multiple-gear train.*

type introduced in the previous section may be used, it is unnecessary if the inertias and frictions are all referred to the motor shaft.

Let
$$\frac{N_2}{N_1} = N_a$$

and
$$\frac{N_3}{N_4} = N_b$$

Viscous friction of mass 2 referred to motor shaft $= \dfrac{F_2}{N_a^2}$

Inertia of mass 2 referred to motor shaft $= \dfrac{J_2}{N_a^2}$

Viscous friction of mass 3 referred to motor shaft $= \dfrac{F_3}{N_a^2 N_b^2}$

Inertia of mass 3 referred to motor shaft $= \dfrac{J_3}{N_a^2 N_b^2}$

Equation of motion is thus

$$T - \left(F_1 + \frac{F_2}{N_b^2} + \frac{F_3}{N_a^2 N_b^2}\right)\frac{\mathrm{d}\theta_1}{\mathrm{d}t} = \left(J_1 + \frac{J_2}{N_a^2} + \frac{J_3}{N_a^2 N_b^2}\right)\frac{\mathrm{d}^2\theta_1}{\mathrm{d}t^2}$$

6.3 Electrical Systems

6.3.1 The Capacitance-Resistance Series Circuit

Let us suppose that an uncharged capacitor of capacitance C is connected in series with a resistor of resistance R; this series circuit is then suddenly connected to a source of constant e.m.f. E. The circuit diagram of the arrangement is shown in Fig. 6.12.

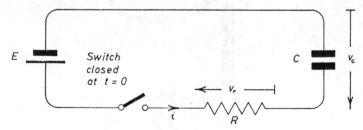

Fig. 6.12 *CR series circuit.*

The object of the analysis is to determine the waveform of the current i which flows after the instant of closing the switch, $t = 0$.

Now, using Kirchhoff's mesh law, we have

$$v_r + v_c = E$$

but
$$v_r = Ri$$

and
$$v_c = \frac{1}{C} \int i \, dt$$

Hence
$$Ri + \frac{1}{C} \int i \, dt = E$$

This equation is not in a suitable form, so differentiating both sides we obtain

$$R\frac{di}{dt} + \frac{i}{C} = 0$$

The auxiliary equation is thus

$$Rm + \frac{1}{C} = 0$$

Hence
$$m = -\frac{1}{CR}$$

The transient response is thus

$$i_t = A \, e^{-t/CR}$$

In D-form the differential equation is

$$\left(RD + \frac{1}{C}\right) i = 0$$

Equating D to zero gives the steady-state response, i.e.

$$i_{ss} = 0$$

∴ complete general solution is given by

$$i = i_t + i_{ss}$$
$$= A \, e^{-t/CR}$$

At $t = 0$ there is no charge on the capacitor, hence $v_c = 0$, thus at the instant $t = 0$,

$$iR + 0 = E$$

∴
$$i = \frac{E}{R}$$

∴
$$\frac{E}{R} = A \, e^{-0/CR}$$

∴
$$A = \frac{E}{R}$$

∴ complete particular solution is

$$i = \frac{E}{R} e^{-t/CR}$$

The waveform of the current i is shown in Fig. 6.13.

This analysis relies on the electrical principles introduced in chapter 4 and on the solution of differential equations discussed in chapter 5. The exponential decay is treated in chapter 2.

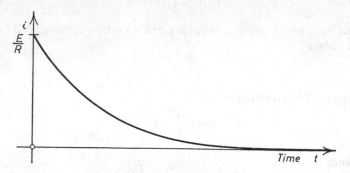

Fig. 6.13 *Response of CR series circuit.*

6.3.2 The Inductance-Resistance Series Circuit

The circuit is as shown in Fig. 6.14. The object is to determine the waveform of the current i when a constant e.m.f. is applied to the circuit at the instant $t = 0$.

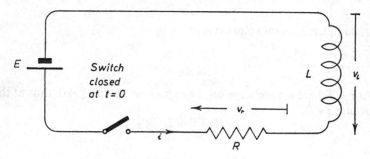

Fig. 6.14 *LR series circuit.*

Using Kirchhoff's mesh law we have

$$v_1 + v_r = E$$

but

$$v_r = Ri$$

and

$$v_1 = L\frac{di}{dt}$$

Hence

$$L\frac{di}{dt} + Ri = E$$

The auxiliary equation is

$$Lm + R = 0$$

$$\therefore \qquad m = -R/L$$

$\therefore$ transient response is given by

$$i_t = A\,e^{-Rt/L}$$

In D-form the differential equation becomes

$$(LD + R)i = E$$

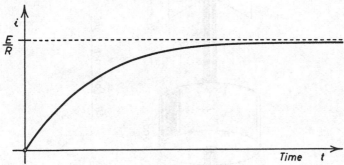

Fig. 6.15 *Response of LR series circuit.*

To obtain the steady-state response we equate D to zero, hence

$$Ri_{ss} = E$$

$$\therefore \qquad i_{ss} = E/R$$

$\therefore$ complete general solution is

$$i = i_t + i_{ss}$$

$$= A\,e^{-Rt/L} + \frac{E}{R}$$

At the instant the switch is closed the inductor possesses no magnetic energy, i.e. $\dfrac{Li^2}{2} = 0$; thus, since $L \neq 0$, $i = 0$ at $t = 0$

$$\therefore \qquad 0 = A\,e^0 + \frac{E}{R}$$

$$A = -\frac{E}{R}$$

Thus complete particular solution becomes

$$i = -\frac{E}{R}e^{-Rt/L} + \frac{E}{R}$$

$$= \frac{E}{R}(1 - e^{-Rt/L})$$

The rise in current is shown in Fig. 6.15.

103

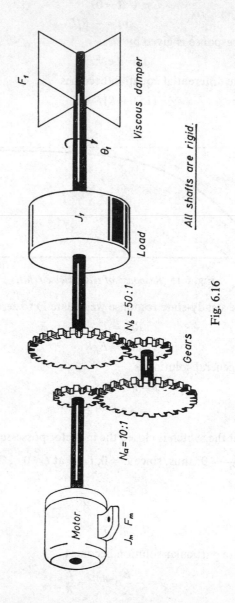

F_1

θ_1

Viscous damper

J_1

Load

All shafts are rigid.

Fig. 6.16

$N_b = 50:1$

Gears

$N_a = 10:1$

Motor

$J_m \; F_m$

EXAMPLES FOR SOLUTION

1. A mass m lies on a smooth horizontal table and has a position x_o. It is connected to one end of a light spring of stiffness k, the opposite end of which has a position x_i. The mass is subjected to a viscous damping force f per unit velocity by means of a dash pot.

(i) Derive the equation of motion for the system.

(ii) Solve this equation assuming that x_i is a step input, that $f = 2\sqrt{(mk)}$ and that at $t = 0$, $x_o = 0$ and $dx_o/dt = 0$.

(iii) Draw the response curve showing the variation of x_o with time t.

2. In the angular positioning system of Fig. 6.4 $J = 1$ kg m^2 and $K = 3$ N m per rad. Determine the value of the viscous frictional constant F such that the frequency of oscillation during a transient is $0 \cdot 1$ c/s.

3. A motor of moment of inertia J_m and constant torque drives a load of moment of inertia J_1 through a torque-magnifying gear-box of ratio $1:N$. Determine the value of N in terms of J_m and J_1 for which the acceleration of the load is maximum. Ignore all friction and assume the inertia of the gears to be included in J_m and J_1.

4. In the angular positioning system of Fig. 6.4, $J = 2$ kg m^2, $K = 3$ N m per rad and the damping is critical. The handwheel is forced to make sinusoidal oscillations of peak amplitude 1 rad at a frequency of $0 \cdot 05$ c/s.

(i) Write down the equation of motion of the system.

(ii) Determine an expression for the *steady-state* motion of the mass in the form

$$\theta_{o\,ss} = \theta_{o\,ss} \sin(\omega t - \phi)$$

stating the values of $\theta_{o\,ss}$ and ϕ.

5. A series capacitance-resistance circuit is suddenly subjected to a ramp e.m.f. e given by

$$e = 2t$$

where $t = $ time in seconds.

The capacitor has a capacitance of 1 μF and the resistor a resistance of 2 MΩ. Assuming the capacitor to have no initial charge determine:

(i) An expression for the instantaneous current i which will flow through the circuit.

(ii) An expression for the p.d. across the resistor v_r.

(iii) An expression for the p.d. across the capacitor v_c.

Sketch waveforms representing i, v_r and v_c.

6. A series capacitance-inductance-resistance circuit is suddenly subjected to a step e.m.f. of 1 V magnitude. The capacitor has a capacitance of 1 μF, the inductor an inductance of 1 H and the resistor a resistance of 1 kΩ. Determine an expression for the instantaneous current i which will flow through the circuit assuming the capacitor to have zero initial charge and the inductor to have no initial stored energy. Sketch the waveform of i.

7. The e.m.f. supplied to a series inductance resistance circuit is suddenly doubled. The circuit has an inductance of 100 H and a resistance of 10 Ω. Calculate the time to increase the current from its original value to 99% of its final value.

8. The motor in Fig. 6.16 produces a torque of 1 N m (assumed constant at all speeds). Other parameters are $J_m = 0 \cdot 1$ kg m^2, $F_m = 0 \cdot 2$ N m per rad/s, $J_1 = 2 \cdot 5$ kg m^2, $F_1 = 6$ N m per rad/s. The gears are inertialess and the coupling shafts are rigid.

(i) Determine the equation of motion for the system referred to the motor shaft.

(ii) Determine the steady-state angular velocity of the load.

(iii) Estimate the time taken for the load to reach its steady-state angular velocity from rest.

(Section 2.3.2 may be helpful.)

105

Chapter Seven

Control System Components

7.1 Introduction

The constitution of a closed-loop control system is discussed in chapter 1; the basic system is defined in terms of three elements, the error detector, the controller and the output element. The number of different types of component used in control systems is enormous and it is only possible to consider in this chapter a cross-section of typical components. For a more comprehensive description the student is advised to consult the literature.[12, 13]

7.2 Error Detectors

7.2.1 General

An error detector is any device or combination of devices used to determine the difference between the desired output (i.e. the input) and the actual output.

In order to compare the output with the input or the reference quantity, the error detector must be capable of accepting signals of different physical natures and often must be able to convert them to a common physical quantity in order to effect the comparison. The output of the error detector, which is the difference between the two signals compared, must be of the proper physical nature to actuate the controller. Error detectors often contain 'transducers' which may be defined as devices which convert signals of one physical form to another.

There are many types of error detector and the few examples considered will be classified according to the physical quantities they are required to compare.

7.2.2 *Positional Error Detectors*

The Potentiometer Bridge

The basic principle of the potentiometer has been mentioned earlier in §4.4.5. A single precision, wire-wound rotary potentiometer may be used as a transducer for converting angular position to a voltage proportional to angular position. Fig. 7.1 shows the arrangement and the schematic diagram.

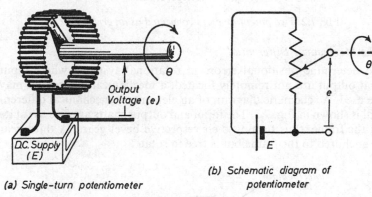

(a) *Single-turn potentiometer*

(b) *Schematic diagram of potentiometer*

Fig. 7.1 *The rotary potentiometer.*

If the potentiometer is linear, then

$$\frac{e}{\theta} = \frac{E}{\theta_{max}}$$

where θ_{max} is the maximum possible shaft rotation;

$$\therefore \qquad e = \left\{\frac{E}{\theta_{max}}\right\}\theta$$

Since E/θ_{max} is constant for a particular arrangement, the voltage e picked off by the slider is proportional to θ, the angular position of the slider.

A pair of potentiometers may be connected as an angular positional error detector as shown in Fig. 7.2.

Now $\qquad e_i = k\theta_i \quad$ and $\quad e_o = k\theta_o$

hence $\qquad e = e_i - e_o = k(\theta_i - \theta_o)$

Thus the voltage e produced by the device is proportional to the difference between the angular positions of the input and the output.

The arrangement is also useful as an error detector for translational motion when translational potentiometers are used.

107

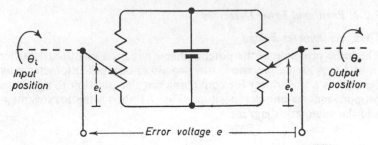

Fig. 7.2 *Two potentiometers connected as an error detector.*

The Mechanical Differential

To determine positional errors in rotational systems, where input and output are not remotely located, a mechanical differential may be used. A schematic diagram of an elementary mechanical differential is shown in Fig. 7.3. The input and output shafts are free to rotate in the frame, thus turning their respective bevel gears. A third gear is anchored to the frame but is free to rotate.

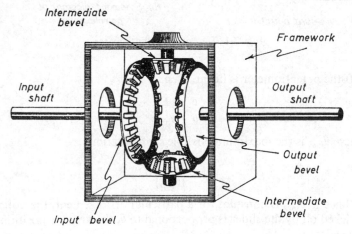

Fig. 7.3 *Mechanical differential.*

Suppose the output shaft is locked in position and the input shaft rotated. The input bevel will rotate, thus causing the intermediate gear to rotate and 'walk' round the locked output bevel. The frame is also forced to rotate, but only through half the angle through which the input rotates, the other half being taken up by the rotation of the intermediate gear. If the output is now rotated, while the input is locked in position, the output bevel will rotate, thus causing the intermediate gear to rotate and walk round the locked input bevel.

The frame is forced to rotate through half the angle turned through by the output.

If both input and output shafts are free to rotate the angle turned through by the frame is half the sum of the input and output angles. If the positive direction of the output shaft is defined oppositely to the positive direction of the input shaft, then the angle turned through by the frame is half the difference between the input and output angles, i.e.

$$\text{angle turned through by frame} = \frac{\theta_i - \theta_o}{2}$$

It is often desirable to convert the motion of the frame, which is a mechanical indication of the error, to an electrical error signal. This may be done by using a rotary potentiometer as an electromechanical transducer, as shown in Fig. 7.4.

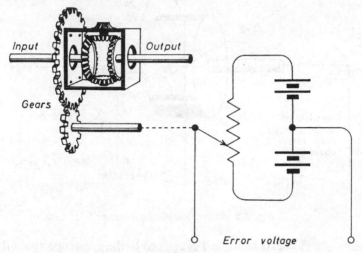

Fig. 7.4 *Conversion of mechanical error signal to electrical signal.*

The device has two limitations. The first is that the input and the output shafts cannot be remotely located and the second is that there will normally be some backlash in the gears; this will give rise to inaccuracy in the detection of errors.

The Positional Gyroscope

In many applications there is no fixed reference axis available and such devices as potentiometer bridges and mechanical differentials become useless. For instance, the angle of roll undergone by a ship or an aircraft could not be measured by a potentiometer, for if the slider itself were attached to the vehicle whose roll was being detected,

109

there would be no fixed point to which the framework carrying the resistor could be attached.

In such cases, where a 'mechanical memory' is required, the positional gyroscope may be used.

Physical bodies which are given large rotational momentum tend to maintain a fixed axial alignment in three-dimensional space. This alignment is not affected by translatory movement but if a torque T is applied, a reaction is set up perpendicular to the axis of the applied torque.

Referring to Fig. 7.5, the spinner, of moment of inertia J, is maintained in motion at a high angular velocity ω about the axis $X'X$ by

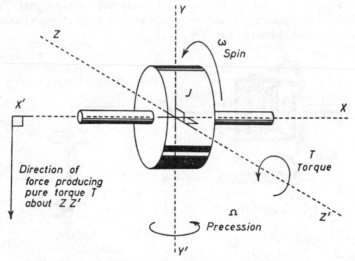

Fig. 7.5 *Basic positional gyroscope.*

means of a motor. If a torque T is applied to the gyroscope about the axis $Z'Z$, the gyroscope reacts by precessing about YY' with an angular velocity Ω. The quantities are related by the formula

$$\Omega = \frac{T}{J\omega}$$

where Ω and ω are in rad/s, and J is in kg m^2 and T is in N m. This formula is derived in most standard texts on applied mechanics (e.g. reference 14).

Precession has been used to stabilize ships and aircraft. A gyroscope can be mounted in such a way that it is allowed to precess in a given plane. This precession provides a torque in a plane at right angles to the precession plane, and this torque may be used to combat the forces that cause an aircraft or ship to pitch or roll. The size of such

110

gyroscopes would be considerable and the preferred method is to use a small, freely-suspended gyroscope as a sensing element and to apply corrective torques via servo-controlled stabilizing elements within the vehicle. An example of such an arrangement is the automatic pilot. Fig. 7.6 shows the pitch circuit of a typical scheme.

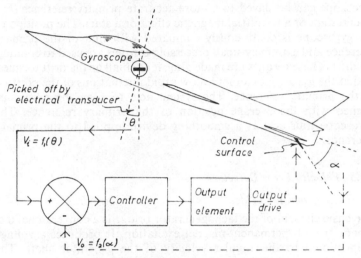

Fig. 7.6 *Pitch circuit of an auto-pilot.*

The object of this system is to relieve the human pilot of the monotonous and heavy work of controlling the aeroplane manually and to improve flying comfort for passengers when riding in rough air.

The gyroscope is freely suspended by a double gimbal and tends to maintain its preset axial alignment. The control system receives a command signal V_i from the gyroscope. V_i is some function $f_1(\theta)$ of the deviation of the aircraft from its set condition in pitch. This signal produces a rotation of the aeroplane's elevator control. The elevator then produces a rate of pitch of the aircraft proportional to the angle α of the elevator rotation, and therefore proportional to the input signal, in such a direction as to reduce the original pitch deviation to zero.

The rotor of a practical gyroscope is not usually a disc but instead consists of the rotor of a three-phase induction or hysteresis motor designed to operate at speeds as high as 24,000 rev/min.

Bearing friction and unbalance of the frameworks or gimbals is a major problem in the construction of gyroscopes and these effects cause 'drift' or change of axial alignment. The relative importance of drift depends entirely on the application. A gyroscope used to establish the directional reference in a guided weapon has a life of only a few minutes and may drift a few degrees per hour without adversely affecting the accuracy of the missile. In an aircraft the gyroscope used as an artificial horizon may be set occasionally and drift may again not be important.

In applications where drift is unallowable, the gyroscope is equipped with small torque motors so that it can be precessed. In this way the gyroscope can be slaved to a more accurate primary reference (e.g. a pendulum or a terrestrial magnetic effect or a star). The position of the gyroscope is continuously compared with that of the primary reference and extremely small precessing torques are used to counteract drift. These torques are made almost as small as the drift torques, so that the gyroscope cannot follow rapid fluctuations of the position of the primary reference. The system acts to keep the gyroscope aligned with the average position of the primary reference. The gyroscope thus acts as a smoothing device applied to the primary reference.

7.2.3 Velocity Error Detectors

The Tachogenerator Bridge

The basic element of the tachogenerator bridge is a conventional d.c. generator with permanent-magnet excitation. It produces a voltage proportional to the angular velocity of the generator shaft. The theory of operation of d.c. generators is introduced in §7.3.2.

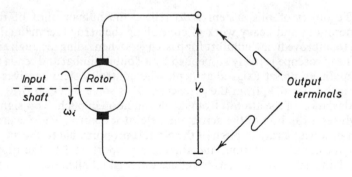

Fig. 7.7 *A tachogenerator.*

The d.c. tachogenerator is symbolized in Fig. 7.7. So long as negligible current is taken from the output terminals it may be shown that

$$V_o = k_n \omega_i$$

where k_n is the tacho constant.

When both input and output signals are in the form of a shaft

112

velocity, a tachogenerator bridge as shown in Fig. 7.8 may be used to detect the velocity error.

Now

$$V = V_i - V_o = k_{n1}\omega_i - k_{n2}\omega_o$$

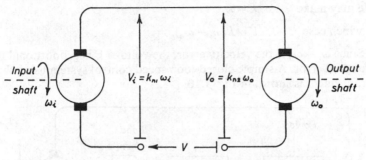

Fig. 7.8 *A tachogenerator bridge.*

If the tachogenerators have equal constants, i.e. $k_{n1} = k_{n2} = k_n$, then

$$V = k_n\omega_i - k_n\omega_o$$

$$= k_n(\omega_i - \omega_o)$$

But $(\omega_i - \omega_o)$ represents the velocity error, hence the voltage V is proportional to the velocity error $\omega_i - \omega_o$.

The Potentiometer-tachogenerator Bridge

Very often, the input signal is required to be the position of a hand-wheel moving against a calibrated scale, whereas the output signal is a shaft velocity. In this case a potentiometer-tachogenerator bridge as shown in Fig. 7.9 may be used.

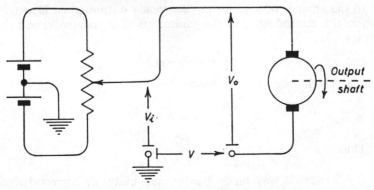

Fig. 7.9 *The potentiometer–tachogenerator bridge.*

113

If V_i is made proportional to required speed ω_i, then we may write $V_i = k\omega_i$. Also the output voltage from the tachogenerator $V_o = k_n \omega_o$.

Hence $$V = V_i - V_o = k\omega_i - k_n \omega_o$$

We may make $$k = k_n$$

in which case $$V = k(\omega_i - \omega_o)$$

Since $\omega_i - \omega_o$ is the velocity error, the voltage V is proportional to the speed error. A simple closed-loop speed control system using this arrangement is shown in Fig. 7.10.

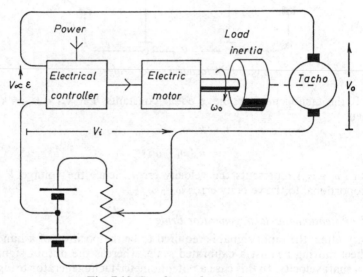

Fig. 7.10 *Simple speed-control system.*

In the absence of load torque the steady output speed $\omega_o = GV$, where G is dependent upon the parameters of the controller and the motor.

But $$V = k(\omega_i - \omega_o)$$

hence, substituting for V, we have

$$\frac{\omega_o}{G} = k(\omega_i - \omega_o)$$

Thus $$\omega_o = \frac{kG}{1 + kG}\omega_i$$

If kG is made very much greater than unity, by correct design, then $\omega_o \simeq \omega_i$.

114

The effect of load torque is to decrease the load speed, but not seriously so long as kG is large.

The Rate Gyroscope

In applications where there is no fixed reference axis a device like a tachogenerator is useless for measuring angular velocities. For instance in aircraft or missiles the rate of roll, pitch or yaw could not be measured by a tachogenerator for if the shaft itself were attached to the vehicle, there would be no fixed point to which the stator could be attached. The rate gyroscope is an important error detector which does not suffer from this deficiency.

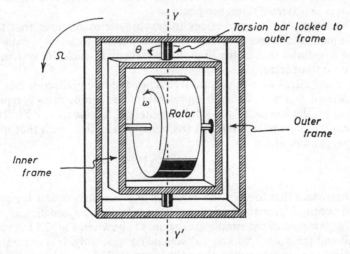

Fig. 7.11 *The rate gyroscope.*

Fig. 7.11 shows a simple form of rate gyroscope. The outer frame is fixed to the member which is expected to rotate. The inner frame is restrained by some spring system such as a torsion bar which is locked at one end to the outer frame. The inner frame can turn through a small angle θ, if a torque is provided about axis YY'.

Now when the outer frame is rotated at angular velocity Ω, the inner frame exerts a torque T on the torsion bar where $T = J\omega\Omega$.

However, the torsion bar will produce a restraining torque $k\theta$, where k is the stiffness of the bar. Thus the inner frame will come to rest about the axis YY' when

$$T = k\theta$$

or
$$J\omega\Omega = k\theta$$

115

Feedback Control Theory for Engineers

where J is the inertia of the rotor.

Therefore
$$\Omega = \frac{k}{J\omega}.\theta$$

Thus since k, J and ω are constants for the system, the device will measure Ω as an angular displacement θ. The angular displacement is normally converted to an electrical signal by a suitable transducer such as a potentiometer.

The rate gyroscope finds considerable application in ships, aircraft and guided missiles for control and stabilization. The device is of great value because its output is dependent almost solely upon the rate of spin about the Ω-axis. Its output remains unaffected by translatory motion or spins about the other two axes and hence it requires no external reference position.

The usage of rate gyroscopes in servo systems requires that the instrument shall have a certain designed natural frequency, usually some two times that of the highest frequency at which the system is required to operate.

For the calculation of natural frequency the rate gyroscope can be considered as a mass with spring restraint. The simple mass is represented by the inertia of the gimbal system J_g about axis YY'. The system will thus have a natural frequency f_n identical with that of a simple pendulum, i.e.

$$f_n = \frac{1}{2\pi}\sqrt{\left\{\left(\frac{k}{J_g}\right)\right\}}$$

This means that to meet the demands of servomechanisms for ever higher natural frequencies we must keep k high and J_g small.

The damping of the simple arrangement shown in Fig. 7.11 is very small and the gimbal is likely to oscillate considerably. It is normal in modern rate gyroscopes to place the inner gimbal in an hermetically sealed cylindrical can and fill the outer case with a viscous fluid. By adjusting the distance between the can and the case any desired degree of damping may be produced. This arrangement is doubly useful because, as well as damping out excessive oscillation, if the can is floated at nominally neutral buoyancy, the gimbal pivots carry very little load which allows the usage of small diameter, low friction pivot bearings.

7.2.4 Temperature Error Detectors

Electrical Temperature Error Detectors
The resistance thermometer may be used in a bridge circuit as shown in Fig. 7.12. The resistance thermometer is placed in a medium whose temperature is to be controlled. The resistance of the reference resistor is proportional to the required temperature, and the resistance of the

thermometer is proportional to the output temperature. A voltage proportional to the difference between these quantities will appear across the terminals AB.

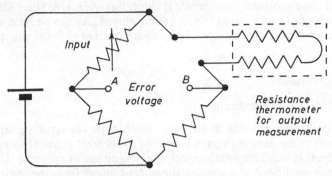

Fig. 7.12 *Resistance thermometer bridge.*

It is also quite possible to employ a thermocouple in a bridge circuit as shown in Fig. 7.13. The bridge is balanced and hence the error is zero when the thermocouple voltage and potentiometer voltage are equal.

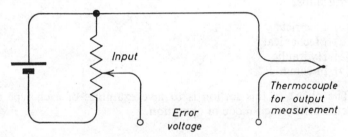

Fig. 7.13 *Thermocouple bridge.*

Mechanical Temperature Error Detectors

The bimetallic strip is perhaps the most commonly used temperature error detector. It is not capable of great precision.

The adjustable contact thermometer is another popular mechanical error detector but is capable of considerable accuracy. It is essentially a simple mercury-in-glass thermometer with two electrical contacts of platinum in the capillary, one static and the other adjustable. It is fitted with an external magnet which, when rotated, affords a precise means of varying the position of the adjustable contact and thus the setting of the required temperature. When used in conjunction with a fairly sophisticated temperature control system it is capable of controlling temperature to an accuracy of ±0·1°C.

117

7.2.5 Conclusion

The above treatment of error detectors is far from exhaustive and many quantities such as acceleration, pressure and rate of flow of fluids have not been considered. It does, however, give some idea as to the various techniques which are employed. As can be seen, error detection is basically the science of measurement of physical quantities.

7.3 Controllers

7.3.1 General Classification

The controller receives at its input the low-power error signal and delivers to the output element power of the correct physical form and of a level in exact accordance with the magnitude of the error. Under normal conditions of operation the output power from the controller will be very much greater than the power contained by the error signal. The controller does not itself generate the extra power but is supplied from an external source with sufficient power to satisfy the greatest needs of the system. The controller merely acts in such a way as to adjust the amount of power available to the output element at any particular instant. Controllers may be broadly classified into four groups:

(1) Electrical
(2) Mechanical
(3) Hydraulic
(4) Pneumatic

The object of this section is to give examples of each type and discuss briefly their mode of operation.

7.3.2 Electrical Controllers

Classification of Electrical Controllers

Electrical controllers may be classified into various groups as follows:

(*a*) *Electronic amplifiers* (employing thermionic vacuum tubes or transistors or both). These are most economical in size and price in the range 0 to 100 watts output power.

(*b*) *Magnetic amplifiers.* These are very robust and have no moving parts but are probably at their best in the power range 100 W to 500 W, although magnetic amplifiers with power outputs of greater than 10 kW are commercially available. The theory of these devices is beyond the scope of this book but may be found in the literature.[15]

(*c*) *Rotary amplifiers.* Such devices as d.c. generators, metadynes and amplidynes are often necessary in systems which require output powers above 500 W. The fact that they rotate means that they require more maintenance than electronic and magnetic amplifiers. They also make noise and require to be driven by a prime mover.

(*d*) *Discontinuous electrical controllers.* In on–off control systems and in certain types of continuous control systems such devices as thyratrons, electrical relays, silicon-controlled rectifiers, ignitrons and mercury arc rectifiers find application. As a group, the output powers range from a few watts to many kilowatts. The treatment of such devices is beyond the scope of this text.

Electronic Amplifiers

It is convenient to represent an electronic amplifier by an approximate equivalent circuit as shown in Fig. 7.14. The representation is not precise but is a useful approximation when the input signals are small and changes do not take place very quickly. It is less exact for transistor circuits than it is for vacuum tube circuits.

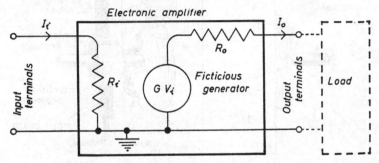

Fig. 7.14 *Equivalent circuit of an electronic amplifier.*

V_i is the input voltage and V_o is the output voltage. Inside the 'black box' we imagine there to be a generator which produces a voltage GV_i where G is the open-circuit 'gain' of the amplifier. The voltage GV_i will only appear at the output terminals when they are not connected to an external load. When a load is connected a current I_o will flow and the voltage $V_o = GV_i - I_o R_o$, where R_o is the output resistance of the amplifier. The input resistance is R_i. Usually R_i is designed to be as high as possible in order not to absorb a significant input current I_i from the source. If R_i is very high compared with external resistances the input can be regarded as an open circuit in order to simplify the analysis.

Electronic amplifiers may be designed with very high values of gain G.

119

Rotary Amplifiers

The ordinary d.c. generator is the simplest example of a rotary amplifier. The basic principle on which the operation of a d.c. generator depends is introduced in §4.4.7.

In the d.c. generator a magnetic field (density B) is produced by a field-winding which is wound on iron pole-pieces. The conductors are forced to move through the magnetic field and they cut the flux at right-angles. For reasons of constructional simplicity the motion of the conductors is pure rotation. The conductors are usually wound

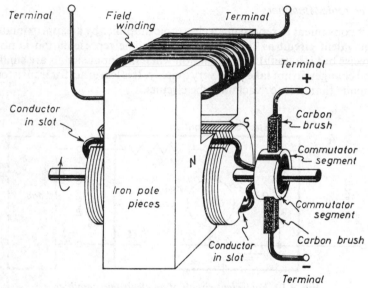

Fig. 7.15 *Simple d.c. generator.*

in slots in a laminated iron armature; only a small air gap exists between the pole-pieces and the armature, so that the reluctance of the magnetic circuit is as low as possible and thus high flux densities can be produced by relatively small m.m.f.'s. A simple single-turn generator is shown in Fig. 7.15.

In this arrangement the two conductors are connected together at the far end of the armature and brought out to 'commutator' segments at the near end. These segments make electrical contact with stationary carbon brushes which are connected to the output terminals of the machine. The commutator is a form of rotary switch and is necessary because the direction of the induced e.m.f. in the conductors reverses during rotation due to the change of direction of motion through the magnetic field.

120

Practical d.c. generators have many conductors laid in successive slots and they are interconnected in complicated patterns. There are many segments in the commutator but its function is essentially the same. It is also more efficient to have more poles than two but the principle of operation of a multipole machine is basically similar.

The e.m.f. generated by a d.c. generator is directly related to the e.m.f. generated in a single conductor. It is discussed in §4.4.7 how, if a conductor of length l is moved with velocity v at right-angles to a magnetic field of density B, then the e.m.f. E is given by

$$E = Blv$$

In the d.c. generator, B is proportional to the total flux per pole Φ and the velocity v is proportional to the angular velocity ω of the

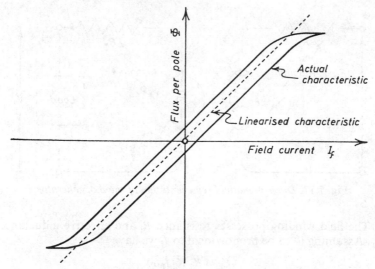

Fig. 7.16 *Graph relating Φ and I_f for a d.c. generator.*

armature. Thus since the length of each conductor is constant, the e.m.f. E_g generated by the machine is given by

$$E_g \propto \Phi\omega$$

or $$E_g = K_1 \Phi\omega$$

When the d.c. generator is used as a controller the speed ω is maintained constant by a prime mover. The field winding is supplied with the input voltage V_i and the current through the field winding I_f produces the flux Φ. The flux Φ and the field current I_f are related non-linearly as shown in the graph of Fig. 7.16.

It is convenient to approximate the non-linear relationship, between

121

Φ and I_f to a linear law for the purposes of elementary analysis. Such an approximation does lead to errors but the results of analysis based on the linear law are of considerable value.

The output voltage V_o of the machine is only equal to the generated voltage E_g when no output current I_o is being taken. Since the armature conductors must possess resistance, a voltage drop must exist across this resistance when current flows.

If the effective armature resistance is R_a then the relationship between V_o and E_g is given by

$$V_o = E_g - I_o R_a$$

It is convenient to represent the d.c. generator as a circuit element as shown in Fig. 7.17.

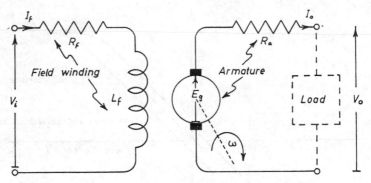

Fig. 7.17 *Diagrammatical representation of the d.c. generator.*

The field winding possesses resistance R_f and effective inductance L_f. Assuming Φ to be proportional to I_f we have

$$E_g = K_1 K_2 I_f \omega$$

where $K_2 I_f = \Phi$.

Since K_1, K_2 and ω are all constants,

$$E_g = K_g I_f$$

where $K_g = K_1 K_2 \omega$;

thus $$V_o = K_g I_f - I_o R_a$$

This relationship is useful in the analysis of control systems involving d.c. generators.

There are several physical effects which have not been considered. One is that the inductance L_f of the field winding is not absolutely constant but varies with I_f. Another is that the armature winding possesses a small inductance. Thirdly, when current is taken by the load, the effect of this current flowing through the armature winding is to produce an 'armature reaction' m.m.f. which is at right angles to the main field. This has the effect of lowering the generated voltage when armature current flows. These effects are fairly small and need not concern the student at the present stage.

There are various forms of d.c. generator which have been developed expressly for use as controllers in control systems, e.g. amplidynes. The student is referred to the literature[16] for a more detailed treatment of the subject.

The tachogenerator is mentioned in §7.2.3 in its application as a component in a velocity error detector. It is a d.c. generator with the flux Φ produced by a permanent magnet. The generated voltage E_g is thus given by

$$E_g = K_s \omega$$

where K_s is a constant for the machine (given by $K_s = K_1 \Phi$) and ω is the angular velocity of the armature. Thus so long as no current is taken, the output of the tachogenerator is directly proportional to the angular velocity of the armature.

7.3.3 A Mechanical Controller—The Torque Amplifier

Fig. 7.18 shows a mechanical torque amplifier arranged to increase the torque transmitted by a shaft which always rotates in the same direction.

The drum is free to rotate on the output shaft and is driven at

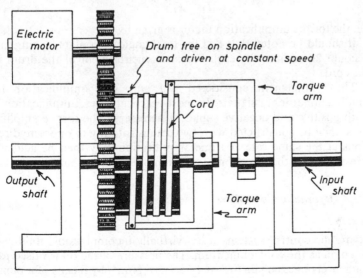

Fig. 7.18 *Simple mechanical torque amplifier.*

constant speed by a motor. A cord is wound round the drum and one end is connected to the input shaft and one to the output shaft.

Referring to Fig. 7.19, let θ = total angle of contact between cord and drum (including 2π radians for each complete encirclement), F_o = tension on cord at point P, F_i = tension in cord at point Q, ($F_o > F_i$), μ = coefficient of friction between drum and cord.

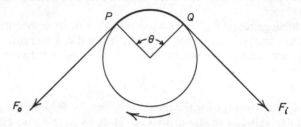

Fig. 7.19 *Showing tensions in the cord.*

Then it has been shown elsewhere[17] that

$$\frac{F_o}{F_i} = e^{\mu\theta}$$

Now if torque arms are of the same length the input torque T_i and the output torque T_o are related by the equation

$$\frac{T_o}{T_i} = \frac{F_o}{F_i} = e^{\mu\theta}$$

i.e. the torque amplification factor is given by $e^{\mu\theta}$.

It should be noted that θ is the total angle of contact, taking into account 2π radians for each complete encirclement of the drum by the cord.

The arrangement considered will only give amplification for unidirectional input signals. In most practical cases, amplification of both positive and negative signals is necessary. The torque amplifier must then be constructed with two drums rotating in opposite directions at the same rate. Torque amplification may then be achieved irrespective of the direction of rotation of the input shaft.

7.3.4 Hydraulic Controllers

General

Hydraulic control systems use a virtually incompressible fluid such as an oil as the control medium. The pressure of the oil is raised to a high level (e.g. 2000 lbf/in² or $1\cdot35 \times 10^7$ N/m²) by means of a pump.

There are two basic types of hydraulic control system. One of these types is termed a pump-controlled system. In this a single, variable-stroke pump supplies a fixed-stroke motor. Control of the motor is exercised by varying the amount of oil delivered by the pump. The arrangement is relatively inexpensive so long as only one motor is to be controlled. When several motors are to be controlled it is more economical to use a common high pressure supply in conjunction with the second basic type of system which is valve controlled. In a valve-controlled system each motor is controlled independently by a fast-acting, accurate 'servo valve'. Servo valves may be used to control powers ranging from as low as a few watts to as high as 5 kW.

Hydraulic control systems have several advantages. The main one is that a hydraulic motor may be made much smaller physically than an electric motor for the same power output. Hydraulic lines are not however, quite as flexible as electric cables and there are many advantages in using electrical error detection and 'pre-amplification' combined with hydraulic power amplification and output drive. Hydraulic systems do, however, require elaborate power supplies and pressure-regulating devices.

The purpose of this section is to introduce a few servo valves.

The Simple Spool Valve

Fig. 7.20 shows a primitive form of spool valve. The position of the cylindrical spool may either be controlled by direct mechanical

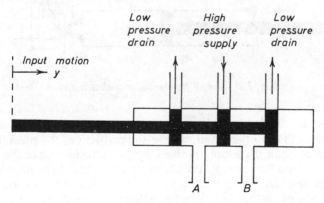

Fig. 7.20 *Primitive form of spool valve.*

linkage to the error detector or in an electrically signalled system, by means of a 'torque-motor' (see §7.4.2).

When the spool is centrally situated ($y = 0$) both channels A and B are cut off. When the spool is moved to the right (y is +ve), A is connected to the high-pressure supply and B is connected to the

125

exhaust. When the spool is moved to the left (y is $-$ve), B is connected to the high-pressure supply and A is connected to the exhaust. For small valve openings (i.e. small values of y) it is usually assumed that the rate of flow of fluid is proportional to the valve opening. It is also assumed that the fluid is incompressible.

There are many practical problems associated with the design and production of spool valves for use in high-performance control systems, and the student is particularly recommended to consult the literature[12] on this subject.

The Flapper Valve

One of the main disadvantages of the spool valve is the existence of axial reaction forces and attempts to reduce these have led to valves which operate on a completely different principle. Fig. 7.21 shows an example of such a valve.

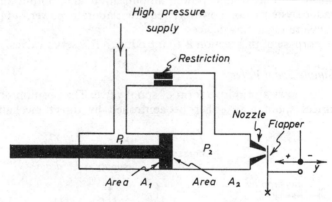

Fig. 7.21 *Simple flapper valve with actuator.*

When the flapper is in the neutral position (i.e. y is zero), oil will flow through the nozzle and, due to the restriction, the pressure p_2 will be less than the supply pressure p_1. Nevertheless, since the area A_1 is less than the area A_2, the forces on each side of the piston will balance and the piston will be stationary. When y is positive, the nozzle will be further closed and p_2 will be increased, with the result that the force on the right-hand side of the piston will be greater than that on the left-hand side; hence the piston will move towards the left. When y is negative, the nozzle will be further opened and p_2 will be reduced. The net force acting on the piston will then move the piston towards the right.

The pressure p_2 is approximately linearly related to the flapper position over a limited range.

126

There are a number of disadvantages associated with the device. One is the hydraulic leakage through the nozzle. Another is the existence of the reaction force on the flapper. The major limitation is that the controlled-pressure chamber must be fairly small to give small time delays. The time delays may be made smaller by using a larger nozzle but this will produce greater reaction forces and a larger leakage. These disadvantages restrict the use of the flapper valve and it is mainly used in the first stage of a two-stage valve.

A Two-stage Flapper-spool Valve

The disadvantages associated with flapper and spool valves can be largely overcome by the use of a two-stage device. A simple example

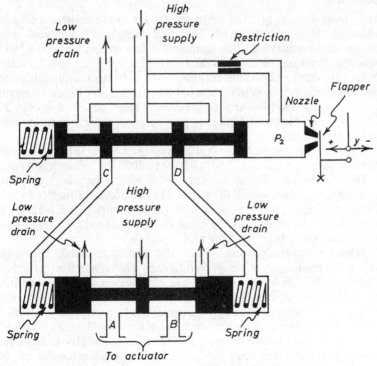

Fig. 7.22 *Simple two-stage flapper-spool valve.*

of a two-stage device which uses both flapper and the spool is shown in Fig. 7.22.

When the flapper is in the neutral position (y is zero), the pressure p_2 produces a force on the upper spool which exactly balances the spring pressure with ports C and D closed. The lower spool remains central with channels A and B both cut off.

127

When the flapper is moved to the left (y is +ve) the pressure p_2 increases and the upper spool moves to the left. Port C is connected to the high-pressure supply and port D to the exhaust. The lower spool is thus forced to the right and channel A is connected to the high-pressure supply and channel B to the low pressure exhaust.

When the flapper is moved to the right (y is −ve) the pressure p_2 decreases and the upper spool moves to the right. Port C is connected to the low-pressure exhaust and port D to the high-pressure supply. The lower spool is thus forced to the left and the channel A is connected to the exhaust and channel B to the high-pressure supply.

7.3.5 Pneumatic Controllers

General

Pneumatic control systems normally use air as the control medium, although this is not always so. They find considerable application in the process control field (see chapter 14) due to their reliability and safeness. Pressures of 15 to 20 lbf/in² ($1 \cdot 02 \times 10^5$ N/m² to $1 \cdot 35 \times 10^5$ N/m²) are employed in conventional process control, although some process control systems make use of 60 to 100 lbf/in². Process control systems using low pressures are relatively slow, soft and spongy in operation. This is an advantage in process control for it reduces wear in the moving parts.

Pneumatic systems are also sometimes used in guided missiles and aircraft where pressures as high as 1000 to 3000 lbf/in² are employed.

For short term use the air may be stored in very-high-pressure storage vessels from which the gas is metered down through reducing valves but more often the air is raised to the working pressure by a compressor. In both cases the used air is exhausted into the atmosphere and there is no need for return piping.

Whilst structurally some pneumatic valves resemble hydraulic valves the philosophy of design is different. The reason for this is that hydraulic fluid is incompressible but air is compressible, and thus pneumatic output elements must be pressure-locked in the required position. The object of the hydraulic valve is to produce a controlled rate of flow, whereas the pneumatic valve must produce a controlled pressure. This controlled pressure must be a function of the mechanical position of the valve. Low-pressure systems make extensive use of nozzle-flapper valves whereas the higher-pressure systems frequently use sliding-plate valves or spool valves similar to those used in hydraulic servos. The object of this section is to introduce a few simple pneumatic controllers.

Simple Proportional Flapper Valve

The most basic pneumatic flapper valve is the proportional type without feedback and is shown in Fig. 7.23.

With the flapper in the central position the controlled pressure p_c will have a nominal medium value. When the flapper is partly closed on to the nozzle p_c will be greater than the medium value and when it is completely closed p_c will tend towards its limiting value p_s. As the flapper is opened away from the nozzle p_c will fall below the medium

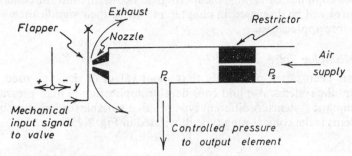

Fig. 7.23 *Proportional flapper valve.*

value, tending to a limit as the flapper is moved completely away. The characteristic relating p_c to the flapper position is very non-linear and can only be regarded as linear for very small flapper excursions. In order to linearize and desensitize the device, pneumatic feedback may be introduced as explained in the next paragraph.

The Proportional Flapper Valve with Pneumatic Feedback

To improve linearity and reduce sensitivity negative feedback is introduced as shown in Fig. 7.24.

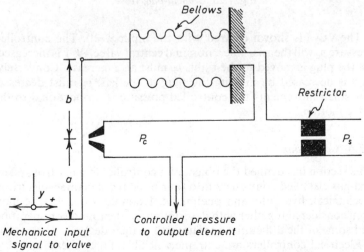

Fig. 7.24 *Proportional flapper valve with feedback.*

129

A bellows which expands an amount proportional to the controlled pressure is used to move the flapper in the opposite direction to the input signal. The sensitivity may be controlled by adjusting the ratio $a:b$.

Flapper valves of this type are used in the process control field. More complicated arrangements to give 'two-term' and 'three-term' control will be discussed in chapter 14, where their significance will be more appreciated.

Conical-plug Valve

It has been stated previously that spool valves of the type used in hydraulic systems also find considerable application in high-pressure pneumatic systems. A different type of valve, suitable for low pressure systems is the conical-plug type illustrated in Fig. 7.25.

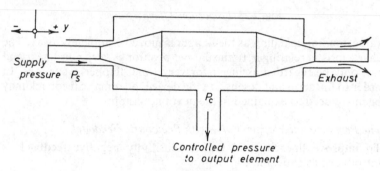

Fig. 7.25 *Conical-plug valve.*

The valve is shown centred with the input $y = 0$. The controlled pressure p_c will then assume a nominal central value. As y is increased, i.e. the plug is moved to the right, p_c must also increase. Conversely, as y is decreased by moving the plug to the left, p_c must decrease. For small movements the controlled pressure is proportional to the valve motion.

7.3.6 Conclusion

This section has defined the object of a controller in a control system and has classified controllers into four basic types, namely electrical, mechanical, hydraulic and pneumatic. Examples of each type have been considered together with descriptions of their mode of operation and some of the difficulties encountered in their design.

Electrical controllers are extremely flexible, fairly cheap and they may be miniaturized but they have not yet become as highly reliable as is necessary in completely automated systems. Mechanical controllers such as the torque amplifier are rather unsophisticated and inflexible and do not find much application in modern systems. Hydraulic controllers are not quite so flexible as electrical controllers and cannot be miniaturized to the same extent; hydraulic output elements, however, have a high power:weight ratio and they are stiff and fast in operation. In general, hydraulic servo-elements are expensive and require elaborate power supplies: the oil must be free from particles of solid matter for the reliable operation of valves. Leaks in hydraulic systems are not dangerous in themselves but the existence of an inflammable vapour in the atmosphere causes a danger of explosion. The use of non-inflammable oils is far more expensive.

Pneumatic controllers are cheap, very reliable, capable of miniaturization and safe at low pressures. Pneumatic systems are slow, soft and spongy in operation but this is no disadvantage in the process-control industry. In airborne applications the pressures have to be very much greater if performances comparable to hydraulic systems are to be achieved. This not only increases the weight of the piping but also makes the chances of a lethal explosion far greater. In pneumatic systems the air is highly compressed and any damage to the air-storage vessel may cause an explosion; in hydraulic systems a puncture merely produces a spray of oil. It is essential in pneumatic systems that the air should be free from particles of solid matter, water and oil, and thus filtering is necessary. Also, transmission of pneumatic signals over an appreciable distance results in a slow speed of response as compared with electrical transmission.

7.4 Output Elements

7.4.1 Introduction

The output element of a control system is required to produce a high-powered output of some physical quantity such as position, velocity, temperature, voltage, etc., the nature of the quantity depending on the specifications of the system. The output elements may therefore be any one of a large number of possibilities. In control of position or velocity it will usually be some form of servo-motor or actuator (electrical, hydraulic or pneumatic) but may possibly be an internal combustion engine or turbine. In the control of temperature the output element may be a resistive or inductive heater or an infra-red heater or an arc heater. In many chemical process systems requiring temperature control the output element consists of copper pipes through which steam passes at a controlled rate. In the control of voltage the output element will often be a conventional d.c. generator, whilst in the control of hydraulic pressure a gear pump may be used.

131

The object of this section is to describe some output elements and to explain their mode of operation and show how they are used in typical control systems.

7.4.2 Electric Output Elements

The D.C. Generator

The d.c. generator has been previously described in §7.3.2 as a controller. It may also be used as an output element in a voltage control system, a typical example of which is shown in Fig. 7.26.

Regulators of this kind are necessary because if the load current I_o is increased, this causes an increased voltage drop across R_{a2}, the armature resistance of the main generator, which causes a decrease in V_o. Also variations in the speed of the drive or in the resistance R_{f2} of the field winding will cause undesirable variations in V_o. If, for example, I_o rises due to increased load requirements, V_o will tend to decrease, but since V_i is set at a constant value, $V_i - V_o$ must increase, i.e. ϵ must increase. Thus I_{f1} increases causing the generated voltage of the pilot generator to go up; this produces an increase in I_{f2}, hence V_o will tend to increase thus counteracting the original tendency for V_o to decrease.

The improvement in the regulation may be made very considerable by correct design.

The D.C. Motor: The Basic Theory

The construction of the d.c. motor is identical to that of the d.c. generator which is described in §7.3.2. However, in the motor a d.c. voltage V_s is applied to the armature brushes. This forces a current I_a to flow through the armature conductors. It has been explained in §4.4.8 how, if a current-carrying conductor of length l is placed at right angles to a magnetic field of flux density B, then a force F given by

$$F = BIl$$

will exist. In the d.c. machine each conductor carries the armature current I_a and the flux density B is proportional to the flux per pole Φ produced by the field winding. The force on each conductor produces an unidirectional torque T on the armature which will tend to make it rotate. It follows that

$$T \propto \Phi I_a$$

or $\qquad T = K_2 \Phi I_a$ (the torque equation)

When the armature is allowed to rotate under the influence of its own torque, its conductors will cut the flux Φ and cause an internal

132

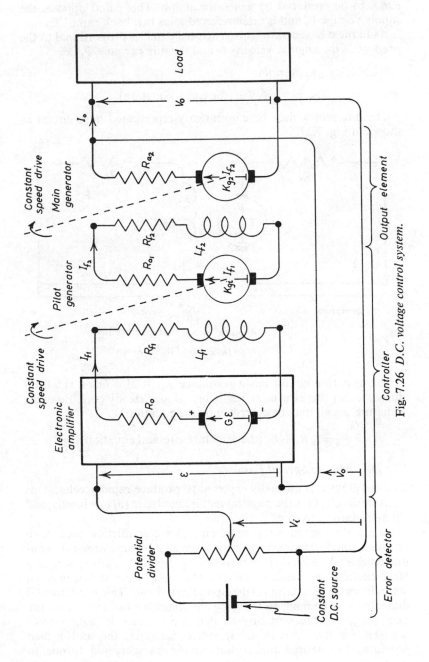

Fig. 7.26 D.C. voltage control system.

e.m.f. to be produced by generator action. This e.m.f. opposes the supply voltage V_s and is often referred to as the 'back e.m.f.' E_b.

As in the d.c. generator this generated e.m.f. is proportional to the product of the angular velocity ω and the flux per pole Φ, i.e.

$$E_b \propto \Phi\omega$$

or
$$E_b = K_1 \Phi\omega \text{ (the e.m.f. equation)}$$

The d.c. motor may be conveniently represented by a circuit as shown in Fig. 7.27.

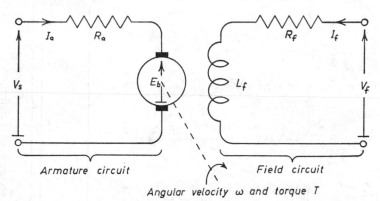

Fig. 7.27 *Circuit diagram of a d.c. motor.*

The armature circuit has a resistance R_a. It also has a small inductance but this is usually negligible. Under steady conditions the armature circuit may be described by the equation

$$V_s = I_a R_a + E_b \text{ (the armature circuital equation)}$$

The D.C. Motor: Special Features

The servomotor is normally expected to produce rapid accelerations from standstill; thus the physical requirements are (a) low inertia, and (b) high starting torque.

To a certain extent these requirements are conflicting because to produce a high starting torque the lever arm of each armature conductor should be as long as possible, i.e. for high starting torque a large diameter armature is required. However, if the armature has a large diameter its inertia is correspondingly large. This fundamental difficulty is overcome by reducing the diameter but increasing the axial length of the armature so that the increase in length compensates for the decrease in armature diameter, the motor then providing the desired torque but having an increased torque to inertia ratio.

The d.c. servomotor is essentially an ordinary d.c. machine designed specifically for separate excitation. That is to say the field and armature circuits are intended to be supplied from different sources.

There are two popular methods of control, armature control and field control. In armature control the armature receives the signal from the controller and the field current is maintained constant. In field control the field receives the signal from the controller and the armature current is maintained constant (or approximately so).

The nature of the field winding depends on the method of control for which the machine is designed. If it is designed specifically for field control, the field winding will consist of many turns of fine wire, so as to give as high a resistance as possible, thus making it suitable for use in conjunction with electronic controllers. Often, when this form of control is to be used, the field winding is split into two identical halves to facilitate 'push–pull' control from electronic amplifiers. In order to avoid large eddy current losses due to variations in the field current, the pole core of a d.c. motor designed for field control must be constructed of laminated steel. Where armature control is to be used the resistance of the field winding need not be high.

Permanent magnet excitation with armature control is now possible owing to the development of Alnico and other modern magnetic alloys. They are only used in small motors, however, with outputs not greater than several hundred watts.

The D.C. Motor: Armature Control

In armature control a voltage V_a, which is the output from the controller, is applied to the armature and the field voltage V_f is held

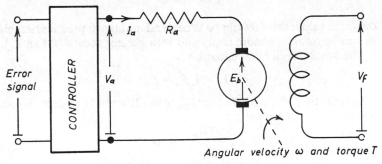

Fig. 7.28 *Armature control.*

constant, producing a constant flux per pole Φ. The arrangement is shown in Fig. 7.28.

The torque-speed characteristic will now be derived. The e.m.f. equation gives

$$E_b = K_1 \Phi \omega$$

135

but since Φ is held constant (ignoring the small effect of armature reaction[18]),

$$E_b = K_v \omega \qquad (1)$$

where $\qquad K_v = K_1 \Phi$ (a constant)

The torque equation gives

$$T = K_2 \Phi I_a$$

but again since Φ is held constant,

$$T = K_t I_a \qquad (2)$$

where $\qquad K_t = K_2 \Phi$ (a constant)

(Note: If K_v is expressed in volts per rad/s and K_t is expressed in N m/ampere then it may be shown that K_t and K_v have numerically

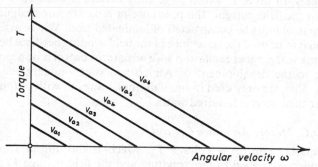

Fig. 7.29 *Torque-speed characteristics for armature-controlled motor.*

the same value; this fact can be used to advantage in practice because K_v can be measured more easily and with greater accuracy than K_t). The armature circuital equation is

$$V_a = I_a R_a + E_b \qquad (3)$$

Substituting in (3) for I_a and E_b from (2) and (1) respectively we obtain

$$V_a = \frac{TR_a}{K_t} + K_v \omega$$

or $\qquad T = \frac{K_t}{R_a} V_a - \frac{K_v K_t}{R_a} \omega$

This equation will give a set of linear torque/speed characteristics for various values of V_a as shown in Fig. 7.29.

One of the disadvantages of armature control is the fact that even for small machines the current required will be large. This normally

136

precludes the direct use of thermionic vacuum tubes as control elements. Whilst it is now possible to achieve armature control of small machines with high-power transistors or thyristors it is usual to employ the Ward-Leonard connection for larger machines. In this a d.c. generator is used as the main controller as shown in Fig. 7.30.

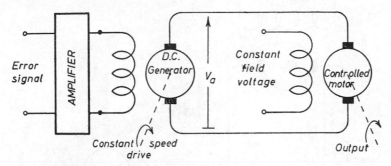

Fig. 7.30 *Ward-Leonard connection for the practical attainment of armature control.*

The advantage of armature control is that it inherently possesses a high speed of response.

The D.C. Motor: Use of Armature Control in a Typical Speed Control System

An important application of the armature-controlled d.c. motor is in the speed regulator. A typical arrangement is shown in Fig. 7.31. It consists of an electronic amplifier which supplies the field winding of a d.c. generator, the armature of which is driven at constant speed. The armature of the d.c. generator is electrically connected to the armature of the d.c. motor which is mechanically coupled to a tacho-generator whose output is V_o. A reference signal V_i is derived from a potential divider connected across a constant voltage d.c. source. The electronic amplifier receives the error signal $V_i - V_o$. The object of the system is to maintain the speed constant at a level proportional to V_i regardless of load torque.

This system will be mathematically analysed for steady-state conditions as an example to illustrate the general method of approach to such problems. The object of the analysis is to find a relationship between the motor speed ω, the reference V_i and the motor torque T.

Parameters of System

G = open-circuit voltage gain of electronic amplifier
K_g = generator voltage per ampere of field current
K_t = motor torque per ampere of armature current

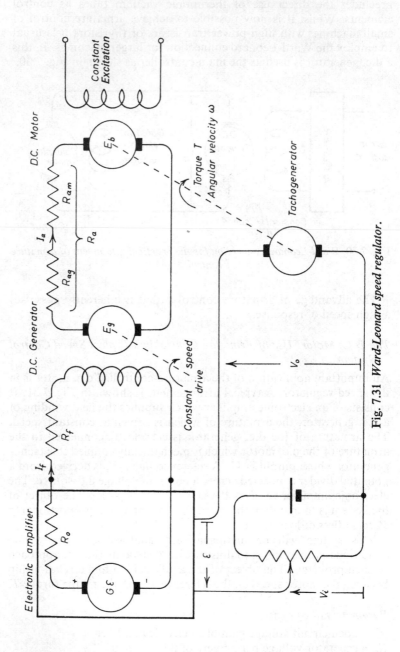

Fig. 7.31 *Ward-Leonard speed regulator.*

K_v = motor back e.m.f. per rad/s of motor speed
K_s = tachogenerator voltage per rad/s of motor speed
$R_a = R_{ag} + R_{am}$ = combined armature circuit resistance

Defining Equations

$$\epsilon = V_i - V_o \tag{1}$$

$$V_o = K_s \omega \tag{2}$$

$$E_g = K_g I_f \tag{3}$$

$$E_b = K_v \omega \tag{4}$$

$$T = K_t I_a \tag{5}$$

Analysis

For the armature circuit we have

$$E_g = I_a R_a + E_b \tag{6}$$

Substituting for E_g, I_a and E_b from equations (3), (4) and (5) respectively we have

$$K_g I_f = \frac{T}{K_t} R_a + K_v \omega \tag{7}$$

But

$$I_f = \frac{G\epsilon}{R_o + R_f}$$

$\therefore$

$$\frac{K_g G\epsilon}{R_o + R_f} = \frac{T}{K_t} R_a + K_v \omega$$

or

$$\omega = \frac{K_g G}{(R_o + R_f) K_v} \epsilon - \frac{R_a}{K_t K_v} T$$

Now let $K_g G/(R_o + R_f) K_v = P$ (a composite system parameter), and let $R_a/K_t K_v = Q$ (a second parameter).

Hence

$$\omega = P\epsilon - QT \tag{8}$$

This equation may be regarded as the open-loop, static characteristic of the system. If, for the moment, we regard ϵ as a constant instead of a function of ω, we see that the no load speed will be $P\epsilon$ and the drop in speed on load will be QT. The static open-loop characteristic is shown in Fig. 7.32.

Now in fact $\epsilon = V_i - V_o$, but using equation (2) we have

$$\epsilon = V_i - K_s \omega$$

$\therefore$

$$\omega = P(V_i - K_s \omega) - QT$$

thus

$$\omega(1 + K_s P) = PV_i - QT$$

or

$$\omega = \frac{P}{1 + K_s P} V_i - \frac{Q}{1 + K_s P} T$$

139

It can be seen that if $K_s P$ is designed to be much greater than unity, then the droop, which becomes $QT/(1 + K_s P)$, is very considerably reduced. The no-load speed becomes approximately V_i/K_s and is thus relatively independent of variations in the parameters of the hardware in the forward path.

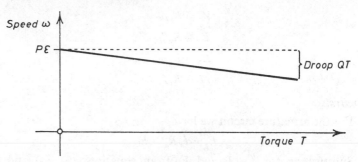

Fig. 7.32 *Static open-loop characteristic of Ward-Leonard system.*

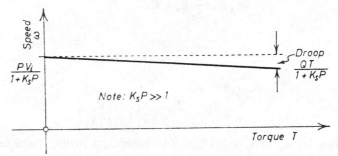

Fig. 7.33 *Static closed-loop characteristic of Ward-Leonard system.*

D.C. Motor: Field Control

In field control a voltage V_f, which is the output from the controller, is applied to the field winding and the armature current is maintained constant as shown in Fig. 7.34.

In order to attain a reasonably linear performance it is necessary to hold I_a constant, despite variations in the back e.m.f. which will occur as the speed ω varies. This problem may be solved in a number of ways, one of which is to connect the armature to a constant voltage supply in series with a high-value resistance. The current is then largely governed by the resistance and is little affected by the back e.m.f.

The static characteristics of the arrangement will now be derived. The flux per pole Φ will be related to the current I_f by the hysteresis loop for the machine as shown in Fig. 7.35.

If saturation and hysteresis are neglected we can say

$$\Phi \propto I_f$$

or
$$\Phi = K_f I_f \tag{1}$$

But the torque
$$T = K_2 I_a \Phi$$

Since I_a is constant
$$T = K_2' \Phi \tag{2}$$

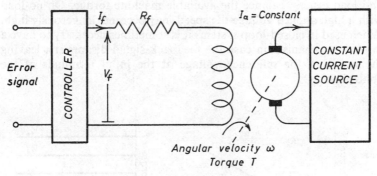

Fig. 7.34 *Field control.*

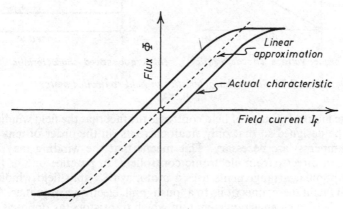

Fig. 7.35 *Flux-current characteristic for the d.c. motor.*

Eliminating Φ between (1) and (2) we have

$$T = K_f K_2' I_f$$

or
$$T = K_f' I_f$$

where
$$K_f' = K_f K_2'$$

Now under static conditions $V_f = I_f R_f$

$$\therefore \qquad T = \frac{K_f'}{R_f} V_f$$

or $$T = K_f'' V_f$$

where $$K_f'' = K_f'/R_f$$

The static characteristics are shown in Fig. 7.36.

It is evident that the speed is independent of both the torque and the field voltage. If the motor is run on open loop, i.e. with V_f held constant, the speed will rise until the torque due to friction, windage and load exactly balance the available machine torque. On no-load with a high applied voltage the speed may become dangerously high. When used in closed-loop systems it is sometimes necessary to have a fail-safe mechanism in case the feedback signal disappears, leaving the whole of the reference voltage at the input terminals of the controller.

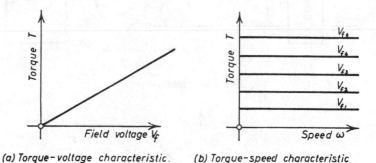

(a) Torque-voltage characteristic.   (b) Torque-speed characteristic

Fig. 7.36 *Static characteristics of field-controlled motor.*

The main advantage of field control is the fact that the field winding may be designed so that only small currents (in the order of tens of milliamperes) are necessary. This means that the winding may be supplied directly from electronic controllers. In practice one of the most popular arrangements uses a motor with a split field winding which facilitates connections to a 'push–pull' electronic amplifier. An example of such an arrangement, in which transistors (as opposed to vacuum tubes) are used in the output stage of the controller, is shown in Fig. 7.37.

A disadvantage of field control is the relatively slow speed of response associated with it.

The D.C. Motor: The Velodyne Speed Control System

An arrangement which is extremely popular in speed control systems for instrument servos is the velodyne. In this, a d.c. motor is field-controlled from an electronic amplifier. The motor armature current is maintained constant and its output shaft is mechanically coupled

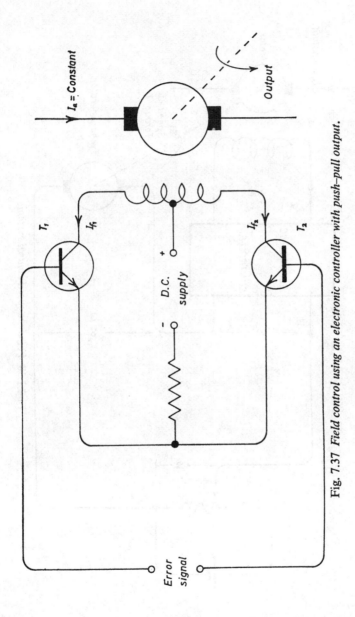

Fig. 7.37 *Field control using an electronic controller with push-pull output.*

143

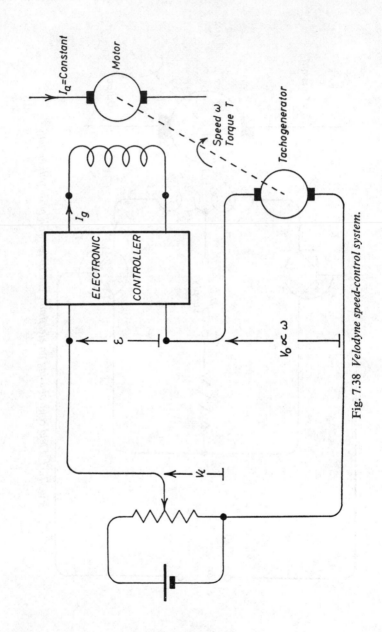

Fig. 7.38 *Velodyne speed-control system.*

to a tachogenerator. A reference signal V_i is derived from a potential divider connected across a constant voltage d.c. source. The electronic amplifier receives the error signal $V_i - V_o$. The object of the system is to maintain the speed constant at a level proportional to V_i regardless of load torque. The system is illustrated in Fig. 7.38.

The method of deriving the static speed-torque characteristic is similar to that used earlier for the Ward-Leonard system.

The Torque Motor

D.C. torque motors are special devices whose output is a rotary displacement that is proportional to the control-winding input. In order to achieve linear operation, the output displacement is usually limited to a maximum of about 10 to 20 degrees. The torque motor thus finds application in the control of hydraulic valves in which very small movements are necessary. In many applications the rotary motion is converted to translatory motion by means of a simple mechanical linkage.

A typical torque motor is shown in Fig. 7.39. The coils wound on poles 1 and 2 carry the same direct current I_a and the coils on poles 3 and 4 carry a second current I_b. I_a and I_b might be the two currents from a push–pull electronic amplifier which receives the error signal at its input. Normally all four coils are identical. The rotor is made of iron and contains no winding. When I_a is equal to I_b poles 1 and 2 exert the same force of attraction on the rotor as poles 3 and 4. The neutral position of the rotor is thus along the axis XX'. When I_a is greater than I_b poles 1 and 2 exert a greater force of attraction than poles 3 and 4. The rotor is thus moved in the direction of the arrow. However, when I_b is greater than I_a poles 3 and 4 exert a greater force of attraction than poles 1 and 2 and the rotor is moved in the opposite direction to the arrow.

Although this type of torque motor is basically stable in any position, springs are sometimes provided to give an additional restraining torque. These springs may either be inbuilt or form part of the hydraulic valve which the torque motor is designed to control.

The static equation for the torque motor is given by

$$T = K_1 i - K_2 \theta$$

where T = torque produced by the motor, $i = I_a - I_b$, θ = angular displacement from axis XX', and K_1 and K_2 are constants for the machine.

If T_r is the restraining torque of the control spring then

$$T_r = K\theta$$

where K is the stiffness of the spring.

145

Thus for static equilibrium $T = T_r$

$$\therefore \qquad K\theta = K_1 i - K_2 \theta$$

$$\therefore \qquad \theta(K + K_2) = K_1 i$$

$$\therefore \qquad \theta = \frac{K_1 i}{K + K_2}$$

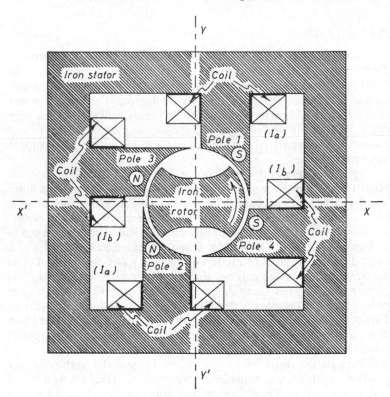

Fig. 7.39 *A d.c. torque motor.*

The angular position of the spring-restrained rotor is hence directly proportional to the difference between the coil currents (which may be termed the 'control current').

7.4.3 Hydraulic Output Elements

General

Hydraulic motors or actuators are of two general types: those intended to produce translatory motion and those whose output is rotational.

The linear actuators are piston devices. They may be obtained in a variety of power capacities with a wide range of stroke lengths. Speed of action can usually be adjusted to meet any reasonable specification. The hydraulic piston may be locked in place, since hydraulic fluid is virtually incompressible. Reversible action is readily provided by proper design.

Rotary hydraulic motors are available in unidirectional or reversible types, and in a wide range of ratings from watts to kilowatts. In general, they have good torque characteristics and are very light in weight considering their power ratings. The rotors have comparatively high torque-to-inertia ratio, which is frequently important in systems having high acceleration requirements.

Linear Actuators

A few typical linear actuators are illustrated in Fig. 7.40.

The spring-loaded piston can be operated from a three-way spool valve. The double acting piston requires a four-way valve. The push–pull actuator contains a pair of single acting pistons, mechanically linked to produce limited rotary motion of the output shaft.

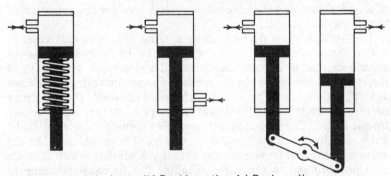

(a) Spring-loaded piston. (b) Double acting. (c) Push-pull.

Fig. 7.40 *Linear actuators.*

Hydraulic actuators are self-lubricating but suffer from marked Coulomb friction, which is most severe when Neoprene seals are fitted. There is relatively little viscous friction and the stiction is not usually very much larger than the dynamic coulomb friction. The value of the pressure drop across a piston necessary to overcome the friction might be as high as 30% of the supply pressure and at best can only be reduced to 10%.

Under static conditions the equations governing the motion of a single piston are

$$Q = L_p P + A_p V \quad \text{and} \quad F = A_p P$$

Feedback Control Theory for Engineers

where Q = total flow into cylinder, L_p = leakage coefficient (piston-cylinder leakage), A_p = area of piston, V = velocity of piston motion, F = force available to do work, P = pressure difference across the piston.

It should be noted that the compressibility of the oil has no effect on the static equations of the device and that L_p is often small enough to be neglected.

Applications of Hydraulic Actuators: Automatic Profile Milling Machine

An application of a hydraulic actuator is shown diagrammatically in Fig. 7.41, where the cutter of a milling machine is caused to rise and fall automatically and thereby reproduce in the finished work the contour of a master template or cam. The controller is a spool valve and the error detector is a direct mechanical link.

Electrically Signalled Fin Servo for Guided Missile

Guided missiles and modern machine tool control systems are electrically signalled. The system illustrated in Fig. 7.42 is an example of a typical remote position control system used for the actuation of fins in a guided missile.

The voltage V_i is derived from a radar (or infra-red) receiver within the missile. This voltage is related to the desired direction of missile motion in a particular plane. The feedback voltage V_o is directly proportional to the fin position θ_o and the voltage difference $V_i - V_o$ is determined by a simple electrical network. The difference or error voltage is amplified and becomes a current signal to the torque motor. The torque motor controls the position of a hydraulic valve. Ideally the rate of flow from this valve is proportional to the valve-opening and imparts to the actuator a velocity which is hence also proportional to the valve-opening. The fin must continue to move until the error signal $V_i - V_o$ is reduced to zero.

Mechanically Signalled Control-surface Servo for Aircraft

Whilst servos in guided missiles are almost exclusively electrically signalled, in the aircraft field electrical signalling of the control-surface hydraulics is still rare. An arrangement in which the input signal is a manual displacement and error detection is carried out by a mechanical linkage is shown in Fig. 7.43.

When the command lever is moved forward (x_i positive), the valve is caused to move through a distance x_e. Port B of the actuator is connected through the valve to the high pressure supply and port A is connected to the low-pressure exhaust. This causes the actuator to move through a distance x_o. This motion will reduce x_e; the motion

148

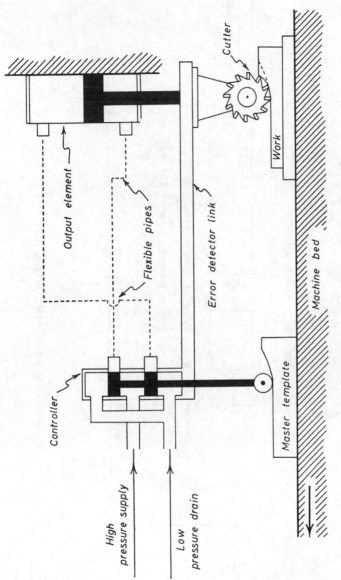

Fig. 7.41 *Profile milling machine.*

149

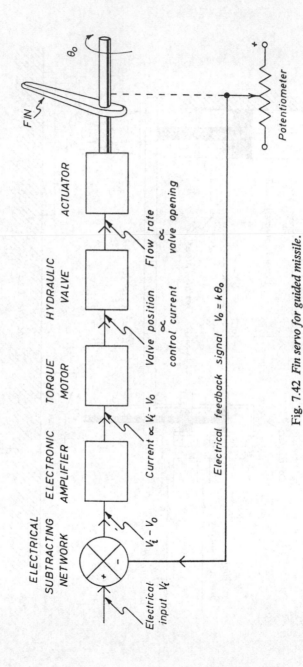

Fig. 7.42 *Fin servo for guided missile.*

150

will only cease when x_e is zero, i.e. the valve is centralized, and x_i and x_o are correctly related.

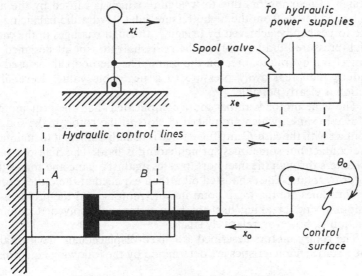

Fig. 7.43 *Control-surface servo for aircraft.*

Rotary Motors

Two typical rotary motors are illustrated in Fig. 7.44.

Gear motors have fewer moving parts than other rotary motors and are the easiest to manufacture. They are simple, rugged, efficient and low in cost.

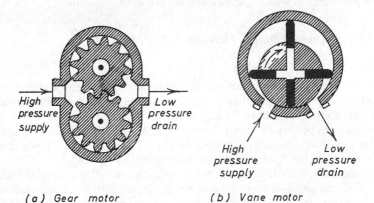

(a) Gear motor   (b) Vane motor

Fig. 7.44 *Rotary hydraulic motors.*

The oil forces its way from the high-pressure inlet into the spaces between the teeth and the housing and impels the gear wheels. The oil is exhausted at the opposite port. A basic difficulty exists in the design of gear motors due to 'wedging' which is caused by the unbalanced forces from the high pressure inlet. Hydraulic balancing of the forces can be achieved by bringing, through passages in the case, high-pressure fluid to bear on the gear shaft at a point designed to cancel the hydraulic force on the gears. The method can be used to reduce the break-away pressure to a negligible value. Reversible action is clearly possible.

The vane motor is rather more complicated than the gear motor. Movable vanes, which are placed in slots in the rotor, make sliding contact with the case. Centrifugal force is usually sufficient to maintain the contact but sometimes spring loading is used. The high-pressure oil enters through the inlet port, presses against a vane and forces the rotor to rotate. The exhausted oil is then expelled at the outlet port.

The vanes are the weak point in vane motors, and the problem of chipping and breaking has not been completely solved. Coulomb friction is, however, relatively small.

The rotary motors described are 'fixed-displacement' devices, and their static characteristics are determined by the following equations:

$$Q = L_m P + D_m \omega \tag{1}$$

and

$$P = \frac{T}{D_m} \tag{2}$$

where Q = total rate of flow to the motor, P = differential motor pressure, ω = motor speed, T = torque produced by motor, L_m = motor leakage coefficient, D_m = motor displacement.

The M.K.S. system of units may, of course, be used in the solution of problems in which these equations are used.

7.4.4 Pneumatic Output Elements

General

A pneumatic motor is an air-operated device wherein a change in input air-pressure produces a mechanical output motion. Pneumatic motors are of two basic kinds, translatory and rotary. The majority of modern pneumatic control systems make use of translatory output devices, the principal types being the capsule, the bellows, diaphragm, ram and piston. These types are illustrated in Fig. 7.45.

With the exception of the pneumatic piston, all the devices illustrated are single-acting and can be operated from three-way valves. The piston is double acting and would require a four-way valve. The capsule and bellows are mainly suitable for low-pressure applications

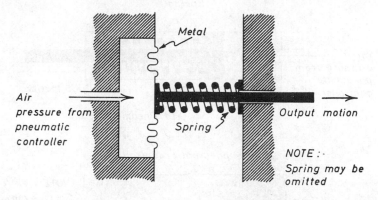

(a) Pneumatic capsule

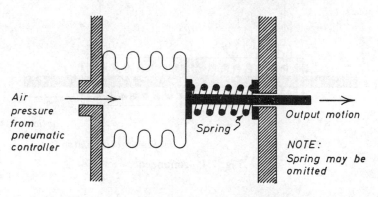

(b) Pneumatic bellows.

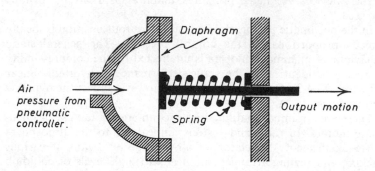

(c) Pneumatic diaphragm.

Fig. 7.45 *Pneumatic motors.*

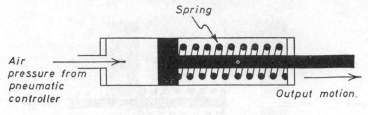

(d) Pneumatic ram

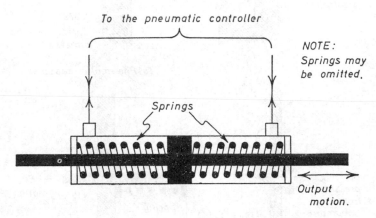

(e) Pneumatic piston

Fig. 7.45 continued.

and for maximum sensitivity the springs may be omitted from each of these devices. At higher pressures, diaphragms, rams and pistons are used.

In the pneumatic motor, the final steady output position is ideally directly proportional to the control pressure. The general static behaviour of pneumatic motors is unaffected by the compressibility of air and is identical to the static performance of hydraulic linear actuators (§7.4.3). Compressibility does, however, affect the dynamic performance.

There are a number of difficulties encountered in the use of pneumatic motors. In rams and pistons air leakage to the atmosphere causes inefficiency. Reduction of air leakage by means of various packing and sealing arrangements leads to high levels of coulomb friction. Air is a poorer lubricant than oil and thus the problem of maintaining seals is more serious than in hydraulic equipment.

The translatory types of pneumatic motor are prevalent because air leakage can be kept within reasonable limits, whereas in the rotary types air leakage is considerable.

Applications of Pneumatic Motors

These devices find considerable application in various fields. Electrically-signalled fin servos using pneumatic valves and actuators rather than hydraulic are often employed in small guided missiles. These systems are basically similar to that described in §7.4.3.

Many systems in the chemical process control field use pneumatic systems and these applications are further discussed in chapter 14.

7.5 Concluding Remarks

In this chapter an attempt has been made to give a representative cross-section of the major elements used in control systems. The static characteristics of many of the elements have been given and some typical applications have been described. In view of the wide field of application of automatic control and of the very varied conditions found in this field, it is not desirable to confine the discussion to any particular type of system (e.g. purely hydraulic). The electrical approach is often the most convenient because it provides flexibility in the experimental stage (the electronic analogue computer, for instance, is a powerful tool in design work). There are many cases, however, in which the final solution with least complexity and cost will involve the use of hydraulic or pneumatic means.

EXAMPLES FOR SOLUTION

1. (*a*) Describe, with the aid of a labelled diagram, the principles of operation of a rate gyroscope and derive the relevant equation relating the angular displacement of the inner framework to the rate of turn of the device about its input axis.

(*b*) A rate gyroscope is required to measure rates of turn of up to 2 rad/s and must have an undamped natural frequency of 60 c/s. The moment of inertia of the rotor is $7 \cdot 00 \times 10^{-4}$ kg m^2 and the moment of inertia of the inner framework about the output axis $9 \cdot 20 \times 10^{-4}$ kg m^2. If the spinner speed is 24,000 rev/min, determine the maximum value of angular displacement of the spinner framework.

2. A velodyne speed control system consists of a d.c. electronic amplifier which supplies the field winding of a field-controlled d.c. motor. The armature current of this motor is kept constant. Coupled to the motor shaft is a tachogenerator which produces a voltage V_o. The d.c. amplifier receives at its input a voltage $(V_i - V_o)$ in which V_i is a d.c. reference voltage derived from a potential divider connected across a constant d.c. source. The parameters of the system are as follows:

Electronic Amplifier: gain on open-circuit = 2000 V/V; output resistance = 2 kΩ; input resistance is infinite.

D.C. Motor: resistance of field winding = 2 kΩ; motor torque T = 8 N m per ampere of field current.

Tachogenerator: $V_o = 3 \cdot 5n$ volts where n is the motor speed in rev/s.

(i) Draw a simplified circuit diagram for the system.

(ii) Derive an equation relating the motor speed n to the reference voltage V and the load torque T.

(iii) If the reference voltage is 100 V calculate the no-load speed and the percentage regulation for a load torque $T = 1 \cdot 5$ N m.

(iv) By what percentage does the no-load speed change if the gain of the electronic amplifier decreases by 20%?

3. A Ward-Leonard system is used for controlling the speed of a d.c. motor. The field of the motor to be controlled is supplied at constant voltage, and the voltage applied to the armature of the motor is derived from a d.c. generator. This generator is driven at constant speed, and has its field supplied from a d.c. electronic amplifier. The input signal to this amplifier is equal to the difference between a steady reference voltage V_i and a voltage V_o generated by a tachogenerator which is coupled to the motor shaft. The details of the system are as follows:

Generator: Resistance of the field circuit including the output resistance of the d.c. amplifier is 200 Ω; generated e.m.f. per ampere of field current is 2000 V.

Amplifier: Gain on open-circuit is 20 V/V; input resistance is to be assumed infinite.

Motor: Torque developed per ampere of armature current is 1·0 N m; generated e.m.f. per rad/s is 1·0 V; armature resistance, including resistance of generator armature is 2·0 Ω.

Tachogenerator: Generated e.m.f. per rad/s of motor speed is 0·5 V.

    (i) Draw a simplified circuit diagram for the system.

    (ii) Derive the equation relating the motor speed ω to the reference voltage V and the torque T.

    (iii) What is the speed when $V_i = 101$ V and T is zero?

    (iv) By what percentage of the no-load speed does the speed fall when $T = 10$ N m assuming $V_i = 101$ V?

4. A d.c. voltage regulator consists of a d.c. electronic amplifier which supplies the field winding of a d.c. generator which is driven at constant speed. The generator supplies an external load with a current I_o at a voltage V_o. The electronic amplifier receives at its input an error voltage $V_i - V_o$, where V_i is a reference voltage derived from a potential divider connected across a constant d.c. voltage source. The particulars of the system are:

Electronic Amplifier: gain into open-circuit = 1000 V/V; output resistance = 350 Ω; input resistance is infinite.

D.C. Generator: generated voltage = 100 volts per ampere of field current, armature resistance = 3 Ω, field resistance = 350 Ω.

    (i) Draw a simplified circuit diagram of the system and derive an expression for V_o in terms of V_i and I_o.

    (ii) Determine the value of V_o when $I_o = 0$ and $V_i = 100$ V.

    (iii) Determine the percentage regulation when $I_o = 20$ A and $V_i = 100$ V.

    (iv) Determine the percentage change in the no-load output voltage if the gain of the electronic amplifier decreases by 50%.

5. (*a*) Describe in detail an experiment to determine the relationship between the rate of precession and the torque applied to a free gyroscope. Show how you would represent the results graphically. In what way does the characteristic obtained experimentally differ from the ideal theoretical characteristic?

(*b*) A free gyroscope has a moment of inertia of 0·048 kg m² and the spinner rotates at a constant speed of 6800 rev/min. If a torque of 1 N m is applied to the gyroscope frame about an axis at right angles to the axis of spin, determine the rate of precession assuming (i) there is no bearing frictional torque opposing the applied torque; (ii) there is a bearing frictional torque of 0·2 N m in direct opposition to the applied torque.

6. Determine the torsion constant of the torsion bar of a rate gyroscope which is required to measure rates of turn of 2 rad/s if the maximum allowable value of angular deflection of the spinner framework is one degree. The spinner has a moment of inertia of $7·32 \times 10^{-4}$ kg m² and a speed of 24,000 rev/min.

Chapter Eight

The Dynamics of a Simple Servomechanism for Angular Position Control

8.1 Introduction

One of the most important problems in control engineering is that of mechanical position control of heavy masses capable of rotation or translation. Such problems occur in machine tool control, automatic steering of aircraft, ships, guided weapons and space craft, automatic positioning of guns, launchers, radar aerials and radio-telescopes, automatic handling of materials, to mention but a few.

In chapter 6 (§6.2.2 to 6.2.5 inclusive) some simple angular position control systems without power amplification are analysed. When it is necessary to position a very heavy mass quickly and precisely, some form of power amplification is necessary. The position of the mass must be controlled by a motor (electric, hydraulic or pneumatic). Open-loop control of the motor is often used (as in hoists, locomotives, lifts, etc.) where absolute precision is unimportant; however, where the load position must be controlled with extreme accuracy (machine tools, guns, launchers, etc.) and without excessive overshoot, a closed-loop system is necessary.

8.2 The Torque-Proportional-to-Error Servomechanism

The simplest continuous control closed-loop system for angular position control is the torque-proportional-to-error servomechanism. It involves a motor, which is the output element, a controller and a positional error detector. In order to obtain a system which is reasonably simple to analyse, we shall assume that the torque produced by the motor is proportional to the error. The error is defined as the difference between the required output (i.e. input θ_i) and actual output θ_o.

157

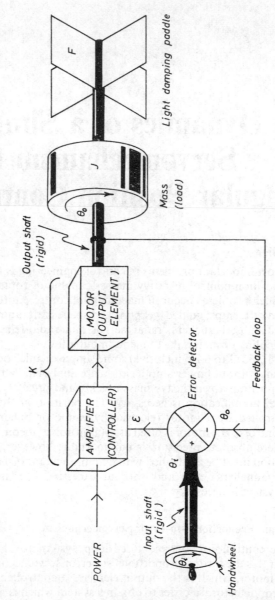

Fig. 8.1 *Schematic diagram of proportional-to-error servomechanism.*

The system inertia is J referred to the output and the system is damped by means of a viscous damping torque F per unit angular velocity. The schematic diagram representing the system is shown in Fig. 8.1.

It should be noted that the system contains ideal components which do not introduce transfer delays and non-linearities as do real components. In practice most components will introduce delays and non-linearities and the analysis which will follow is useful mainly as a basis for comparison.

Now the torque from the motor $T_m = K\epsilon$

$\therefore$
$$T_m = K(\theta_i - \theta_o)$$

The retarding torque due to the damping paddle $T_f = F\dfrac{d\theta_o}{dt}$.

Resultant torque T available to produce acceleration is given by

$$T = T_m - T_f$$
$$= K(\theta_i - \theta_o) - F\frac{d\theta_o}{dt}$$

But Newton's second law gives us that

$$T = J\alpha$$

where
$$\alpha = \frac{d^2\theta_o}{dt^2}$$

$\therefore$
$$K(\theta_i - \theta_o) - F\frac{d\theta_o}{dt} = J\frac{d^2\theta_o}{dt^2}$$

Hence
$$J\frac{d^2\theta_o}{dt^2} + F\frac{d\theta_o}{dt} + K\theta_o = K\theta_i$$

This differential equation is identical to the equation obtained in §6.2.3 for the flexible-shaft positioning system. However, K here is the 'gain' of the system, i.e. the torque output per unit error. The transient solution may again take three possible forms—overdamped, underdamped and critically damped.

There are various tests of merit used to assess the performance of the servomechanism; the step-input and the ramp-input are two such tests and these will be considered.

8.3 Response of Servomechanism to a Step Input

The differential equation for the system in D-form is

$$(JD^2 + FD + K)\,\theta_o = K\theta_i$$

If θ_i is a step-input and the boundary conditions are that at $t = 0$, θ_o and $d\theta_o/dt = 0$, and we consider the most important condition of damping, namely underdamping (for which $F < 2\sqrt{(JK)}$), we may rewrite the solution derived in §6.2.3. The solution must be the same as that obtained previously because the differential equation and the initial conditions are identical, i.e.

$$\theta_o = \theta_i \left[1 - e^{-\alpha t} \sqrt{\left\{ 1 + \left(\frac{\alpha}{\omega_r} \right)^2 \right\}} \sin \left(\omega_r t + \tan^{-1} \frac{\omega_r}{\alpha} \right) \right]$$

where

$$\alpha = \frac{F}{2J}$$

and

$$\omega_r = \sqrt{\left\{ \frac{K}{J} - \frac{F^2}{4J^2} \right\}}$$

The response is shown in Fig. 8.2.

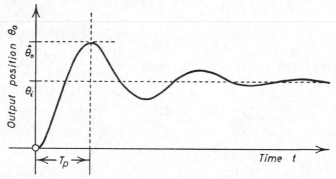

Fig. 8.2 *Response of servomechanism to a step-input.*

The time to rise to the first maximum (T_p) and the percentage overshoot are of considerable interest. Now it will be shown that $T_p = \pi/\omega_r$. Differentiating we have

$$\frac{d\theta_o}{dt} = \alpha e^{-\alpha t} \sqrt{\left\{ 1 + \left(\frac{\alpha}{\omega_r} \right)^2 \right\}} \sin \left(\omega_r t + \tan^{-1} \frac{\omega_r}{\alpha} \right)$$

$$- \omega_r e^{-\alpha t} \sqrt{\left\{ 1 + \left(\frac{\alpha}{\omega_r} \right)^2 \right\}} \cos \left(\omega_r t + \tan^{-1} \frac{\omega_r}{\alpha} \right)$$

Now θ_o has a maximum or minimum value when $d\theta_o/dt$ is zero, thus,

$$0 = \alpha e^{-\alpha t} \sqrt{\left\{ 1 + \left(\frac{\alpha}{\omega_r} \right)^2 \right\}} \sin \left(\omega_r t + \tan^{-1} \frac{\omega_r}{\alpha} \right) \dots$$

$$- \omega_r e^{-\alpha t} \sqrt{\left\{ 1 + \left(\frac{\alpha}{\omega_r} \right)^2 \right\}} \cos \left(\omega_r t + \tan^{-1} \frac{\omega_r}{\alpha} \right)$$

or $$\alpha \sin\left(\omega_r t + \tan^{-1}\frac{\omega_r}{\alpha}\right) = \omega_r \cos\left(\omega_r t + \tan^{-1}\frac{\omega_r}{\alpha}\right)$$

$$\therefore \qquad \frac{\sin\left(\omega_r t + \tan^{-1}\omega_r/\alpha\right)}{\cos\left(\omega_r t + \tan^{-1}\omega_r/\alpha\right)} = \frac{\omega_r}{\alpha}$$

$$\therefore \qquad \tan\left(\omega_r t + \tan^{-1}\omega_r/\alpha\right) = \frac{\omega_r}{\alpha}$$

$$\therefore \qquad \omega_r t + \tan^{-1}\omega_r/\alpha = (\tan^{-1}\omega_r/\alpha) \pm n\pi$$

where n is an integer whose value lies between zero and infinity.

$$\therefore \qquad \omega_r t = \pm n\pi$$

Negative values of t given by this are physically impossible, thus considering only the positive values, we have

$$\omega_r t = n\pi$$

Now when $n = 0$ we have $t = 0$; this corresponds to the minimum value of θ_o at the origin. For $n = 1$ we have $\omega_r t = \pi$; this value of time corresponds to the first maximum for which $t = T_p$, i.e.

$$\omega_r T_p = \pi$$

$$\therefore \qquad T_p = \frac{\pi}{\omega_r}$$

Now if we substitute for $t = \pi/\omega_r$ in the expression for θ_o we shall find the value of $\hat{\theta}_o$, i.e.

$$\hat{\theta}_o = \theta_i\left[1 - e^{-\alpha\pi/\omega_r}\sqrt{\left\{1 + \left(\frac{\alpha}{\omega_r}\right)^2\right\}}\sin\left(\pi + \tan^{-1}\frac{\omega_r}{\alpha}\right)\right]$$

$$\therefore \qquad \hat{\theta}_o = \theta_i\left[1 + e^{-\alpha\pi/\omega_r}\sqrt{\left\{1 + \left(\frac{\alpha}{\omega_r}\right)^2\right\}}\sin\left(\tan^{-1}\frac{\omega_r}{\alpha}\right)\right]$$

Now $$\sin\left(\tan^{-1}\frac{\omega_r}{\alpha}\right) = \frac{\omega_r}{\sqrt{(\omega_r^2 + \alpha^2)}}$$

$$\therefore \qquad \hat{\theta}_o = \theta_i\left[1 + e^{-\alpha\pi/\omega_r}\sqrt{\left\{1 + \left(\frac{\alpha}{\omega_r}\right)^2\right\}}\frac{\omega_r}{\sqrt{(\omega_r^2 + \alpha^2)}}\right]$$

$$= \theta_i(1 + e^{-\alpha\pi/\omega_r})$$

The percentage overshoot is thus $100\,e^{-\alpha\pi/\omega_r}$.

8.4 Response of the Servomechanism to a Ramp Input

The purpose of the ramp input test is to determine the steady-state performance of the system. We will assume that the input is given by $d\theta_i/dt = \omega_i$.

161

The differential equation for the system has been shown to be:

$$(JD^2 + FD + K)\,\theta_o = K\theta_i$$

Now $\theta_o = \theta_i - \epsilon$, thus, substituting for θ_o in the differential equation, we have

$$(JD^2 + FD + K)(\theta_i - \epsilon) = K\theta_i$$

or
$$(JD^2 + FD + K)\,\epsilon = (JD^2 + FD)\,\theta_i$$

Now since the input velocity $d\theta_i/dt = \omega_i$, then $D\theta_i = \omega_i$ and hence the input acceleration $D^2\theta_i = 0$. Thus the differential equation becomes

$$(JD^2 + FD + K)\,\epsilon = F\omega_i$$

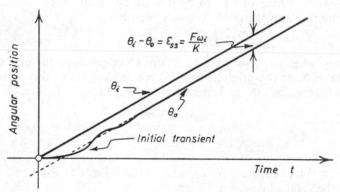

Fig. 8.3 *Response of servomechanism to input ramp of slope ω_i.*

Although the solution in ϵ will be composed of the transient ϵ_t and the steady-state ϵ_{ss}, it is only the steady-state solution which is of interest in this test. Since the driving function is a constant, we may find ϵ_{ss} by putting D equal to zero, i.e.

$$K\epsilon_{ss} = F\omega_i$$

∴
$$\epsilon_{ss} = \frac{F\omega_i}{K}$$

We may conclude that the servomechanism responds to a ramp input with an initial transient (which may or may not be oscillatory) and then the output settles down and follows the input with a constant steady error. This error is called the 'velocity lag'. It is as well to note that it is a positional lag for a constant velocity input and does not imply a difference between input and output velocities. The response is shown in Fig. 8.3.

It is evident that in positional systems which are required to follow dynamic inputs precisely (e.g. machine tools, target-illuminating radar sets, A.A. guns, etc.) a velocity lag is a disadvantage. Thus in many applications its minimization is important, whereas in others it may be necessary to eliminate it completely.

8.5 The Response to a Suddenly-applied Load Torque

Many position control systems are liable to have load torques suddenly applied to them (e.g. radar trackers, guns and launchers will have load torques due to wind gusts).

The performance of the proportional-to-error system when subjected to suddenly-applied load torques will now be investigated.

Let the applied torque have a value $\pm T_L$. The motor torque will be $K\epsilon$ and will act on the inertia in addition to the load torque. The viscous damping torque $Fd\theta_o/dt$ will act in opposition to the torque tending to produce motion. Hence the resultant torque T tending to accelerate the mass is given by

$$T = \pm T_L + K\epsilon - F\frac{d\theta_o}{dt}$$

But Newton's second law gives

$$T = J\frac{d^2\theta_o}{dt^2}$$

hence

$$J\frac{d^2\theta_o}{dt^2} = \pm T_L + K\epsilon - F\frac{d\theta_o}{dt}$$

But

$$\epsilon = \theta_i - \theta_o$$

$\therefore$

$$J\frac{d^2\theta_o}{dt^2} + F\frac{d\theta_o}{dt} + K\theta_o = \pm T_L + K\theta_i$$

Suppose there is no command signal, i.e. $\theta_i = 0$, then the equation becomes

$$J\frac{d^2\theta_o}{dt^2} + F\frac{d\theta_o}{dt} + K\theta_o = \pm T_L$$

The transient response will be similar to the solution obtained for a step-input and may be underdamped, overdamped or critically damped.

The steady-state performance will be given by

$$(JD^2 + FD + K)\theta_o = \pm T_L$$

Hence, putting $D = 0$, we have

$$\theta_{o\,ss} = \pm \frac{T_L}{K}$$

The response of the system to a step applied torque is represented graphically in Fig. 8.4. The graph is sketched for $+T_L$ and for the underdamped condition ($F < 2\sqrt{(JK)}$).

The worst practical feature of the response is the permanent off-set T_L/K which has been produced. If K is large this off-set can be made small, but in systems where extreme accuracy is required, such effects must be eliminated.

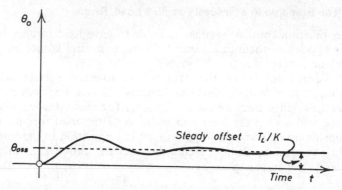

Fig. 8.4 *Response of underdamped servomechanism to a step-applied torque.*

Worked Example

A servomechanism is used to control the angular position θ_o of a mass via command signals θ_i applied to a handwheel. The moment of inertia of the moving parts is 0.1 kg m^2 and the motor produces a torque of 20 N m per radian of error. The system is damped by viscous friction which is half that necessary to produce critical damping.

(i) Develop an expression for the response of the servomechanism to a step input of 1 radian and determine the frequency of transient oscillation and the time to rise to the first maximum.

(ii) Determine the velocity lag when the handwheel is rotated at a constant angular velocity of 10 rev/min.

(iii) Determine the steady error which exists when a steady load torque of 1 N m is applied.

Solution

(i) If F is the viscous frictional torque per unit angular velocity then using Newton's second law,

$$0.1D^2\,\theta_o = 20(\theta_i - \theta_o) - FD\theta_o$$

hence

$$(0.1D^2 + FD + 20)\,\theta_o = 20\theta_i$$

Now for critical damping

$$F = 2\sqrt{(0.1 \times 20)}$$

164

but F is only half that necessary to produce critical damping, i.e.

$$F = \sqrt{(0 \cdot 1 \times 20)}$$

i.e.

$$F = 1 \cdot 41$$

$\therefore$ differential equation becomes

$$(0 \cdot 1 D^2 + 1 \cdot 41 D + 20)\, \theta_o = 20 \theta_i$$

If θ_i is a step of magnitude 1 radian, then

$$(0 \cdot 1 D^2 + 1 \cdot 41 D + 20)\, \theta_o = 20$$

Putting D equal to zero gives $\theta_{o\,ss}$, i.e.

$$\theta_{o\,ss} = 1$$

The transient solution is

$$\theta_{o\,t} = e^{-7 \cdot 05 t}\,(A \sin \omega_r t + B \cos \omega_r t)$$

where

$$\omega_r = \sqrt{\left\{ \frac{20}{0 \cdot 1} - \left(\frac{1 \cdot 41}{2 \times 0 \cdot 1} \right)^2 \right\}}$$

$$= \sqrt{(200 - 49 \cdot 7)}$$

$$= \sqrt{150 \cdot 3}$$

$$= 12 \cdot 26 \text{ rad/s}$$

This is the angular frequency of oscillation during the transient, thus if f_r is the actual frequency then

$$2\pi f_r = \omega_r$$

i.e.

$$f_r = \frac{12 \cdot 26}{2\pi}$$

$$= 1 \cdot 95 \text{ c/s}$$

The time to rise to the first maximum is π/ω_r or $1/2 f_r$, i.e.

$$1/(2 \times 1 \cdot 95) \text{ or } 0 \cdot 256 \text{ sec}$$

Now

$$\theta_{o\,t} = e^{-7 \cdot 05 t}\,(A \sin 12 \cdot 26 t + B \cos 12 \cdot 26 t)$$

The complete solution for $\theta_o = \theta_{o\,ss} + \theta_{o\,t}$, i.e.

$$\theta_o = 1 + e^{-7 \cdot 05 t}\,(A \sin 12 \cdot 26 t + B \cos 12 \cdot 26 t)$$

Now, assuming the system to be initially at rest, we have at $t = 0$, $\theta_o = 0$ and $d\theta_o/dt = 0$. Thus

$$0 = 1 + B$$

$\therefore$

$$B = -1$$

$\therefore$

$$\theta_o = 1 + e^{-7 \cdot 05 t}\,(A \sin 12 \cdot 26 t - \cos 12 \cdot 26 t)$$

165

$$\therefore \qquad \frac{d\theta_o}{dt} = -7{\cdot}05\,e^{-7{\cdot}05t}(A\sin 12{\cdot}26t - \cos 12{\cdot}26t)$$

$$+ e^{-7{\cdot}05t}(12{\cdot}26A\cos 12{\cdot}26t + 12{\cdot}26\sin 12{\cdot}26t)$$

$$\therefore \qquad 0 = 7{\cdot}05 + 12{\cdot}26A$$

$$\therefore \qquad A = -7{\cdot}05/12{\cdot}26$$

$$= -0{\cdot}576$$

The complete particular solution is thus

$$\theta_o = 1 - e^{-7{\cdot}05}(0{\cdot}576\sin 12{\cdot}26t + \cos 12{\cdot}26t)$$

This may be converted to the form

$$\theta_o = 1 - 1{\cdot}15\,e^{-7{\cdot}05}\sin(12{\cdot}26t + 1{\cdot}05)$$

(ii) The velocity lag is given by

$$\epsilon_{ss} = \frac{F}{K}\omega_i$$

Here $\qquad F = 1{\cdot}41\,\text{N m per rad/s}$

$$K = 20\,\text{N m/rad}$$

and $\qquad \omega_i = 10\,\text{rev/min} = (10 \times 2\pi)/60\,\text{rad/s}$

$$= 1{\cdot}05\,\text{rad/s}$$

$$\therefore \qquad \epsilon_{ss} = \frac{1{\cdot}41}{20} \times 1{\cdot}05\,\text{rad}$$

$$= 0{\cdot}074\,\text{rad}$$

(iii) Now the steady error ϵ_{ss} which exists due to a load torque T_L is given by

$$\epsilon_{ss} = \frac{T_L}{K}$$

where $\qquad K = $ motor torque per radian of error

$$= 20\,\text{N m/rad}$$

Thus if $\qquad T_L = 1\,\text{N m},$

$$\epsilon_{ss} = \tfrac{1}{20} = 0{\cdot}05\,\text{rad}$$

8.6 Techniques for Improving the General Performance of the Servomechanism

8.6.1 The Use of Viscous Damping

It is evident from the previous discussion (§§8.3 and 8.4) that if the system is to be underdamped, as is practically desirable, then the value of α, the exponential damping must be suitably chosen. Let us call the per-unit overshoot μ, then from previous analysis (§8.3) it has been shown that μ is given by

$$\mu = e^{-\alpha\pi/\omega_r}$$

Supposing the value of the time to rise to the first overshoot is defined as a system specification (T_p) and μ is also defined (typical values of μ lie between 0 and 0·2); then taking logs of both sides we have

$$\log_e \mu = \frac{-\alpha\pi}{\omega_r}$$

but

$$\frac{\pi}{\omega_r} = T_p$$

thus

$$\frac{\log_e \mu}{T_p} = -\alpha$$

or

$$\frac{\log_e \dfrac{1}{\mu}}{T_p} = \alpha$$

Thus for a given specification of rise-time to first maximum and peak overshoot we may determine the necessary value of α, where $\alpha = F/2J$. One method of adjusting α is to adjust the value of F, the viscous frictional torque. This has two disadvantages, however. Firstly energy is continually expended by the system in overcoming the frictional torque. This is uneconomical both in power consumed and size of output element required. Secondly the velocity lag ϵ_{ss} is given by,

$$\epsilon_{ss} = \frac{F}{K} \cdot \omega_i$$

and thus is directly affected by the choice of F. In fact once μ and T_p have been specified, ϵ_{ss} is automatically fixed for a given value of ω_i.

8.6.2 *The Use of Negative Velocity Feedback*

A common method of achieving the desired response from a system is to use negative velocity feedback. A transducer (in this case a tachogenerator) is used to convert the output positional signal to a signal proportional to the angular velocity of the output shaft. It is fed back negatively as shown in Fig. 8.5. It is assumed that there is viscous friction also present in the system; as will be shown, viscous frictional damping is no longer a requirement for stability, but in all practical systems some residual viscous friction is always present.

167

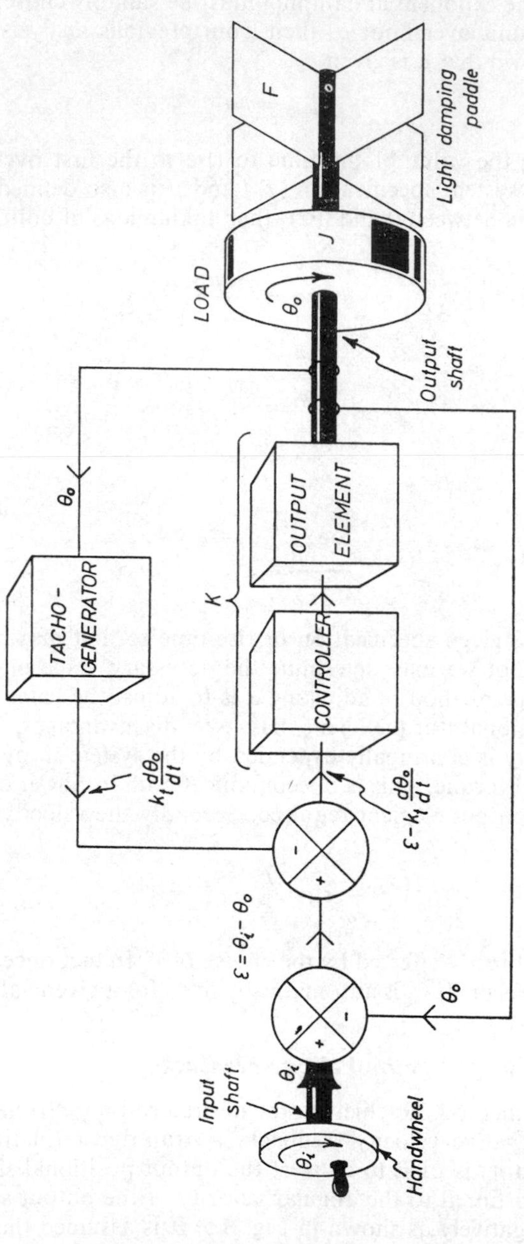

Fig. 8.5 *Servomechanism with velocity feedback.*

The signal actuating the controller is now $\epsilon - k_t \, d\theta_o/dt$, thus the differential equation representing the motion of the system becomes:

$$J\frac{d^2\theta_o}{dt^2} = K\left(\epsilon - k_t\frac{d\theta_o}{dt}\right) - F\frac{d\theta_o}{dt}$$

Or in D-form

$$\{JD^2 + (Kk_t + F)D\}\,\theta_o = K\epsilon$$

Now

$$\theta_o = \theta_i - \epsilon$$

$\therefore$

$$\{JD^2 + (Kk_t + F)D\}\,(\theta_i - \epsilon) = K\epsilon$$

$\therefore$

$$\{JD^2 + (Kk_t + F)D + K\}\,\epsilon = \{JD^2 + (Kk_t + F)D\}\,\theta_i$$

With the equation in this form we see that:

(i) The value of α is increased from $F/2J$ to $(Kk_t + F)/2J$.

(ii) The value of the velocity lag ϵ_{ss} is increased from $F\omega_i/K$ to $(Kk_t + F)\omega_i/K$.

Hence this method of damping will directly affect the velocity lag as does viscous frictional damping. The method does, however, possess the advantage that no extra energy is expended to overcome the extra frictional torque necessary to produce adequate damping. The physical reason for this is that the feedback signal controls the amount of energy entering the output element; it does not, as in the case of a viscous torque, load the output element and require work to be done during motion.

8.6.3 The Use of Positive Acceleration Feedback

Here an accelerometer is used to derive a feedback signal proportional to output acceleration. The arrangement is shown in Fig. 8.6.

It should be noted that here viscous damping (or auxiliary negative velocity feedback) is necessary. The signal actuating the controller is now $\epsilon + k_a \, d^2\theta_o/dt^2$, thus the system equation becomes:

$$J\frac{d^2\theta_o}{dt^2} = K\left(\epsilon + k_a\frac{d^2\theta_o}{dt^2}\right) - F\frac{d\theta_o}{dt}$$

or in D-form

$$\{(J - Kk_a)D^2 + FD\}\,\theta_o = K\epsilon$$

Using the fact that $\theta_o = \theta_i - \epsilon$, the above equation may be rewritten in the form

$$\{(J - Kk_a)D^2 + FD + K\}\,\epsilon = \{(J - Kk_a)D^2 + FD\}\,\theta_i$$

From this we note:

(i) The value of α is increased from $F/2J$ to $F/2(J - Kk_a)$. The effect of positive acceleration feedback has been to reduce the effective value of the load inertia.

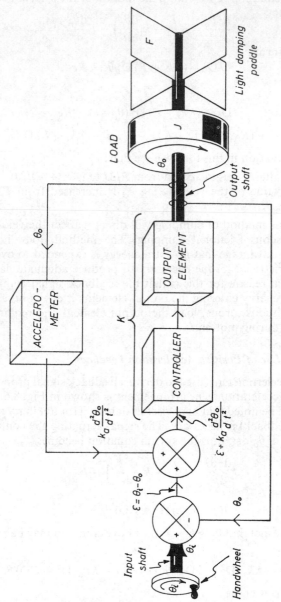

Fig. 8.6 *Servomechanism with acceleration feedback.*

(ii) The value of the velocity lag ϵ_{ss} has not increased; it remains at $F\omega_i/K$.

8.6.4 The Effect of Error-rate Damping

An economical and effective method of increasing the damping is to connect in cascade with the controller a device which will 'operate' on the error and thus change the nature of the signal actuating the system. This method of damping calls for a device which accepts at its input a signal equal to the error and gives out a signal equal to the sum of two quantities, one being proportional to the error and the other being proportional to the derivative of the error with respect to time. Devices which approximately perform such an operation may often be cheaply produced to suit a particular system. Electrical and pneumatic devices of this type do not usually present any difficult problems of design. Fig. 8.7 shows a suitable arrangement.

Since the actuating signal is now $k_1 \epsilon + k_2 \, d\epsilon/dt$ we have,

$$J\frac{d^2\theta_o}{dt^2} = K\left(k_1 \epsilon + k_2 \frac{d\epsilon}{dt}\right) - F\frac{d\theta_o}{dt}$$

In D-form

$$(JD^2 + FD)\,\theta_o = K(k_1 + k_2 D)\,\epsilon$$

Thus, since $\theta_o = \theta_i - \epsilon$, we have,

$$\{JD^2 + (Kk_2 + F)\,D + Kk_1\}\,\epsilon = (JD^2 + FD)\,\theta_i$$

From this equation we note that:

(i) The value of α is increased from $F/2J$ to $(Kk_2 + F)/2J$. This represents a large increase in α without the energy loss associated with viscous damping.

(ii) The value of the velocity lag ϵ_{ss} has been altered from $F\omega_i/K$ to $F\omega_i/Kk_1$. Thus if k_1 is made greater than unity, the velocity lag may be reduced.

The term responsible for damping is $(Kk_2 + F)$ and this may be made as large as necessary by adjustment of Kk_2; thus the viscous frictional component F may be kept as low as physically possible. A certain amount of viscous friction is of course inevitable in any mechanical arrangement. The smaller it can be made however, the smaller the velocity lag will become. *With the other methods of damping, i.e. viscous frictional damping, velocity feedback and acceleration feedback, the velocity lag is fixed automatically once the rise time and percentage overshoot are specified. With error-rate damping the velocity lag is not fixed by these specifications. The extent to which it may be reduced is limited only by the minimum value of viscous friction which can be achieved.*

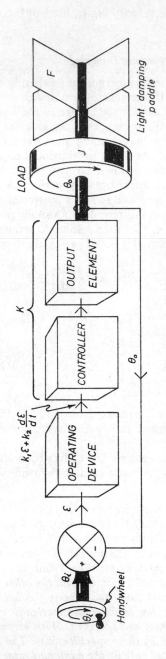

Fig. 8.7 *Servomechanism with error-rate damping.*

The response to a step input of the error-rate system is different from the normal second order response. This has a zero initial velocity when the system is initially at rest whereas the error-rate system has theoretically a finite initial velocity. The value of the initial velocity can be determined in a number of ways; perhaps the simplest method to understand is that given directly by the differential equation. Now this may be rewritten as

$$\{J D^2 + (F + Kk_2) D + Kk_1\} \theta_o = (Kk_2 D + Kk_1) \theta_i$$

Integrating both sides between limits $t = 0-$ and $t = 0+$ (infinitesimally small times before and after application of the step-input) we obtain

$$\int_{0-}^{0+} J D^2 \theta_o \, dt + \int_{0-}^{0+} (F + Kk_2) D\theta_o \, dt + \int_{0-}^{0+} Kk_1 \theta_o \, dt$$

$$= \int_{0-}^{0+} Kk_2 D\theta_i \, dt + \int_{0-}^{0+} Kk_1 \theta_i \, dt$$

$$\therefore \quad [J D\theta_o]_{0-}^{0+} + (F + Kk_2) [\theta_o]_{0-}^{0+} + Kk_1 \int_{0-}^{0+} \theta_o \, dt$$

$$= Kk_2 [\theta_i]_{0-}^{0+} + Kk_1 \int_{0-}^{0+} \theta_i \, dt$$

There can be no change in the output position in this infinitesimally small time interval, thus $(F + Kk_2)[\theta_o]_{0-}^{0+}$ must be zero; also the area enclosed under the curve of output position over this time interval is zero: i.e.

$$Kk_1 \int_{0-}^{0+} \theta_o \, dt = 0$$

Now although the input moves from zero to say θ_i in this time interval, the area under the curve of θ_i for the interval must be zero, i.e.

$$Kk_1 \int_{0-}^{0+} \theta_i \, dt = 0$$

Thus eliminating the terms which are zero we have

$$[J D\theta_o]_{0-}^{0+} = Kk_2 \theta_i$$

The term $[D\theta_o]_{0-}^{0+}$ is the initial velocity, thus, at $t = 0$,

$$\frac{d\theta_o}{dt} = \frac{Kk_2}{J} \theta_i$$

where θ_i is the magnitude of the input step.

In general this initial velocity has the effect of making the system respond more quickly but with slightly more overshoot than an ordinary second-order system having the same values of α and ω_r. A complete mathematical analysis of the step response of the error-

173

rate system is left to the reader as an exercise. The underdamped response is given by

$$\theta_o = \theta_i \left\{ 1 - e^{-\alpha t} \left(\cos \omega_r t - \frac{Kk_2/J - \alpha}{\omega_r} \sin \omega_r t \right) \right\}$$

where
$$\alpha = \frac{F + Kk_2}{2J}$$

and
$$\omega_r = \sqrt{\left\{ \frac{Kk_1}{J} - \frac{(F + Kk_2)^2}{4J^2} \right\}}$$

8.6.5 Integral Control

Second-order systems having viscous frictional damping, auxiliary negative velocity feedback, auxiliary positive acceleration feedback or any combination of these may be described by a differential equation of the form:

$$(J'D^2 + F'D + K)\theta_o = K\theta_i$$

where J', F' are the 'effective' values of inertia and friction.

If a system is specified in terms of T_p and μ as defined in §8.6.1 then

$$\alpha = \frac{F'}{2J'} = \frac{\log_e(1/\mu)}{T_p} \tag{1}$$

as shown previously.

Also
$$\omega_r = \frac{\pi}{T_p} = \sqrt{\left\{ \frac{K}{J'} - \alpha^2 \right\}}$$

$$\therefore \qquad \frac{\pi^2}{T_p^2} + \alpha^2 = \frac{K}{J'}$$

$$\therefore \qquad \frac{\pi^2}{T_p^2} + \left\{ \frac{\log_e(1/\mu)}{T_p} \right\}^2 = \frac{K}{J'} \tag{2}$$

From (1) and (2)

$$\frac{F'}{K} = \frac{2T_p \log_e(1/\mu)}{\pi^2 + \{\log_e(1/\mu)\}^2} \tag{3}$$

The velocity lag of such a system is $F'\omega_i/K$ where ω_i is the velocity of the input. Thus if T_p and μ are specified it is evident that the velocity lag is fixed by equation (3).

In the error-rate system described in §8.6.4 the situation is different because the driving function is modified by the introduction of the operating network. Then for a given T_p and μ it is possible to achieve a genuine reduction in velocity lag. As previously explained, the magnitude of the velocity lag is then dependent only on the inherent viscous friction.

Thus in all the methods of damping previously described there is no possibility of complete elimination of velocity lag. In many applications the velocity lag must be entirely eliminated. When this is necessary a device may be placed in cascade with the main elements which operates on the error. This device must produce an output which consists of the sum of two signals, one proportional to the error and the other proportional to the time-integral of the error. The arrangement is shown in Fig. 8.8.

Now the signal actuating the controller is $k_1 \epsilon + k_2 \int \epsilon \, dt$, thus the system equation becomes:

$$J\frac{d^2 \theta_o}{dt^2} = K\left(k_1 \epsilon + k_2 \int \epsilon \, dt\right) - F\frac{d\theta_o}{dt}$$

Differentiating both sides with respect to time we have:

$$J\frac{d^3 \theta_o}{dt^3} = K\left(k_1 \frac{d\epsilon}{dt} + k_2 \epsilon\right) - F\frac{d^2 \theta_o}{dt^2}$$

In D-form this equation becomes,

$$(JD^3 + FD^2)\theta_o = K(k_1 D + k_2)\epsilon$$

But $$\theta_o = \theta_i - \epsilon$$

∴ $$(JD^3 + FD^2)(\theta_i - \epsilon) = K(k_1 D + k_2)\epsilon$$

or $$(JD^3 + FD^2 + Kk_1 D + Kk_2)\epsilon = (JD^3 + FD^2)\theta_i$$

If the input signal is a ramp then the terms in $D^3 \theta_i$ and $D^2 \theta_i$ on the right-hand side disappear and the equation for ϵ becomes:

$$(JD^3 + FD^2 + Kk_1 D + Kk_2)\epsilon = 0$$

Thus to find ϵ_{ss} we may put D equal to zero,

∴ $$\epsilon_{ss} = 0$$

Thus the velocity lag has been eliminated.

However, the differential equation has now become third order and the possibility of absolute instability exists. Absolute instability implies an exponential build up of sinusoidal oscillations. The Routh stability criterion (see chapter 9) can be used to relate the parameters in such a way as to ensure absolute stability. It may be shown in fact that to achieve absolute stability

$$Fk_1 > Jk_2$$

The determination of the transient response and the design of the system so as to achieve adequate damping and correct response time cannot readily be treated by using the differential equation approach. Frequency response methods (as described in chapters 10 to 13 inclusive) are far more powerful.

175

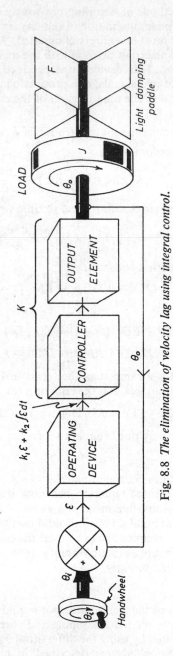

Fig. 8.8 *The elimination of velocity lag using integral control.*

There is a further advantage in using integral control, namely the elimination of the off-set produced by constant load torques (see §8.5).

In the presence of a constant load torque $\pm T_L$ applied at $t = 0$, the differential equation becomes

$$J\frac{d^2\theta_o}{dt^2} = \pm T_L + K\left(k_1\epsilon + k_2\int\epsilon\,dt\right) - F\frac{d\theta_o}{dt}$$

Differentiating both sides with respect to time we have

$$J\frac{d^3\theta_o}{dt^3} = K\left(k_1\frac{d\epsilon}{dt} + k_2\epsilon\right) - F\frac{d^2\theta_o}{dt^2}$$

or, since $\epsilon = \theta_i - \theta_o$

$$J\frac{d^3\theta_o}{dt^3} + F\frac{d^2\theta_o}{dt^2} + Kk_1\frac{d\theta_o}{dt} + Kk_2\theta_o = Kk_1\frac{d\theta_i}{dt} + Kk_2\theta_i$$

If there is no command signal, $\theta_{o\,ss} = 0$ and hence the off-set normally associated with the load torque $\pm T_L$ has disappeared.

8.6.6 Elimination of Velocity lag using 'Feed-forward'

The velocity lag may be eliminated by using a feed-forward element, the input to which is the input signal θ_i and the output from which is proportional to the derivative of the input signal. The controller is supplied with the error signal plus the derivative signal as shown in Fig. 8.9.

The signal actuating the controller is $\epsilon + k_1\dfrac{d\theta_i}{dt}$, thus the system equation becomes

$$J\frac{d^2\theta_o}{dt^2} = K\left(\epsilon + k_1\frac{d\theta_i}{dt}\right) - F\frac{d\theta_o}{dt}$$

In D-form the equation becomes

$$JD^2\theta_o = K\epsilon + Kk_1\,D\theta_i - FD\theta$$

$\therefore$
$$(JD^2 + FD)\theta_o = K\epsilon + Kk_1\,D\theta_i$$

But
$$\theta_o = \theta_i - \epsilon$$

$\therefore$
$$(JD^2 + FD)(\theta_i - \epsilon) = K\epsilon + Kk_1\,D\theta_i$$

or
$$(JD^2 + FD + K)\epsilon = \{JD^2 + (F - k_1 K)D\}\theta_i$$

If the signal is a ramp the term $D^2\theta_i$ on the right-hand side disappears and $D\theta_i = \omega_i$, hence the equation becomes

$$(JD^2 + FD + K)\epsilon = (F - k_1 K)\omega_i$$

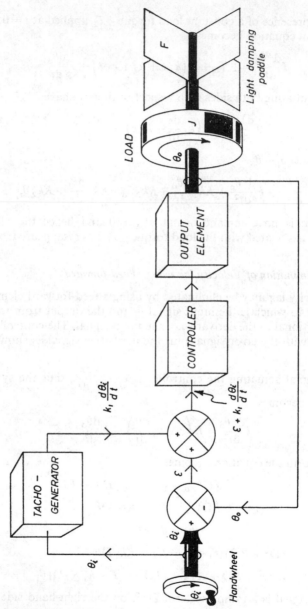

Fig. 8.9 *Elimination of velocity lag using feed-forward.*

Hence the steady-state solution for ϵ is found by putting $D = 0$, thus

$$K\epsilon_{ss} = (F - k_1 K)\omega_i$$

$$\therefore \qquad \epsilon_{ss} = \frac{(F - k_1 K)\omega_i}{K}$$

If the value of k_1 is adjusted so that $F = k_1 K$, then $\epsilon_{ss} = 0$ and the velocity lag becomes zero. The stability of the system is unaltered by the introduction of this feed-forward signal.

The system suffers from the disadvantage that the feed-forward arrangement is open-loop in character. Should any of the parameters F, k_1 or K vary from the designed value, a velocity lag (or even a lead if $k_1 K$ becomes greater than F) will be produced. Furthermore the method does not eliminate any off-set due to the existence of a constant load torque (see §§8.5 and 8.6.5) as does integral control. The method is thus not as useful as integral control in practice.

Worked Example

A closed-loop position control system with negligible friction has a torque of 10 N m per radian of input to the controller. The moment of inertia of the moving parts is 1 kg m^2. Auxiliary negative velocity feedback $k_t d\theta_o/dt$ combined with auxiliary positive acceleration feedback $k_a d^2\theta_o/dt^2$ is to be used in producing a system with an overshoot of 20% and a time to rise to the first maximum (T_p) of 1 sec. Determine suitable values of k_t and k_a.

Solution

The signal entering the controller is

$$\epsilon - k_t D\theta_o + k_a D^2 \theta_o$$

where ϵ = error.

Since there is no friction and $J = 1$ kg m^2 we have

$$D^2 \theta_o = 10(\epsilon - k_t D\theta_o + k_a D^2 \theta_o)$$

Thus, since $\epsilon = \theta_i - \theta_o$, we have

$$\{(1 - 10k_a) D^2 + 10k_t D + 10\} \theta_o = 10\theta_i$$

Thus

$$\alpha = \frac{10k_t}{2(1 - 10k_a)}$$

Now per unit overshoot $= e^{-\alpha\pi/\omega_r}$

but

$$\frac{\pi}{\omega_r} = T_p$$

179

$\therefore$ per unit overshoot $= e^{-\alpha T_p}$

But $\qquad\qquad T_p = 1$ sec and per unit overshoot $= 0.2$

$\therefore \qquad\qquad\qquad e^{-\alpha} = 0.2$

or $\qquad\qquad\qquad e^{\alpha} = 5$

$\therefore \qquad\qquad\qquad \alpha = \log_e 5$

or $\qquad\qquad\qquad \alpha = 1.61$

$\therefore \qquad\qquad \dfrac{10k_t}{2(1 - 10k_a)} = 1.61$

$$k_t = 0.322(1 - 10k_a)$$

Also $\qquad\qquad \omega_r = \sqrt{\left(\dfrac{10}{1 - 10k_a} - \alpha^2\right)}$

But $\qquad\qquad \omega_r = \dfrac{\pi}{T_p} = \pi$

$\therefore \qquad\qquad \pi = \sqrt{\left(\dfrac{10}{1 - 10k_a} - 1.61^2\right)}$

$\therefore \qquad\qquad \pi^2 + 1.61^2 = \dfrac{10}{1 - 10k_a}$

or $\qquad\qquad 1 - 10k_a = \dfrac{10}{12.46}$

$\therefore \qquad\qquad 1 - 0.802 = 10k_a$

i.e. $\qquad\qquad k_a = 0.0198$ rad per rad/s^2

Also $\qquad\qquad k_t = 0.322(1 - 10k_a)$

$\qquad\qquad\qquad\quad = 0.322(1 - 0.198)$

$\qquad\qquad\qquad\quad = 0.322 \times 0.802$

i.e. $\qquad\qquad k_t = 0.258$ rad per rad/s

8.7 The Use of Non-dimensional Notation

The response of the second-order servomechanism has so far been expressed in terms of:

(i) The intrinsic constants of the system J, F and K.
(ii) Two convenient parameters α and ω_r.

Now α and ω_r are combinations of J, F and K and although convenient (especially in the study of the root-locus method[19]) can usefully be replaced by two other parameters, namely, the undamped natural angular frequency ω_n, and the damping ratio ζ. One of these quantities ω_n, has the dimensions of radians per second and the other one ζ, is dimensionless. A study of the behaviour of the system in dimensionless form can then be made.

The quantity ω_n is defined as the angular frequency of transient oscillation of the system when the viscous damping constant F is zero.

Now for any value of F, the angular frequency of oscillation ω_r has been shown to be given by

$$\omega_r = \sqrt{\left(\frac{K}{J} - \frac{F^2}{4J^2}\right)}$$

When F is zero $\omega_r = \omega_n$, thus by definition

$$\omega_n = \sqrt{\left(\frac{K}{J}\right)}$$

The parameter ζ, the damping ratio is the ratio of actual damping to critical damping. Critical damping F_c is given by

$$F_c = 2\sqrt{(JK)}$$

The damping ratio is then

$$\zeta = \frac{\text{actual damping}}{F_c} = \frac{F}{2\sqrt{(JK)}}$$

If ω_n and ζ as parameters are used to replace appropriate combinations of J, F and K in the basic equations, and ω_r and α in the solutions, all the equations thus far derived may be rewritten in a new form which provides not only greater facility to our work but also more clarity to our thinking.

Now the basic equation for the proportional-to-error servomechanism has been shown to be

$$(J\mathrm{D}^2 + F\mathrm{D} + K)\,\theta_o = K\theta_i$$

Dividing through by J we have,

$$\left(\mathrm{D}^2 + \frac{F}{J}\mathrm{D} + \frac{K}{J}\right)\theta_o = \frac{K}{J}\theta_i$$

Now

$$\frac{F}{J} = 2\zeta\omega_n$$

and

$$\frac{K}{J} = \omega_n^2$$

thus

$$(\mathrm{D}^2 + 2\zeta\omega_n \mathrm{D} + \omega_n^2)\,\theta_o = \omega_n^2 \theta_i$$

181

The solution to a step input of magnitude θ_i has previously been shown to be given by

$$\theta_o = \theta_i\left[1 - e^{-\alpha t}\bigg/\sqrt{\left\{1 + \left(\frac{\alpha}{\omega_r}\right)^2\right\}}\sin\left(\omega_r t + \tan^{-1}\frac{\omega_r}{\alpha}\right)\right]$$

Now

$$\alpha = \frac{F}{2J} = \zeta\omega_n$$

and

$$\omega_r = \sqrt{\left\{\frac{K}{J} - \frac{F^2}{4J^2}\right\}}$$

$$= \sqrt{\{\omega_n^2 - \omega_n^2\zeta^2\}}$$

$$= \omega_n\sqrt{\{1 - \zeta^2\}}$$

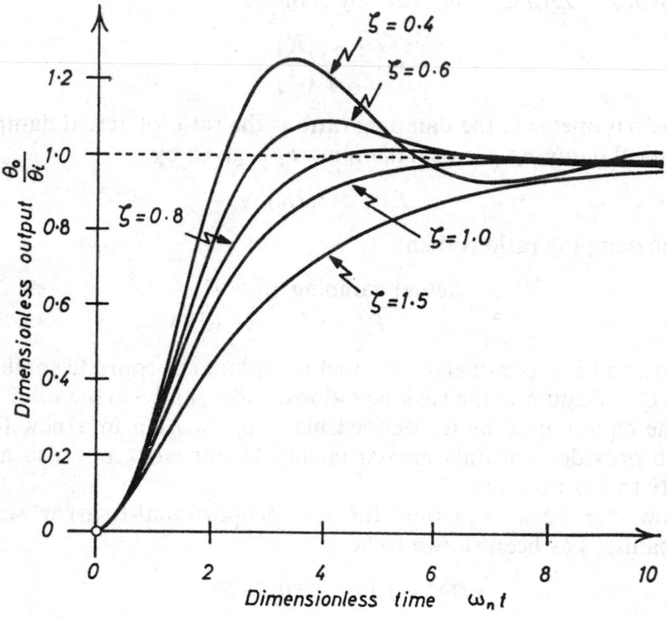

Fig. 8.10 *Dimensionless transient response curves for servomechanism.*

The step-response may be written:

$$\theta_o = \theta_i\left[1 - \frac{e^{-\zeta\omega_n t}}{\sqrt{(1 - \zeta^2)}}\sin\{\omega_n\sqrt{(1 - \zeta^2)}\,t + \phi\}\right]$$

where

$$\phi = \tan^{-1}\frac{\sqrt{(1 - \zeta^2)}}{\zeta}$$

The dimensionless graphs of Fig. 8.10 show the response curves of the system for various values of ζ.

The per unit overshoot is also a function of ζ. It has been shown that the per unit peak overshoot μ is given by,

$$\mu = e^{-\alpha\pi/\omega_r}$$

Substituting for α and ω_r, we have

$$\mu = e^{-\zeta\pi/\sqrt{(1-\zeta^2)}}$$

Values of μ may be plotted as a function of ζ for values of ζ lying between zero and unity.

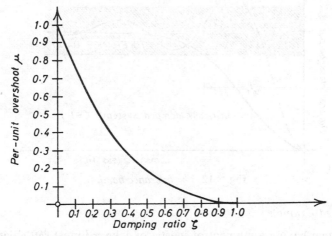

Fig. 8.11 *The per-unit overshoot plotted as a function of the damping ratio.*

8.8 Choosing the Optimum Value of Damping Ratio

The design specification may be phrased in a number of ways. Possibly the value of the per-unit peak overshoot μ may be specified, in which case the value of the desirable damping ratio ζ may be read off the graph given in Fig. 8.11. It is also possible that the problem may specify that the system must reach the final value fastest; the solution here is that the damping must be critical in which case the required value of ζ is unity. However, frequently a 'tolerance band' is specified and the problem is to get the system into the tolerance band fastest without coming out of it again.

It is seen from Fig. 8.12 that the underdamped system enters the tolerance band without coming out again after a 'time' $\omega_n t_2$. This is quicker than it can be done with the system critically damped (time $\omega_n t_1$).

In general the time $\omega_n t_m$ taken for the system to get into the tolerance band without coming out again is called the 'settling time'.

183

The optimum value of ζ is thus the value for which the settling time is minimum. A table of optimum values of ζ for various percentage tolerances, showing the settling times is given below.

Tolerance, %	1	2	3	4	5	7	10	15	20
Optimum ζ	0·82	0·80	0·75	0·72	0·69	0·63	0·59	0·52	0·46
Settling Time, $\omega_n t_m$	4	3·5	3·2	3·0	2·8	2·6	2·3	2·0	1·8

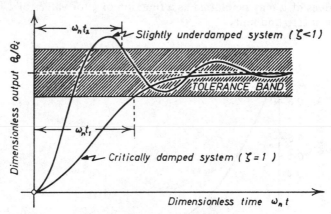

Fig. 8.12 *The tolerance band.*

Worked Example

A system having a moment of inertia of 1 kg m² must settle within a 5% tolerance band in a time not greater than 2 sec. Determine the necessary values of K and effective F. Determine also:

(i) The velocity lag per rad/s of input velocity assuming the system damping to be entirely viscous.

(ii) The velocity lag per rad/s of input velocity if 90% of the effective F is due to error rate damping and the remainder is due to viscous friction.

Solution

From the table $\zeta = 0·69$ and $\omega_n t_m = 2·8$.

$$\text{Now} \qquad t_m = 2 \text{ sec} \quad \text{and} \quad \omega_n = \sqrt{\frac{K}{J}}$$

$$\therefore \qquad 2\sqrt{\frac{K}{J}} = 2·8$$

$$\text{but} \qquad J = 1 \text{ kg m}^2$$

$$\therefore \qquad 2\sqrt{K} = 2·8$$

$$\therefore \qquad K = 1·96 \text{ N m/rad}$$

184

Now $\qquad \zeta = \dfrac{F}{2\sqrt{(JK)}}$

$\therefore \qquad 0.69 = \dfrac{F}{2\sqrt{1.96}}$

$\therefore \qquad F = 0.69 \times 2 \times \sqrt{1.96}$

$\qquad\qquad = 1.93$ N m per rad/s

(i) $\qquad \epsilon_{ss} = \dfrac{F}{K}\omega_i$

and $\qquad \omega_i = 1$ rad/s

$\therefore \qquad \epsilon_{ss} = \dfrac{1.93}{1.96} = 0.985$ rad

i.e. velocity lag per rad/s of input velocity is 0·985 rad.

(ii) If 90% of the effective F is due to error rate damping, then only 10% is due to viscous friction. It is only this 10% which is then responsible for causing velocity lag, i.e.

$$\text{Velocity lag} = \dfrac{10}{100} \times 0.985$$

$$= 0.0985$$

i.e. velocity lag per rad/s of input velocity is 0·0985 rad.

8.9 The Frequency Response Test

8.9.1 The Sinusoidal Input

So far we have used only step and ramp inputs as tests of merit. A test signal of great importance in control engineering is the sinusoidal input. If the input $\theta_i(t)$ to a linear system is given by

$$\theta_i(t) = A \sin \omega t$$

it is always true that the *steady-state* output $\theta_o(t)$ is given by

$$\theta_o(t) = B \sin(\omega t + \phi)$$

The term 'frequency characteristic' refers to the magnitude and phase relationship between the input and output. The normal way in which a frequency response test is performed is with the amplitude A fixed, the values of B and ϕ are determined for a suitable range of values of frequency. The frequency characteristic may be represented in a number of ways which will be considered later.

In an ideal or perfect follow-up system the output response would exactly correspond to the input for all values of frequency, i.e.

$$B = A \quad \text{and} \quad \phi = 0$$

No physical system can achieve this condition on account of the energy stored and dissipated within it.

Physically realizable systems operate over a finite frequency band and it is within this band that the frequency response studies have great value.

For the proportional-to-error (i.e. second order) servomechanism there is direct correlation between the steady-state frequency response and the transient response. For higher order systems the correlation between frequency and transient 'domains' is more obscure. However it is often the case that for higher order systems, little error is introduced by assuming that correlations developed for the second-order system hold true.

8.9.2 *Frequency Response of the Torque-proportional-to-error Servomechanism*

It has been shown (§8.7) that the differential equation for the torque-proportional-to-error system (in terms of ω_n and ζ) may be written

$$\frac{d^2 \theta_o(t)}{dt^2} + 2\zeta\omega_n \frac{d\theta_o(t)}{dt} + \omega_n^2 \theta_o(t) = \omega_n^2 \theta_i(t)$$

Suppose $\theta_i(t) = \hat{\theta}_i \sin \omega t$, where $\hat{\theta}_i$ is the maximum value of the input signal and ω is any frequency.

The frequency response is concerned only with the steady-state solution. The method described in §5.3.5 will thus be used to extract the steady-state solution as a complex number.

The driving function of the differential equation is the vector $\omega_n^2 \hat{\theta}_i \sin \omega t$ which will be represented by the complex number $\omega_n^2 \hat{\theta}_i e^{j\omega t}$. In D-form the differential equation becomes

$$(D^2 + 2\zeta\omega_n D + \omega_n^2)\, \bar{\theta}_o(j\omega) = \omega_n^2 \hat{\theta}_i e^{j\omega t}$$

where $\bar{\theta}_o(j\omega) = $ steady state vector output represented as a complex number.

For the sake of simplicity let us represent the vector input $\hat{\theta}_i e^{j\omega t}$ by $\bar{\theta}_i(j\omega)$.

Hence, putting $D = j\omega$, we have

$$\{(j\omega)^2 + 2\zeta\omega_n(j\omega) + \omega_n^2\}\, \bar{\theta}_o(j\omega) = \omega_n^2 \bar{\theta}_i(j\omega)$$

$$\therefore \quad \frac{\bar{\theta}_o}{\bar{\theta}_i}(j\omega) = \frac{\omega_n^2}{(j\omega)^2 + 2\zeta\omega_n(j\omega) + \omega_n^2}$$

$$= \frac{\omega_n^2}{(\omega_n^2 - \omega^2) + j(2\zeta\omega_n \omega)}$$

This complex relationship may be expressed in terms of the magnitude $\left|\dfrac{\theta_o}{\theta_i}(j\omega)\right|$ and the phase angle $\phi(j\omega)$

where

$$\left|\frac{\theta_o}{\theta_i}(j\omega)\right| = \frac{\omega_n^2}{\sqrt{\{(\omega_n^2 - \omega^2)^2 + (2\zeta\omega_n\,\omega)^2\}}}$$

and

$$\phi(j\omega) = -\tan^{-1}\frac{2\zeta\omega_n\,\omega}{\omega_n^2 - \omega^2}$$

The instantaneous steady-state output is given by

$$\theta_o(t) = \frac{\hat{\theta}_i\,\omega_n^2 \sin(\omega t + \phi)}{\sqrt{\{(\omega_n^2 - \omega^2)^2 + (2\zeta\omega_n\,\omega)^2\}}}$$

It is useful to define a new variable u as

$$u = \frac{\omega}{\omega_n}$$

This variable may be thought of as the 'frequency ratio' or the 'normalized driving frequency'. The equations for the magnitude and phase may now be expressed as functions of ju.

Thus

$$\left|\frac{\theta_o}{\theta_i}(ju)\right| = \frac{1}{\sqrt{\{(1 - u^2)^2 + (2\zeta u)^2\}}}$$

and

$$\phi(ju) = -\tan^{-1}\frac{2\zeta u}{1 - u^2}$$

It is evident that as $u \to 0$, $\left|\dfrac{\theta_o}{\theta_i}(ju)\right| \to 1$ and as $u \to \infty$, $\left|\dfrac{\theta_o}{\theta_i}(ju)\right| \to 0$.
The magnitude characteristics are shown in Fig. 8.13 for various values of ζ.

The value of $\phi \to 0$ as $u \to 0$ and also as $u \to \infty$, $\phi \to -\pi$. When $u = 1$, $\phi = -\pi/2$. Curves of ϕ as a function of u for various values of ζ are shown in Fig. 8.14.

Both the phase and magnitude characteristics may be represented on a polar diagram (Fig. 8.15).

The value of u for which the magnitude $|\theta_o/\theta_i(ju)|$ has a maximum value is important. Let us call the magnitude M, then

$$M = \frac{1}{\sqrt{\{(1 - u^2)^2 + (2\zeta u)^2\}}}$$

Now

$$\frac{dM}{du} = -\tfrac{1}{2}\{u^4 + 1 - 2u^2 + 4\zeta^2 u^2\}^{-3/2}(4u^3 - 4u + 8\zeta^2 u)$$

For values of $M > 1$, the frequency u at which M is a maximum, defined as M_{pf}, is given by $dM/du = 0$. That is, M_{pf} occurs when

$$4u^3 - 4u + 8\zeta^2 u = 0$$

or when

$$u = \sqrt{(1 - 2\zeta^2)}$$

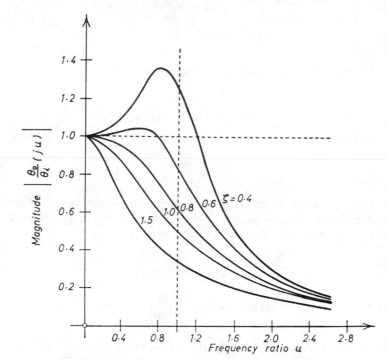

Fig. 8.13 *Frequency response magnitude characteristic.*

The value of ω at which M is maximum is called the resonant angular frequency in the frequency domain and will be referred to as ω_{rf}. Thus since $u = \omega/\omega_n$,

$$\frac{\omega_{rf}}{\omega_n} = \sqrt{(1 - 2\zeta^2)}$$

$\therefore$
$$\omega_{rf} = \omega_n\sqrt{(1 - 2\zeta^2)}$$

The value of M_{pf} may be found by substituting the value $u = \sqrt{(1 - 2\zeta^2)}$ in the general equation for M; thus

$$M_{pf} = \frac{1}{2\zeta\sqrt{(1 - \zeta^2)}}$$

It should be noted that a maximum for values $u = \sqrt{(1 - 2\zeta^2)}$ only occurs for values of $\zeta < 0.707$. This is clearly illustrated in Fig. 8.13.

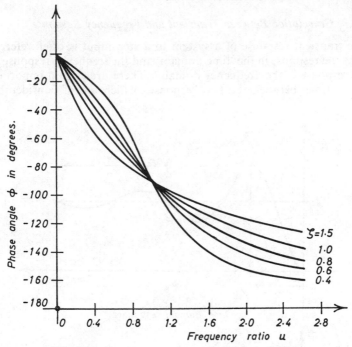

Fig. 8.14 *Frequency response phase characteristic.*

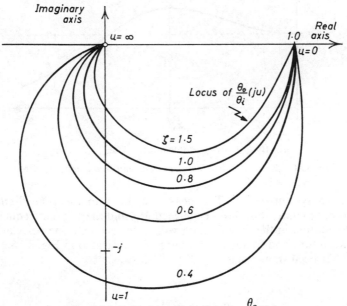

Fig. 8.15 *Polar plot of the function* $\frac{\theta_o}{\theta_i}(ju)$.

189

8.9.3 *Correlation Between Transient and Frequency Response*

The transient response of a system to a step-input is often referred to as the response in the 'time domain' and the frequency response as the response in the 'frequency domain'. There are certain important correlations between the two responses which are of considerable

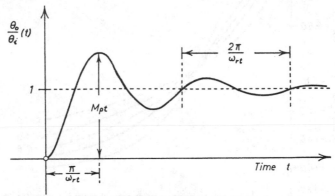

(a) Time domain response.

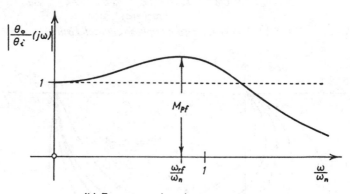

(b) Frequency domain response.

Fig. 8.16 *Correlation between transient and frequency responses.*

value in system design. The peak overshoot in the time domain (referred to unity input) will be termed M_{pt} and the angular frequency of oscillation in the time domain will be termed ω_{rt}. The correlation between time and frequency domains are illustrated in Fig. 8.16.

It has been shown that

$$\omega_{rt} = \omega_n \sqrt{(1 - \zeta^2)}$$

and

$$\omega_{rf} = \omega_n \sqrt{(1 - 2\zeta^2)}$$

190

$$\therefore \quad \frac{\omega_{rt}}{\omega_{rf}} = \sqrt{\left\{\frac{1-\zeta^2}{1-2\zeta^2}\right\}}$$

Alse

$$M_{pf} = \frac{1}{2\zeta\sqrt{(1-\zeta^2)}}$$

and

$$M_{pt} = 1 + e^{-\zeta\pi/\sqrt{(1-\zeta^2)}}$$

For an overshoot of 20%, ζ must be about 0·45, thus M_{pf} must have a value of about 1·25. Fig. 8.17 shows the variation of both M_{pt} and M_{pf} with damping ratio.

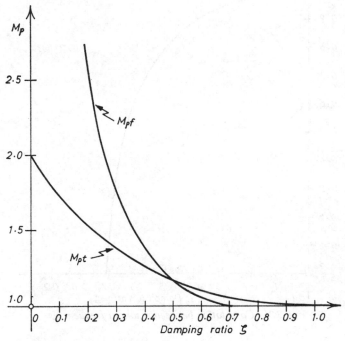

Fig. 8.17 M_{pf} and M_{pt} as functions of the damping ratio ζ.

The correlation between ω_{rt} and ω_{rf} is also important because it is quite evident that to obtain a fast response ω_{rt} must be high; it thus follows that ω_{rf} must be correspondingly high. When $\zeta = 0·45$, $\omega_{rt} = 1·15\omega_{rf}$. The variation of ω_{rf}/ω_{rt} with ζ is shown in Fig. 8.18.

8.9.4 Correlation Between Frequency and Transient Response for Higher-Order Systems

Most practical systems contain energy storage and dissipative elements which give rise to transfer delays. These all tend to increase

191

the order of the resulting differential equation. The frequency and transient responses are always related through the Fourier integral and as a general consequence when the frequency response is known, the transient response may be determined and *vice versa*. Correlation by use of the Fourier integral is, however, very laborious.

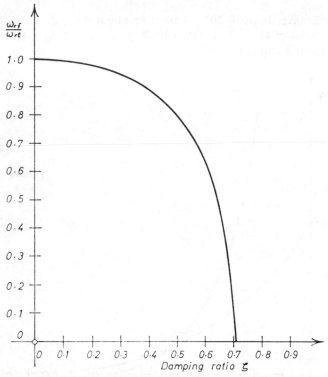

Fig. 8.18 *Correlation between resonant frequencies.*

More often it is profitable to use second-order system correlations for higher-order systems. The results of such use obviously are not exact and must be interpreted with engineering judgement and finally checked by computation. The need for such usage is easy to explain; when a higher-order system is encountered, transient analysis using the differential equation is laborious and also the information thus obtained is phrased in obscure combinations of system parameters.

It is not usually directly evident from the solution how variation of given parameters will affect the response. Synthesis would therefore have to proceed on a trial and error basis with little hope of a quick solution. However, the computation of the frequency response is relatively simple and design procedures which adjust frequency-response characteristics are easy to apply.

The physical problem is always one of control in the time domain however, and design in the frequency domain is only useful so long as correlation may be used to obtain a reasonable estimate of the transient performance.

The control engineer will usually have a design specification which may be phrased in terms of the time-domain parameters M_{pt}, ω_{rt} and ζ. These may be related by second-order correlations to the frequency-domain parameters M_{pf} and ω_{rf} and the frequency response may be adjusted to give approximately the desired values. The resultant design will not be exact for higher-order systems and sound engineering judgement is necessary in order to estimate the degree of accuracy possible in any given problem.

The justification for expecting an acceptable approximation from such techniques is beyond the scope of this book but it is usually included in the more advanced texts on the subject.

Worked Example

A servomechanism designed to control the position of a rotatable mass via a handwheel has an output torque of 0·1 N m per radian of error and is viscously damped with a damping ratio of 0·3. The moment of inertia of the moving parts is 10^{-3} kg m². Steady sinusoidal motion of peak amplitude 0·5 rad at a frequency of 1 c/s is applied to the handwheel. Determine the steady state output motion. At what frequency would the motion of the mass have its maximum amplitude?

Solution

The differential equation of the system is

$$(JD^2 + FD + K)\,\theta_o = K\theta_i$$

The angular frequency of the input signal is 2π rad/s

thus $\qquad\qquad \theta_i = 0.5 \sin 2\pi t$

also $\qquad\qquad J = 10^{-3}\,\text{kg m}^2$

and $\qquad\qquad K = 0.1\,\text{N m/rad}$

also $\qquad\qquad \zeta = 0.3$

but $\qquad\qquad \zeta = \dfrac{F}{2\sqrt{(JK)}}$

$\therefore \qquad\qquad F = 2\zeta\sqrt{(JK)}$

$\qquad\qquad\qquad = 2 \times 0.3\sqrt{10^{-4}}$

$\qquad\qquad\qquad = 6 \times 10^{-3}$

$\therefore$ differential equation becomes

$$(10^{-3} D^2 + 6 \times 10^{-3} D + 0 \cdot 1) \theta_o = 0 \cdot 05 \sin 2\pi t$$

or

$$(D^2 + 6D + 100) \theta_o = 50 \sin 2\pi t$$

Let $\bar{\theta}_o$ represent steady-state vector output represented as a complex number, hence putting $D = j\omega = j2\pi$ we have

$$\{(j2\pi)^2 + 6(j2\pi) + 100\} \bar{\theta}_o = 50 e^{j2\pi t}$$

$$\bar{\theta}_o = \frac{50 e^{j2\pi t}}{(j2\pi)^2 + 6(j2\pi) + 100}$$

$$= \frac{50 e^{j2\pi t}}{60 \cdot 5 + j37 \cdot 7}$$

$\therefore$ instantaneous steady state output motion is given by

$$\theta_o = \frac{50}{\sqrt{(60 \cdot 5^2 + 37 \cdot 7^2)}} \sin\left(2\pi t - \tan^{-1} \frac{37 \cdot 7}{60 \cdot 5}\right)$$

$\therefore$

$$\theta_o = 0 \cdot 7 \sin(2\pi t + 0 \cdot 557)$$

The output motion will have a peak amplitude at an angular frequency ω_{rf} given by

$$\omega_{rf} = \omega_n \sqrt{(1 - 2\zeta^2)}$$

where

$$\omega_n = \sqrt{(K/J)} = \sqrt{(0 \cdot 1/10^{-3})}$$

$$= 10 \, \text{rad/s}$$

$\therefore$

$$\omega_{rf} = 10 \sqrt{(1 - 2 \times 0 \cdot 3^2)}$$

$$= 9 \cdot 05 \, \text{rad/s}$$

Resonant frequency $f_{rf} = \omega_{rf}/2\pi$

$$= 9 \cdot 05/2\pi$$

$$= 1 \cdot 44 \, \text{c/s}$$

EXAMPLES FOR SOLUTION

1. The angular position of a rotatable mass is controlled from a handwheel by means of an electrical servomechanism which is critically damped by viscous friction. Set up the differential equation for the system. Derive an expression for the angular position of the mass at any time if, with the system initially at rest, the control wheel is suddenly turned an angle θ_i.

Given that the moment of inertia of the moving parts is 250 kg m² and the motor torque is 1000 N m per radian of misalignment, and that $\theta_i = 90°$, calculate the angle of misalignment 2 sec after moving the control wheel.

2. A closed-loop electrical system is used to control the angular position of a rotatable mass in response to the rotation of a control handwheel. The rotation of the mass is subject to viscous damping. Draw a block diagram for a suitable scheme and set up the differential equation of the system.

The Dynamics of a Simple Servomechanism

In a particular case, where a mass is required to follow the movement of a handwheel, the moment of inertia of the moving parts, referred to the mass under control, is 100 kg m². The driving torque, also referred to the mass, is 25 N m per minute of misalignment. If the system is critically damped, calculate the steady-state angular error when the control handwheel is continuously rotated at 2 rev/min.

3. A servomechanism is employed to control the angular position θ_o of a rotatable mass having a moment of inertia J, and subject to a viscous frictional torque F per unit angular velocity. The angular input θ_i is applied to the system by means of a control handwheel. A torque $T = K(\theta_i - \theta_o)$ is produced by the controller and output element. Draw a block diagram for the system and develop the differential equation for the output θ_o in terms of θ_i.

If θ_i is a unit step function determine the steady-state and transient response of θ_o for the oscillatory case, and calculate the frequency of oscillation of a particular servomechanism for which

$$J = 15 \times 10^{-6}\,\text{kg m}^2$$

$$K = 6 \times 10^{-3}\,\text{N m/radian}$$

and the damping torque per unit angular velocity is one half of that necessary to produce critical damping.

4. The angular position of a flywheel which is driven by an electric motor is controlled from a handwheel employing a closed-loop motor control system. The rotation of the flywheel is damped by viscous friction. Draw the block diagram for a suitable scheme and set up the differential equation of the system.

The moment of inertia of the moving parts, referred to the position of the flywheel is 2000 kg m², and the motor torque is 4 N m per minute of misalignment. The total frictional torque, also referred to the flywheel position, is 4000 N m per rad/s. At time $t = 0$, with the equipment at rest, the handwheel is set in motion with a constant angular velocity of 20 rev/min.

(i) Determine whether or not the transient response is oscillatory.

(ii) Determine the magnitude of the steady-state error, proving any formula used.

(iii) Sketch a graph of the position of the flywheel as a function of time.

5. The angular position of a flywheel which is driven by an electric motor is controlled from a handwheel employing a closed-loop control system. The rotation of the flywheel is damped by viscous damping. Describe such a scheme with the aid of a block diagram and set up the differential equation of the system.

The moment of inertia of the moving parts, referred to the flywheel, is 1000 kg m², and the motor torque is 2 N m per minute of misalignment. The total frictional torque, also referred to the flywheel, is 2000 N m per rad/s. At time $t = 0$, with the equipment at rest, the handwheel is set in motion with a constant angular velocity of 20 rev/min. Derive the equation of the subsequent angular position of the flywheel in relation to time, and make a sketch of this function.

6. A servomechanism is employed to control the angular position θ_o of a rotatable mass having a moment of inertia J, and subject to a viscous frictional torque F per unit angular velocity. The angular input θ_i is applied to the system by means of a control handwheel. The torque T produced by the controller and output element is directly proportional to the input to the controller, the constant of proportionality being K_t.

The system is stabilized by negative velocity feedback $-K_v\, d\theta_o/dt$. Draw the block diagram of such a system and develop the differential equation for the error ϵ in terms of θ_i where $\epsilon = \theta_i - \theta_o$.

In a particular servomechanism $J = 1000$ kg m², $K_t = 10{,}000$ N m/rad, and the total damping is such that the system is critically damped. Calculate the steady-state angular error, if the control handwheel is continuously rotated at 2 rev/min.

7. A position control system has an inertia referred to the output shaft of 1 kg m². Find the constant of proportionality K and the viscous frictional constant F such that the peak overshoot is 20% and the time to rise to the first maximum is 1 sec.

8. A servomechanism, designed to control the position of a rotatable mass, is stabilized by means of acceleration feedback. The moment of inertia of the system is 10^{-5} kg m², the viscous frictional torque per radian per second is 10^{-4} N m and the motor torque is given by

$$T_m = 4 \times 10^{-3} \left(\epsilon + k \frac{d^2 \theta_o}{dt^2} \right) \text{N m}$$

where $\epsilon = (\theta_i - \theta_o)$ is the angular positional error in radians between input and output shafts, and $kd^2\theta_o/dt^2$ is the additional feedback signal proportional to the acceleration of the output shaft.

(i) Draw a block diagram for the system.

(ii) Establish the differential equation for the system.

(iii) Determine the value to be assigned to k in order that the damping shall be critical.

(iv) Determine the value of the steady-state error for an input signal which has a constant angular velocity of 20 rev/min.

Prove any formula used.

9. A servomechanism is designed to control the angular position θ_o of a rotatable mass having a moment of inertia J, and subject to a viscous frictional torque F per unit angular velocity. The angular input θ_i is applied to the system by means of a control handwheel. The system is stabilized by means of velocity feedback and the motor torque T_m is given by

$$T_m = K_t \left(\epsilon - K_v \frac{d\theta_o}{dt} \right)$$

where $\epsilon = \theta_i - \theta_o$ and K_t and K_v are constants. Establish the differential equation for this system and determine:

(i) The steady-state positional error when the input signal has a constant velocity given by $\dfrac{d\theta_i}{dt} = \omega_i$.

(ii) The value of K_v in terms of the other constants, if the system is to be critically damped.

10. The angular position of a rotatable mass is controlled from a handwheel by means of a closed-loop system which is critically damped by viscous friction. The moment of inertia of the moving parts is 500 kg m² and the motor-torque per radian of misalignment is 2000 N m.

(i) Draw the block diagram of a suitable arrangement and establish the differential equation for the system.

(ii) Determine the steady positional error which exists when the handwheel is rotated at a constant angular velocity of 1 rev/min.

(iii) Describe a technique whereby the velocity-lag associated with this type of system may be entirely eliminated. Support your description with any necessary mathematical explanation.

11. The response of a proportional-to-error servomechanism to a unit input step-function is given by

$$\theta_o = \theta_i \{ 1 + 0 \cdot 207\, e^{-60 \cdot 6t} - 1 \cdot 207\, e^{-10 \cdot 4t} \}$$

Determine the value of the undamped resonant frequency ω_n and the damping ratio ζ for the servomechanism.

12. The specification given on a certain second-order feedback control system is that the overshoot of the step response should not exceed 10%. What are the corresponding limiting values of the damping ratio ζ and the frequency response resonance peak M_{pf}?

Determine the necessary natural undamped angular frequency of the system if the peak overshoot is to be reached in 0·18 sec. What is the value of the resonant angular frequency in the frequency domain ω_{rf}?

13. A simple velocity control system consists of an amplifier and a motor which produce an instantaneous output torque equal to K newton metres per unit error. The moment of inertia of the moving parts is J. The error signal is the difference between a reference input velocity ω_i and the output velocity ω_o.

(i) Draw a block diagram representing the system and derive the differential equation relating the output velocity to the reference. Ignore friction.

(ii) Solve this equation for a step-input velocity, assuming that the system be initially at rest.

(iii) In a practical system $K = 10$ N m per rad/s and $J = 10$ kg m^2. Determine the time taken for output velocity to reach 98% of the final value in response to a step input assuming the system to be initially at rest. Through what angle does the output shaft turn in achieving this velocity (i.e. 98% of the final value) assuming that the magnitude of the input step be 1 rad/s?

Chapter Nine

Transfer Functions

9.1 Introduction

The transient analysis of the torque-proportional-to-error servo-mechanism is treated in chapter 8 on the basis of two assumptions:

(i) That at the instant θ_i and θ_o change their values, the error detector produces a signal directly proportional to their difference ϵ.

(ii) That at the instant the signal ϵ appears at the input of the controller, a torque directly proportional to ϵ is available at the load.

Whilst assumption (i) may often be almost exactly true, assumption (ii) is never true in practical systems. This is because the majority of elements encountered in control systems possess the ability to store energy; this energy cannot be transferred from one element to another immediately. The transfer of signals through a chain of elements is thus delayed. In mechanical devices any element containing masses which must be moved or springs which must be stretched or compressed will cause such delays. In electrical systems it is the presence of inductance or capacitance which causes delay.

In order to illustrate the point in a simple manner let us consider the non-practical mechanical system shown in Fig. 9.1.

Both the spring and the viscous damper are reckoned to possess negligible mass. Let us assume that the spring is compressed by an amount x at any instant t. Thus if an input position x_i is applied to the point A, then the force applied to the damper is kx. This force must be balanced by an equal and opposite force from the damper $f\,dx_o/dt$.

$\therefore$
$$f\frac{dx_o}{dt} = kx$$

But $x = x_i - x_o$.

$$\therefore \qquad f\frac{dx_o}{dt} = k(x_i - x_o)$$

or

$$f\frac{dx_o}{dt} + kx_o = kx_i$$

Hence

$$(fD + k)x_o = kx_i \qquad (1)$$

Let us assume that x_i is an input step and that at $t = 0$, $x_o = 0$. Equating D to zero we find the steady-state solution

$$x_{o\,ss} = x_i$$

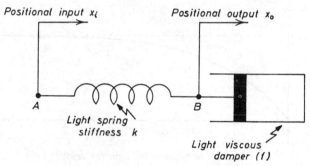

Fig. 9.1 *Illustrating transfer delay.*

The auxiliary equation is

$$(fm + k) = 0$$

$$\therefore \qquad m = -\frac{k}{f}$$

$\therefore$ transient solution is given by

$$x_{o\,t} = A\,e^{-kt/f}$$

$\therefore$ complete solution $x_o = x_{o\,ss} + x_{o\,t}$

$$= x_i + A\,e^{-kt/f}$$

At $t = 0$, $x_o = 0$, hence $A = -x_i$

$$\therefore \qquad x_o = x_i(1 - e^{-kt/f})$$

This represents an exponential rise towards x_i with a time constant f/k (see §2.3.2). The curve is shown in Fig. 9.2.

If we imagine x_i to be a positional signal which has to be transferred from point A to point B, then we can fully realize that there is a delay before the full value of this signal appears at B. Equation (1), which

199

is the differential equation relating the two quantities x_i and x_o, can itself be used to assess both the nature and the magnitude of the delay. The equation can be rewritten as a function of the operator D, i.e.

$$\frac{x_o}{x_i}(D) = \frac{k}{fD + k}$$

$$= \frac{1}{\dfrac{f}{k}D + 1}$$

i.e.
$$\frac{x_o}{x_i}(D) = \frac{1}{TD + 1} \qquad (2)$$

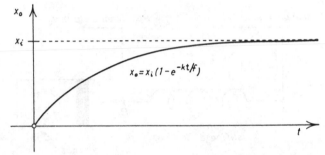

Fig. 9.2 *An exponential transfer delay.*

where T = the time constant of the exponential delay $(T = f/k)$.

It becomes evident that we can, simply by looking at the form of equation (2), deduce much about the step response of the system. For instance, by putting $D = 0$ we have $x_{o\,ss}/x_i = 1$. Also we can see by inspection that the time-constant is T and we know that the system will take $5T$ sec to reach 99.3% of the total rise x_i. Hence if we had a system such that

$$\frac{x_o}{x_i}(D) = \frac{10}{3D + 1}$$

we could deduce all we required to know about the step-response of the system by inspection of this equation. The steady-state value of x_o is $10x_i$ and the time-constant is 3 sec.

The equation (2) is referred to as the general 'transfer function' or 'transmittance' of the device. Often in the literature, instead of D, the Laplace variable s or the Heaviside operator p is used.

To obtain the vector relationship between x_o and x_i when x_i is a steady sinusoidal signal we simply substitute $j\omega$ in place of D.

Transfer functions are of great value because, as will be shown later, it is possible to obtain the overall transfer function of a complicated system by combining the transfer functions of the individual elements. Much about the performance of a system can be deduced from a fairly simple inspection of the transfer function, no matter how complicated this transfer function becomes.

It is necessary first to show how the transfer functions of various elements may be deduced.

9.2 Derivation of Typical Transfer Functions

9.2.1 *Hydraulic Spool-Valve and Actuator*

Negligible Load Reaction

The transfer function to be derived relates the position of the piston x_o to the position of the spool x_i when the load reaction is negligible.

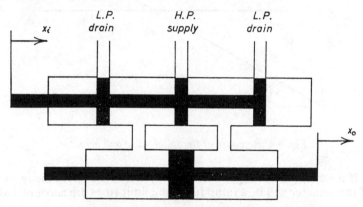

Fig. 9.3 *Spool-valve and actuator.*

When the valve is opened an amount x_i, the rate of flow of oil into the piston is directly proportional to x_i. In order to produce a simple transfer function we will assume that forces opposing the motion of the actuator are negligible. It is then accurate to ignore the oil leakage across the piston, in which case the piston velocity must be proportional to the rate of flow of oil and hence to valve opening. Therefore

$$\frac{\mathrm{d}x_o}{\mathrm{d}t} = Cx_i$$

where C is a constant.

or
$$\mathrm{D}x_o = Cx_i$$

$\therefore$
$$\frac{x_o}{x_i}(\mathrm{D}) = \frac{C}{\mathrm{D}}$$

201

This represents the general transfer function of the system. The transfer function may be viewed in another way:

$$\frac{dx_o}{dt} = Cx_i$$

∴
$$x_o = C \int x_i \, dt$$

Thus the system is ideally a pure integrator. It should be noted that this is an idealized approach and the effects of non-linearities have been neglected.

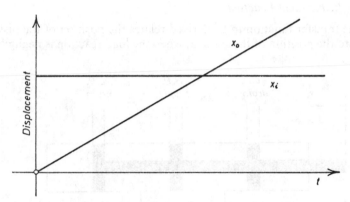

Fig. 9.4 *Response of the spool-valve and actuator.*

If a step-input of magnitude x_i is applied to the spool the motion of the actuator will be a ramp (until the limit stops are encountered).

Finite Load Reaction

Let us assume the piston of Fig. 9.3 is driving a load of mass m against viscous friction (f newtons per m/s) and a spring force (k newtons per metre). In order to analyse the system we will use the static equations for the actuator stated in §7.4.3. The effects of oil compressibility and coulomb friction will be neglected.

Rate of flow of oil $\qquad Q = L_p P + A_p V \qquad\qquad$ (1)

and force $\qquad\qquad\quad F = A_p P \qquad\qquad\qquad\qquad$ (2)

The force opposing F is $f\dfrac{dx_o}{dt} + kx_o$, thus the net force available to produce acceleration is

$$F - \left(f\frac{dx_o}{dt} + kx_o \right)$$

Thus, using Newton's second law we have

$$F - \left(f\frac{dx_o}{dt} + kx_o \right) = m\frac{d^2 x_o}{dt^2}$$

$\therefore$

$$F = m\frac{d^2 x_o}{dt^2} + f\frac{dx_o}{dt} + kx_o \tag{3}$$

$\therefore$ eliminating F between (2) and (3) and putting the result in D-form.

$$A_p P = (mD^2 + fD + k)x_o$$

or

$$P = \frac{(mD^2 + fD + k)}{A_p} x_o \tag{4}$$

Now considering equation (1) we know that Q is proportional to the valve motion x_i, i.e.

$$Q = k_v x_i \tag{5}$$

where k_v is the valve constant.

Also the velocity of the piston $V = dx_o/dt$, thus equation (1) may be rewritten as

$$k_v x_i = L_p P + A_p Dx_o \tag{6}$$

Using (4) we may eliminate P from equation (6) thus

$$k_v x_i = \frac{L_p}{A_p}(mD^2 + fD + k)x_o + A_p Dx_o$$

or

$$k_v x_i = \frac{L_p}{A_p}\left\{ mD^2 + \left(f + \frac{A_p^2}{L_p} \right)D + k \right\}x_o$$

$\therefore$

$$\frac{x_o}{x_i}(D) = \frac{A_p k_v/L_p}{mD^2 + (f + A_p^2/L_p)D + k}$$

The above expression is the general transfer function of the spool valve–actuator combination with load reaction. It is usually called a 'quadratic' transfer function. If a step input of magnitude x_i is applied, then the final value of the output $x_{o\,ss}$ may be found by putting D equal to zero, i.e.

$$x_{o\,ss} = \left\{ \frac{A_p k_v/L_p}{k} \right\}x_i$$

The transient response may be overdamped, critically damped or underdamped, depending on the relative values of the constants in the denominator of the transfer function. A typical response is shown in Fig. 9.5.

We may thus regard this device as an open-loop position control system.

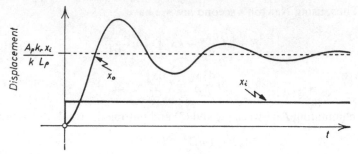

Fig. 9.5 *Underdamped transient response for valve-actuator with load reaction.*

The Use of Negative Positional Feedback

Negative positional feedback can be introduced into the valve–actuator combination by means of a mechanical link as shown in Fig. 9.6 (*a*). The valve motion v can be related to the input and output motion from the geometry of Fig. 9.6 (*b*).

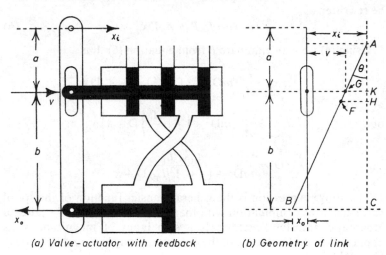

(a) *Valve-actuator with feedback*   (b) *Geometry of link*

Fig. 9.6 *Negative positional feedback.*

Suppose the input position is such that the upper end of the link is at point A and the output position is such that the lower end of the link is at point B.

Now
$$\sin \theta = \frac{BC}{AB} = \frac{x_o + x_i}{a + b} \qquad (1)$$

Also
$$\sin \theta = \frac{FH}{AF}$$

204

If the motion of the valve is small $FH \simeq GK$

$$\therefore \qquad \sin \theta \simeq \frac{GK}{AF}$$

But
$$GK = x_i - v$$

$$\therefore \qquad \sin \theta = \frac{x_i - v}{a} \qquad (2)$$

Hence, equating (1) and (2), we have

$$\frac{x_o + x_i}{a + b} = \frac{x_i - v}{a} \qquad (3)$$

Also, as explained above

$$\frac{dx_o}{dt} = Cv \qquad (4)$$

Hence, substituting for v in (3) from (4) and putting in D-form, we have

$$\frac{x_o + x_i}{a + b} = \frac{x_i - Dx_o/C}{a}$$

$$\therefore \qquad \left\{ a + \frac{(a + b)D}{C} \right\} x_o = bx_i$$

$$\therefore \qquad \frac{x_o}{x_i}(D) = \frac{b}{a + \frac{(a + b)D}{C}}$$

$$= \frac{b/a}{1 + TD}$$

where $T = \dfrac{a + b}{aC}$ = effective time constant of the system.

If the input is a step of magnitude x_i, the steady-state output position $x_{o\,ss} = bx_i/a$ and the rise is an exponential of time constant T.

9.2.2 The Rate Gyroscope

The rate gyroscope is described in §7.2.3. The transfer function is the relationship between the angular position θ of the inner framework about the output axis and the angular velocity Ω of the instrument about the input axis.

The spinner is mounted in a sealed can and the space between the case and the can is filled with oil giving viscous damping F newton metres per unit angular velocity. Let the other parameters of the gyroscope be symbolized as follows:

J = moment of inertia of spinner about its axis of spin, J_g = moment of inertia of can and its contents about output axis, ω = angular velocity of spinner, K = stiffness of torsion bar.

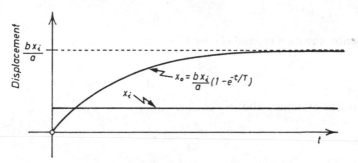

Fig. 9.7 *Transient response of the valve-actuator with feedback.*

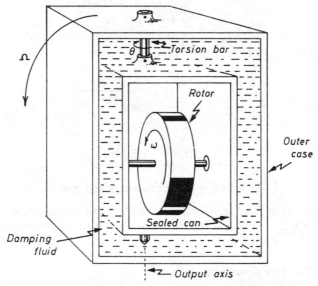

Fig. 9.8 *Rate gyroscope with viscous damping.*

Now the gyroscope torque acting on the can about the output axis due to the input motion is given by

$$T = J\omega\Omega$$

This torque is opposed by the torsion bar which produces an opposing torque $K\theta$ and by the viscous frictional torque $Fd\theta/dt$. Thus the net torque available to produce motion is given by

$$J\omega\Omega - K\theta - Fd\theta/dt$$

Thus using Newton's second law we have

$$J\omega\Omega - K\theta - Fd\theta/dt = J_g d^2\theta/dt^2$$

or in D-form

$$J\omega\Omega = (J_g D^2 + FD + K)\theta$$

$$\therefore \qquad \frac{\theta}{\Omega}(D) = \frac{J\omega}{J_g D^2 + FD + K}$$

The steady output position for a step velocity input is thus given by $\theta_{ss} = J\omega/K$. The form of the transient response is governed by factors in the quadratic denominator of the transfer function and it can be made underdamped, critically damped or overdamped by the selection of the value of F.

9.2.3 The D.C. Generator

The transfer function of the d.c. generator relates the generated voltage (i.e. the open-circuit output voltage v_o) to the field voltage v_i.

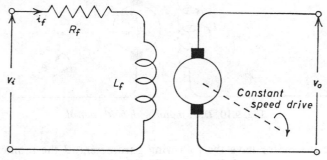

Fig. 9.9 *D.C. generator.*

If saturation and hysteresis are neglected (see §7.3.2) the generated voltage is related to the field current by the equation

$$v_o = k_g i_f \qquad (1)$$

But applying Kirchhoff's mesh law to the field circuit we have

$$v_i = L_f \frac{di_f}{dt} + R_f i_f$$

or

$$v_i = (L_f D + R_f)i \qquad (2)$$

Thus substituting in (2) for i_f from (1) we have

$$v_i = (L_f D + R_f)\frac{v_o}{K_g}$$

$$\therefore \qquad \frac{v_o}{v_i}(D) = \frac{K_g}{L_f D + R_f}$$

$$= \frac{K_g/R_f}{\frac{L_f}{R_f}D + 1}$$

$$= \frac{K_g/R_f}{T_f D + 1}$$

where T_f = time constant of field winding (L_f/R_f).

9.2.4 The Field-Controlled D.C. Motor

The transfer function relates either the armature velocity or the armature position θ_o to the field voltage v_i.

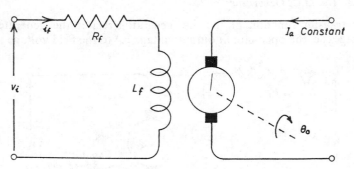

Fig. 9.10. *D.C. motor with field control.*

Let the motor have the following parameters: J the moment of inertia of armature, F the viscous-frictional torque per unit angular velocity, K the torque produced per unit field current (saturation and hysteresis will be neglected).

Hence the motor torque T is given by

$$T = Ki_f \qquad (1)$$

Analysing the field circuit we have

$$v_i = L_f\frac{di_f}{dt} + R_f i_f$$

or $\qquad\qquad v_i = (L_f D + R_f)i_f \qquad (2)$

Hence eliminating i_f between (1) and (2) we have

$$\frac{Kv_i}{L_f D + R_f} = T \tag{3}$$

Now the resultant torque available to accelerate the motor is $T - F d\theta_o/dt$.

Hence, using Newton's second law we have

$$T - F d\theta_o/dt = J d^2 \theta_o/dt^2$$

or
$$T = D(JD + F)\theta_o \tag{4}$$

Hence, eliminating T between (3) and (4) we have

$$\frac{Kv_i}{L_f D + R_f} = D(JD + F)\theta_o$$

Thus
$$\frac{\theta_o}{v_i}(D) = \frac{K}{D(JD + F)(L_f D + R_f)}$$

$$= \frac{K/FR_f}{D(T_m D + 1)(T_f D + 1)}$$

where T_m = mechanical time constant (J/F), and T_f = field circuit time constant (L_f/R_f).

This represents the 'positional transfer function'.

The angular velocity $\omega_o = D\theta_o$, hence

$$\frac{\omega_o}{v_i}(D) = \frac{D\theta_o}{v_i}(D) = \frac{K/FR_f}{(T_m D + 1)(T_f D + 1)}$$

This is the velocity transfer function.

9.2.5 *The Armature-Controlled D.C. Motor*

The transfer function relates either the armature velocity or the armature position θ_o to the armature voltage v_i.

Let the motor have the following parameters: J the moment of inertia of armature, F the viscous frictional torque per unit angular velocity, K_v the generated e.m.f. per unit angular velocity, K_t the torque per unit armature current.

Thus we have
$$e_b = K_v d\theta_o/dt \tag{1}$$

and motor torque
$$T = K_t i_a \tag{2}$$

The small inductance of the armature circuit will be neglected, thus the circuital equation for the armature becomes

$$v_i = i_a R_a + e_b \tag{3}$$

$\therefore$ substituting for i_a and e_b from (2) and (1) in (3) we have

$$v_i = \frac{TR_a}{K_t} + K_v \, d\theta_o/dt \tag{4}$$

Using Newton's second law, we have

$$T - F d\theta_o/dt = J d^2\theta_o/dt^2$$

or
$$T = D(JD + F)\theta_o \tag{5}$$

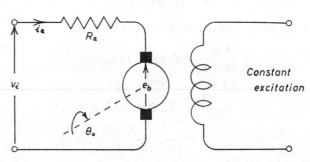

Fig. 9.11 *D.C. motor with armature control.*

Eliminating T between (4) and (5) gives

$$v_i = \frac{R_a}{K_t} D(JD + F)\theta_o + K_v D\theta_o$$

or
$$v_i = D\left\{\frac{JR_a}{K_t}D + \frac{R_a F}{K_t} + K_v\right\}\theta_o$$

Normally in practice $\dfrac{R_a F}{K_t} \ll K_v$, and thus

$$v_i \simeq D\left(\frac{JR_a}{K_t}D + K_v\right)\theta_o$$

$$\therefore \qquad \frac{\theta_o}{v_i}(D) \simeq \frac{1}{D\left(\dfrac{JR_a}{K_t}D + K_v\right)}$$

$$\simeq \frac{1/K_v}{D(T_e D + 1)}$$

where $T_e = \dfrac{JR_a}{K_t K_v}$ and represents the effective time constant of the device.

210

If we were to analyse the system more accurately and take the term R_aF/K_t into account we should have arrived at

$$T_e = \frac{JR_a}{K_t\left\{\dfrac{R_aF}{K_t} + K_v\right\}}$$

$$= \frac{J}{F + K_tK_v/R_a}$$

It is interesting to compare the value of this time constant with the mechanical time constant J/F produced in the field-controlled motor. Actually the term K_tK_v/R_a is much larger than F under normal circumstances and so T_e is very much smaller than J/F. Thus the armature-controlled motor is inherently faster than the field controlled motor, not only because the method gives a single time constant but mainly because that single time constant is very much smaller than the larger of the two time constants associated with field control.

The velocity transfer function of the system is given by

$$\frac{\omega_o}{v_i}(D) = \frac{D\theta_o}{v_i}(D) = \frac{1/K_v}{T_e D + 1}$$

9.2.6 The Torque Motor

The construction and steady-state operation of the torque motor are discussed in §7.4.2. The dynamic operation is somewhat more complicated. The coils on the two axes of the machine are usually driven by a push–pull electronic amplifier. Thus if the current through the coils on one axis increases by an amount $i/2$, the current through the coils on the other axis decreases by an amount $i/2$ and the control current is then i. Since the torque motor is invariably driven from an electronic amplifier, it will be advantageous to compute the overall transfer function relating the position of the rotor θ_o to the input of the amplifier v_i. A simplified diagram representing the amplifier and torque motor is shown in Fig. 9.12.

The circuital equation is complicated by the fact that as the rotor moves an e.m.f. is generated in the coils due to the change in flux-linkages. The e.m.f. is proportional to the angular velocity of the motor $d\theta_o/dt$. Thus the circuital equation becomes

$$Gv_i = (2R_o + 2R_c)\frac{i}{2} + 2L_c\frac{d(i/2)}{dt} + K_b\frac{d\theta_o}{dt}$$

where K_b is a constant.

Thus
$$Gv_i = (R_o + R_c)i + L_c\frac{di}{dt} + K_b\frac{d\theta_o}{dt}$$

211

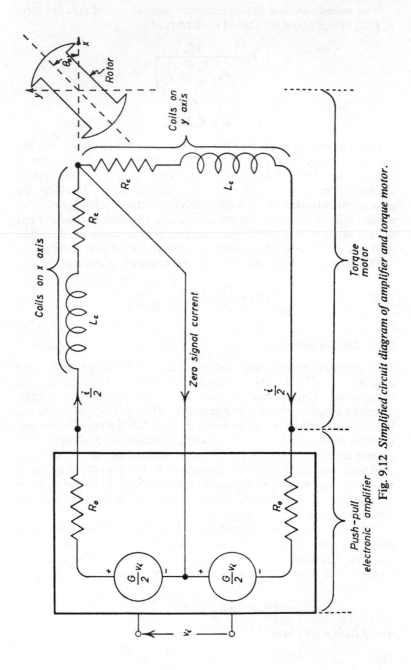

Fig. 9.12 *Simplified circuit diagram of amplifier and torque motor.*

or
$$i = \frac{Gv_i - K_b D\theta_o}{R + L_c D} \tag{1}$$

where $R = R_o + R_c$.

Now the torque T produced by the device is given by

$$T = K_1 i - K_2 \theta_o \tag{2}$$

where K_1 and K_2 are constants for the device.

It will be assumed that the motion is opposed by inbuilt springs of stiffness K and is viscously damped with a damping torque F per unit angular velocity. The net torque available to accelerate the rotor is thus

$$T - K\theta_o - F d\theta_o / dt$$

Thus, if the rotor has a moment of inertia J, using Newton's second law gives

$$T - K\theta_o - F\frac{d\theta_o}{dt} = J\frac{d^2\theta_o}{dt^2}$$

or in D-form

$$T - K\theta_o - FD\theta_o = JD^2\theta_o \tag{3}$$

Eliminating T between (2) and (3) we have

$$K_1 i - K_2\theta_o - K\theta_o - FD\theta_o = JD^2\theta_o$$

$$\therefore \qquad K_1 i = \{JD^2 + FD + (K_2 + K)\}\theta_o \tag{4}$$

Thus eliminating i between (1) and (4) gives

$$K_1\left\{\frac{Gv_i - K_b D\theta_o}{R + L_c D}\right\} = \{JD^2 + FD + (K_2 + K)\}\theta_o$$

$$\therefore \quad Gv_i - K_b D\theta_o = \frac{(R + L_c D)\{JD^2 + FD + (K_2 + K)\}\theta_o}{K_1}$$

$$\therefore \qquad Gv_i = \frac{(R + L_c D)\{JD^2 + FD + (K_2 + K)\}\theta_o + K_1 K_b D\theta_o}{K_1}$$

$$\therefore \qquad \frac{\theta_o}{v_i}(D) = \frac{GK_1}{(R + L_c D)\{JD^2 + FD + (K_2 + K)\} + K_1 K_b D}$$

$$\therefore \qquad \frac{\theta_o}{v_i}(D) = \frac{GK_1}{L_c JD^3 + (RJ + L_c F)D^2 + \{K_1 K_b + RF + L_c(K_2 + K)\}D + R(K_2 + K)}$$

$$= \frac{GK_1/R(K_2 + K)}{\dfrac{L_c J}{R(K_2 + K)}D^3 + \dfrac{RJ + L_c F}{R(K_2 + K)}D^2 + \dfrac{\{K_1 K_b + RF + L_c(K_2 + K)\}}{R(K_2 + K)}D + 1}$$

Further simplification is difficult except by arithmetic methods, when the transfer function can be reduced to the form

$$\frac{\theta_o}{v_i}(D) = \frac{N}{(T_m D + 1)(D^2 + 2\zeta\omega_n D + \omega_n^2)}$$

The values of N, T_m, ζ and ω_n would then have to be computed by arithmetic methods.

This transfer function, whilst being precise, is complicated. A simplified version can be produced if we regard the electronic amplifier as having a very high output resistance R_o. This is frequently the case in practice. The output current is then independent of the characteristics of the torque motor and

$$\frac{i}{2} = \left(\frac{G}{2}v_i\right)\bigg/ R_o$$

$\therefore$
$$i = \frac{G}{R_o}v_i$$

The quantity G/R_o is the transconductance of the amplifier and will be represented by the symbol Y, i.e.

$$i = Yv_i \tag{5}$$

Now $\qquad\qquad$ torque $T = K_1 i - K_2 \theta_o$ $\qquad\qquad\qquad$ (6)

Thus from (5) and (6)

$$T = K_1 Yv_i - K_2 \theta_o \tag{7}$$

Eliminating T between (7) and (3) gives

$$K_1 Yv_i - K_2 \theta_o - K\theta_o - FD\theta_o = JD^2 \theta_o$$

or
$$\frac{\theta_o}{v_i}(D) = \frac{K_1 Y}{JD^2 + FD + (K_2 + K)}$$

It must be appreciated that this approximate transfer function is only valid when the output resistance of the amplifier is very high indeed; otherwise the more complicated form must be used.

9.2.7 Other Transfer Functions

There is a vast range of components used in control systems and their transfer functions can usually be derived quickly by using a few physical laws. The space available in this book for such derivations is limited and the examples selected for analysis in the preceding paragraphs have been chosen to illustrate the general approach to the problem.

Electronic amplifiers have a transfer function which relates the output voltage to the input voltage and is thus simply the open-circuit gain of the device. The delays introduced by the effects of stray capacitances are usually small enough to be neglected.

Positional error detectors such as potentiometer bridges introduce negligible delays and their transfer functions may be expressed in terms of how many units of output they produce per radian of error. A potentiometer bridge will possess a transfer function equal to its sensitivity in volts per radian of error.

A tachogenerator is a device which gives a constant output voltage for a constant input velocity and it is thus a pure differentiator and has a transfer function of the form

$$\frac{v_o}{\theta_i}(D) = k_s D$$

where v_o = output voltage, θ_i = input position, and k_s = a constant for the machine.

The transfer functions of certain pneumatic elements are derived in chapter 14.

9.3 Determination of the Overall Open-loop Transfer Function

When several elements whose transfer functions are known, are connected in cascade, it is possible to determine the overall transfer function of the combination by a very simple technique. Consider the chain of devices shown in Fig. 9.13.

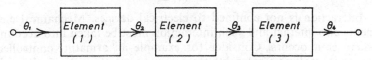

Fig. 9.13 *Elements connected in cascade.*

Let the transfer functions of elements (1), (2) and (3) be H_1, H_2 and H_3 respectively.

The overall transfer function is θ_4/θ_1; however

$$\frac{\theta_4}{\theta_1} = \frac{\theta_2}{\theta_1} \times \frac{\theta_3}{\theta_2} \times \frac{\theta_4}{\theta_3}$$

but $\qquad \dfrac{\theta_2}{\theta_1} = H_1 \quad$ and $\quad \dfrac{\theta_3}{\theta_2} = H_2 \quad$ and $\quad \dfrac{\theta_4}{\theta_3} = H_3$

Thus $\qquad \dfrac{\theta_4}{\theta_1} = H_1 H_2 H_3$

215

In words, therefore, we have that the overall transfer function of a chain of cascaded elements is the product of the transfer functions of the individual elements.

It is extremely important to observe that to apply this rule correctly the transfer functions of the elements must take into account the fact that they are connected to other elements. That is, element (2) will interact with element (1) and element (3) will interact with element (2). Hence the 'open-circuit' transfer functions derived in §9.2 will require slight modification before being used in this manner. Fortunately, the effect of interaction is usually very easy to take into account. Consider, for example, the problem of an electronic amplifier supplying the field winding of a d.c. generator (Fig. 9.14).

The transfer function of the electronic amplifier is G on open circuit, but when supplying the field winding with current, the output terminal voltage will be less than Gv_i because of the voltage drop across R_o. That is to say the second element is interacting with the first. To overcome the computational difficulty involved, we may artificially shift R_o forward to combine it with R_f. This is of course a theoretical shift, not an actual one. The artificial circuit together with its block diagram is shown in Fig. 9.15.

Thus we define an artificial field resistance $R_f' = R_o + R_f$ and the effective field-circuit time constant becomes $T_f' = L_f/R_f'$.

Hence the overall transfer function becomes

$$\frac{v_o}{v_i} = \frac{v_2}{v_i} \times \frac{v_o}{v_2}$$

$$= G \times \frac{K_g/R_f'}{(T_f' D + 1)}$$

Interaction is not confined to electrical devices. Mechanical elements also interact and such interaction must be taken into account wherever it occurs. Consider for example an armature-controlled motor controlling a rotatable mass of moment of inertia J_1 through an ideal step-down gear-box of teeth ratio $1:N$ (Fig. 9.16).

The mechanical effect of J_1 is transmitted back through the gear-box and will thus alter the transfer function of the motor. The best method of approach here is to use the concept of referred moments of inertia introduced in §6.2.6. The moment of inertia of the mass referred to the motor shaft is thus J_1/N^2. The total moment of inertia referred to the motor shaft is thus $J_m + J_1/N^2$ which will be represented by J_m'. The circuit diagram may now be replaced by a block diagram as shown in Fig. 9.17.

Here
$$T_e' = J_m' R_a/K_t K_v$$

Thus
$$\frac{\theta_o}{v_i} = \frac{\theta_m}{v_i} \times \frac{\theta_o}{\theta_m} = \frac{1/K_v}{D(T_e' D + 1)} \cdot \frac{1}{N}$$

216

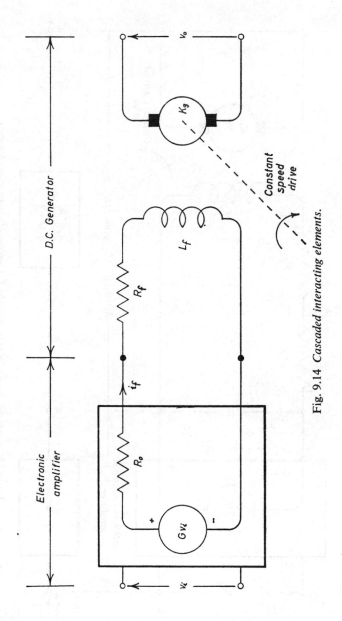

Fig. 9.14 *Cascaded interacting elements.*

217

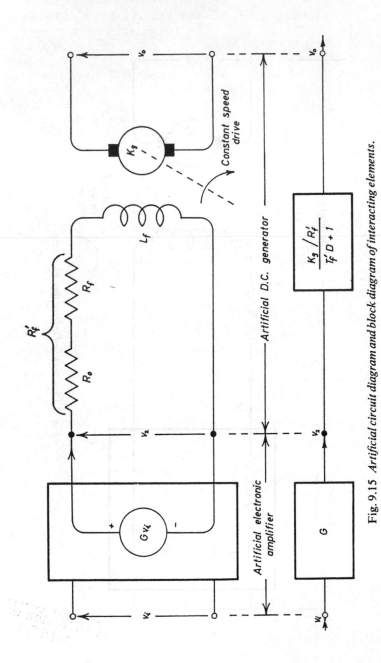

Fig. 9.15 *Artificial circuit diagram and block diagram of interacting elements.*

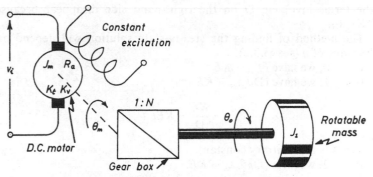

Fig. 9.16 *Mechanical interaction.*

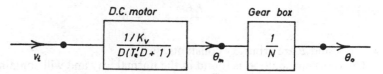

Fig. 9.17 *Block diagram.*

9.4 Determination of the Open-loop Step Response from the Open-loop Transfer Function

Whilst the purpose of this book is largely to describe how closed-loop systems are analysed and designed, it is noteworthy that the open-loop step response of a system can readily be determined from the open-loop transfer function.

In general a system may have an open-loop transfer function of the form

$$\frac{\theta_o}{\epsilon}(D) = \frac{K(1 + DT_a)(1 + DT_b), \text{etc.}}{D^n(1 + DT_1)(1 + DT_2), \text{etc.}}$$

where T_a, T_b, T_1, T_2, etc. are time constants, K is a constant, and n is an integer.

Sometimes there may be a quadratic lag term in the denominator of this transfer function having a general form $(K_1 D^2 + K_2 D + 1)$. This does not materially affect the method.

If ϵ is a step function of magnitude E, the response is given by the solution of the differential equation

$$\theta_o = \left\{ \frac{K(1 + DT_a)(1 + DT_b), \text{etc.}}{D^n(1 + DT_1)(1 + DT_2), \text{etc.}} \right\} E$$

i.e. $\qquad \{D^n(1 + DT_1)(1 + DT_2), \text{etc.}\}\, \theta_o = KE$

219

(the terms involving D on the right-hand side disappear because $DE = 0$).

The method of finding the steady-state solution will depend on the value of n (see §5.3.2).

If $n = 0$, we have $\theta_{o\,ss} = KE$.

If $n = 1$, we have $(D\theta_o)_{ss} = KE$.

$$\therefore \qquad \theta_{o\,ss} = \frac{KE}{D} = KEt + A$$

where A is an arbitrary constant.

If $n = 2$, we have $(D^2\theta_o)_{ss} = KE$.

$$\therefore \qquad (D\theta_o)_{ss} = KEt + A$$

$$\therefore \qquad \theta_{o\,ss} = \frac{KEt^2}{2} + At + B$$

where A and B are arbitrary constants.

The transient solution is found in the normal way and will contain terms such as $Ce^{-t/T_1} + Fe^{-t/T_2}$, etc.

A quadratic term with complex roots will give an exponentially damped sinusoid.

The complete general response is found by adding the steady-state and transient solutions. A complete particular response involves the evaluation of the arbitrary constants, A, B, etc. by using the initial conditions.

9.5 Determination of the Closed-loop Performance from the Open-loop Transfer Function

9.5.1 Closed-loop Transfer Function

When a system has a known open-loop transfer function θ_o/ϵ the closed-loop transfer function may readily be determined.

Consider the unity feedback system shown in Fig. 9.18.

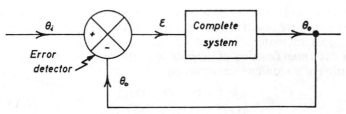

Fig. 9.18 *Closed-loop system.*

Now
$$\frac{\theta_o}{\theta_i} = \frac{\theta_o}{\epsilon + \theta_o}$$

$$= \frac{\theta_o/\epsilon}{1 + \theta_o/\epsilon}$$

Now $\theta_o/\epsilon = $ open-loop transfer function.

Hence to determine the closed-loop transfer function of a unity feedback system we divide the open-loop transfer function by one plus the open-loop transfer function.

When a system has non-unity feedback, the block diagram is as shown in Fig. 9.19.

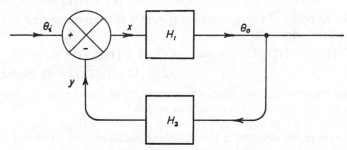

Fig. 9.19 *Non-unity feedback system.*

The elements in the forward path are described by the transfer function H_1 and those in the feedback path by H_2.

Now
$$y = H_2\,\theta_o \tag{1}$$
and
$$\theta_o = H_1\,x \tag{2}$$
also
$$x = \theta_i - y \tag{3}$$

We must eliminate x and y between these equations, hence substituting for x and y in (3) from (2) and (1) we have

$$\frac{\theta_o}{H_1} = \theta_i - H_2\,\theta_o$$

$$\theta_i = \theta_o\left\{\frac{1}{H_1} + H_2\right\}$$

$$= \theta_o\left\{\frac{1 + H_1 H_2}{H_1}\right\}$$

$$\therefore \quad \frac{\theta_o}{\theta_i} = \frac{H_1}{1 + H_1 H_2}$$

The above result is extremely useful in the analysis of single and multiloop systems (see §9.7). Note also, when $H_2 = 1$, as in the unity feedback system, $\theta_o/\theta_i = H_1/(1 + H_1)$ as shown previously.

221

9.5.2 Closed-loop Response

When we have a unity feedback system with an open-loop transfer function given by

$$\frac{\theta_o}{\epsilon}(D) = \frac{K(T_a D + 1)(T_b D + 1), \text{ etc.}}{D^n(T_1 D + 1)(T_2 D + 1), \text{ etc.}}$$

then the closed-loop transfer function

$$\frac{\theta_o}{\theta_i}(D) = \frac{\theta_o/\epsilon}{1 + \theta_o/\epsilon}$$

$$= \frac{K(T_a D + 1)(T_b D + 1), \text{ etc.}}{D^n(T_1 D + 1)(T_2 D + 1), \text{ etc.} + K(T_a D + 1)(T_b D + 1), \text{ etc.}}$$

The response of the closed-loop system is thus characterized by the differential equation:

$$\{D^n(T_1 D + 1)(T_2 D + 1), \text{ etc.} + K(T_a D + 1)(T_b D + 1), \text{ etc.}\}\theta_o$$

$$= \{K(T_a D + 1)(T_b D + 1), \text{ etc.}\}\theta_i$$

The steady-state solution for a step input can easily be found because the right-hand side reduces to $K\theta_i$.

Hence, if $n = 0$, $\theta_{o\,ss} = K\theta_i/(K+1)$, and if $n > 0$, $\theta_{o\,ss} = \theta_i$.

However, to determine the transient solution, the left-hand side must be factorized. This is only directly possible when the order of the function of D is not greater than two. The closed-loop transient response may be determined by approximate graphical methods (e.g. the root locus method) but even then, the determination of the arbitrary constants of integration by using the initial conditions will be extremely tedious except in very simple cases.

9.5.3 Closed-loop Stability—the Routh-Hurwitz Criterion

Whilst exact determination of the transient performance involves considerable labour, it is, however, possible to determine whether or not the system will be stable or unstable on closed loop. A system is said to be absolutely stable if the output eventually settles down after a small disturbance. The system is absolutely unstable if a small disturbance causes the output to build up. Normally in practical systems the build-up is limited by a non-linearity and the instability is exhibited by a 'limit-cycle' which is virtually a sinusoidal oscillation.

In §9.5.2 it is shown how the closed-loop transfer function of a unity-feedback system has the form

$$\frac{\theta_o}{\theta_i}(D) = \frac{K(T_a D + 1)(T_b D + 1), \text{ etc.}}{D^n(T_1 D + 1)(T_2 D + 1), \text{ etc.} + K(T_a D + 1)(T_b D + 1), \text{ etc.}}$$

By equating the denominator to zero we arrive at the *characteristic equation*:

$$D^n(T_1 D + 1)(T_2 D + 1), \text{ etc.} + K(T_a D + 1)(T_b D + 1), \text{ etc.} = 0$$

If any of the roots of this equation should contain positive real parts, this will mean that the transient response will contain exponentials with positive indices of the form $A\,e^{+t/T}$. The existence of such terms must give rise to an ever-increasing output and hence to an unstable system.

The Routh-Hurwitz criterion is a method of determining whether or not the characteristic equation has any roots containing real positive parts. The characteristic equation is written in the form

$$a_m D^m + a_{m-1} D^{m-1} + \ldots a_1 D + a_0 = 0$$

To ensure that there are no positive real roots and that the system is thus stable two conditions must be held.

1. All of the coefficients of the characteristic equation must have the same sign.
2. Each member of the sequence of determinants $R_1, R_2 \ldots R_{m-1}$ defined below must be positive.

$$R_1 = a_1 \quad R_2 = \begin{vmatrix} a_1 & a_0 \\ a_3 & a_2 \end{vmatrix} \quad R_3 = \begin{vmatrix} a_1 & a_0 & 0 \\ a_3 & a_2 & a_1 \\ a_5 & a_4 & a_3 \end{vmatrix}$$

The arrangement of coefficients shown below may serve as an aid to the memory for the construction of the determinants.

R_1	a_1	a_0	0	0	$0 \ldots$
R_2	a_3	a_2	a_1	a_0	$0 \ldots$
R_3	a_5	a_4	a_3	a_2	$a_1 \ldots$
R_4	a_7	a_6	a_5	a_4	$a_3 \ldots$
$\vdots$	$\vdots$	$\vdots$	$\vdots$	$\vdots$	$\vdots$

The array is formed by writing down the coefficients in rows by pairs in the order shown ending in a_0. One pair is shifted to the right in each successive row. When a_{m-1} first appears in the diagonal the process is stopped and the array is completed by writing zeros in the spaces. The determinant so formed will always be $m - 1$ square. Any coefficient absent in a particular characteristic equation is replaced by a zero. Thus a fifth-order equation does not contain coefficients a_7 and a_6 which appear in R_4, the highest order determinant to be considered.

Worked Example

A system has a characteristic equation given by

$$7D^4 + 3D^3 + 8D^2 + 5D + 9 = 0$$

determine whether the system is stable on closed loop.

Solution

The first condition which is that all the coefficients must have the same sign for stability is satisfied.

We also have

$$a_m = a_4 = 7$$

$$a_{m-1} = a_3 = 3$$

$$a_2 = 8$$

$$a_1 = 5$$

$$a_0 = 9$$

$$\therefore \qquad R_1 = a_1 = 5$$

$\therefore R_1$ is positive.

$$R_2 = \begin{vmatrix} a_1 & a_0 \\ a_3 & a_2 \end{vmatrix} = \begin{vmatrix} 5 & 9 \\ 3 & 8 \end{vmatrix} = 13$$

$\therefore R_2$ is positive.

$$R_3 = \begin{vmatrix} a_1 & a_0 & 0 \\ a_3 & a_2 & a_1 \\ 0 & a_4 & a_3 \end{vmatrix} = \begin{vmatrix} 5 & 9 & 0 \\ 3 & 8 & 5 \\ 0 & 7 & 3 \end{vmatrix} = -136$$

$\therefore R_3$ is negative.

The second condition which is that R_1, R_2 and R_3 must be positive for stability is thus not satisfied. Hence the system is unstable on closed loop.

The Routh-Hurwitz criterion gives a method of assessing the stability of a system directly from the transfer function. It is also possible to determine the permissible variation of the parameters of a system. The transfer function must be known in analytic form because the criterion cannot be applied if only experimental results are available. Furthermore, the method can only be used to tell whether or not the system will be stable on closed loop; it cannot be used to suggest methods of stabilizing an absolutely unstable system or of improving the performance of a relatively unstable system. Evaluation of the determinant becomes lengthy for fifth- or higher-order systems.

9.5.4 Types of System

Closed-loop control systems may be classified according to the nature of their steady-state errors. Consider a system whose open-loop transfer function is given by

$$\frac{\theta_0}{\epsilon} = \frac{K(T_a D + 1)(T_b D + 1), \text{ etc.}}{D^n(T_1 D + 1)(T_2 D + 1), \text{ etc.}} \tag{1}$$

The value of n gives the *type number* of the system. If $n = 0$, the system is 'type 0'; if $n = 1$, the system is 'type 1', etc. The nature of the steady-state errors existing in various types of system will be investigated. Let the numerator of the transfer function be X, and the denominator be Y, then $\dfrac{\theta_o}{\epsilon} = \dfrac{X}{Y}$, but $\theta_o = \theta_i - \epsilon$,

$$\therefore \quad \frac{\theta_i - \epsilon}{\epsilon} = \frac{X}{Y}$$

$$\therefore \quad \frac{\theta_i}{\epsilon} = \frac{X + Y}{Y}$$

or

$$\frac{\epsilon}{\theta_i} = \frac{Y}{X + Y} \tag{2}$$

(a) Type 0 system

When $n = 0$, we may combine equations (1) and (2) to give

$$\frac{\epsilon}{\theta_i} = \frac{(T_1 D + 1)(T_2 D + 1), \text{ etc.}}{K(T_a D + 1)(T_b D + 1), \text{ etc.} + (T_1 D + 1)(T_2 D + 1), \text{ etc.}}$$

If θ_i is a step-input, then the steady-state error may be found by putting $D = 0$, i.e.

$$\epsilon_{ss} = \frac{\theta_i}{K + 1}$$

If the input is a ramp, the error will increase steadily.

(b) Type 1 system

When $n = 1$, combining (1) and (2) gives

$$\frac{\epsilon}{\theta_i} = \frac{D(T_1 D + 1)(T_2 D + 1), \text{ etc.}}{K(T_a D + 1)(T_b D + 1), \text{ etc.} + D(T_1 D + 1)(T_2 D + 1), \text{ etc.}}$$

Thus if the input is a step, $\epsilon_{ss} = 0$; but if the input is a ramp defined by $D\theta_i = \omega_i$, then $\epsilon_{ss} = \omega_i/K$. A constant acceleration input gives rise to a steadily increasing error.

(c) Type 2 system

When $n = 2$, combining (1) and (2) gives

$$\frac{\epsilon}{\theta_i} = \frac{D^2(T_1 D + 1)(T_2 D + 1), \text{ etc.}}{K(T_a D + 1)(T_b D + 1), \text{ etc.} + D^2(T_1 D + 1)(T_2 D + 1), \text{ etc.}}$$

Thus if the input is a step or a ramp, $\epsilon_{ss} = 0$. If the input is a constant acceleration defined by $D^2 \theta = \alpha_i$ then $\epsilon_{ss} = \alpha_i/K$.

225

The subject matter introduced in this paragraph is summarized in tabular form below.

It is evident that the value of K in a particular type of system governs the magnitude of the steady-state error. The constant K is thus termed

Type	Open-loop Transfer Function θ_o/ϵ	Typical Responses	Applications
0	$\dfrac{K(T_a D + 1)(T_b D + 1), \text{etc.}}{(T_1 D + 1)(T_2 D + 1), \text{etc.}}$		Regulators where high positional accuracy is not vital and follow-up is not required
1	$\dfrac{K(T_a D + 1)(T_b D + 1), \text{etc.}}{D(T_1 D + 1)(T_2 D + 1), \text{etc.}}$		Positional servos where dynamic accuracy is not vital (e.g. instrument servos, recorders, fin-servos)
2	$\dfrac{K(T_a D + 1)(T_b D + 1), \text{etc.}}{D^2(T_1 D + 1)(T_2 D + 1), \text{etc.}}$		Positional servos where dynamic accuracy is vital (e.g. machine-tool control systems)

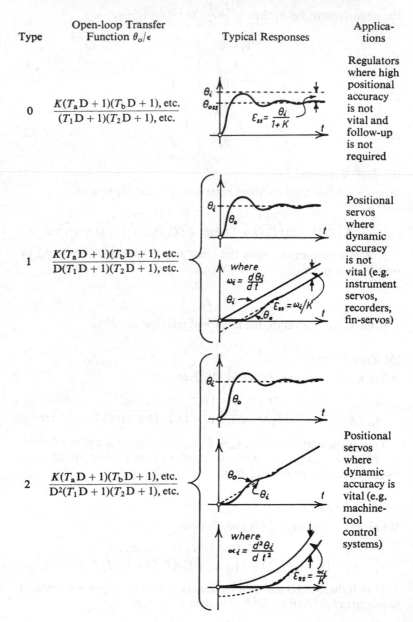

226

the 'error coefficient' or 'error constant'. In type 1 systems K is often called the '*velocity* error constant' and type 2 systems, the '*acceleration* error constant'.

9.6 Worked Example

A servomechanism has an armature-controlled d.c. motor driving a load of moment of inertia 1 kg m^2 through a frictionless 10:1 step-down gear-box. The field winding of the motor is supplied at constant current and the armature is connected to the armature of a d.c. generator which is driven at constant speed. The field winding of the d.c. generator is connected to the output terminals of a d.c. electronic amplifier the input of which is supplied from the error detector. The error detector is a potentiometer bridge with the slider of the input potentiometer mechanically coupled to a light handwheel and the slider of the output potentiometer coupled to the load.

The parameters of the system are as follows:

D.C. Motor: armature resistance is 1 Ω, generated e.m.f. per rad/s of armature velocity is 2 V, torque per armature ampere is 2 N m, moment of inertia is 10^{-2} kg m^2, viscous frictional torque is negligible.
D.C. Generator: armature resistance is 1 Ω, generated e.m.f. per field ampere is 2000 V, resistance of field winding is 1000 Ω, inductance of field winding is 10 H.
D.C. Amplifier: gain into open circuit is 100 V/V, output resistance is 1000 Ω.
Potentiometer Bridge: sensitivity is 10 V per radian.

(i) Draw a simplified circuit diagram for the system.
(ii) Draw a block diagram and determine the overall open-loop transfer function.
(iii) Determine the characteristic equation and thus determine whether or not the system is absolutely stable on closed loop.
(iv) Determine the velocity lag when the input shaft is moving with a steady angular velocity of 1 rev/min.

Solution

(i) A simplified circuit diagram is shown in Fig. 9.20.

(ii) A block diagram giving transfer functions is shown in Fig. 9.21.

For the potentiometer bridge the sensitivity K_b is 10 V/rad, i.e.

$$\frac{V_e}{\epsilon} = 10$$

For the electronic amplifier

$$\frac{V_a}{V_e} = 100$$

227

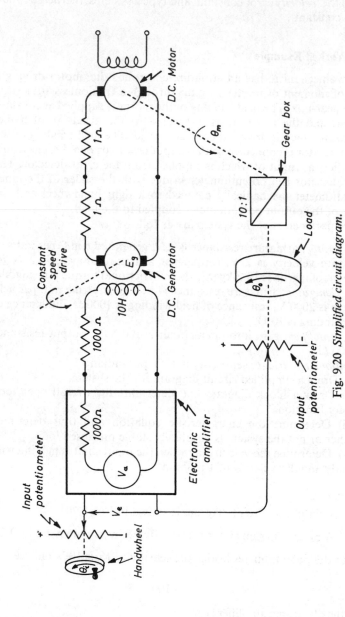

Fig. 9.20 *Simplified circuit diagram.*

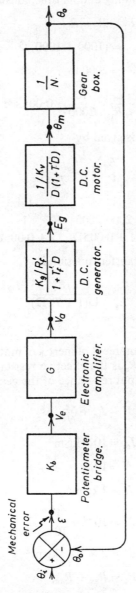

Fig. 9.21 *Computation of individual transfer functions.*

For the d.c. generator, the output resistance of the electronic amplifier must be taken into account when calculating the effective resistance of the field winding and its time constant, i.e.

$$R'_f = R_f + R_o$$

$$= (1000 + 1000)\,\Omega$$

$$= 2000\,\Omega$$

$$\therefore \qquad T'_f = \frac{L_f}{R'_f} = \frac{10}{2000} = 0{\cdot}005\,\text{sec}$$

The transfer function is given by

$$\frac{E_g}{V_a} = \frac{K_g/R'_f}{1 + T'_f\,\text{D}}$$

where $K_g = 2000$ V/A.

$$\therefore \qquad \frac{E_g}{V_a} = \frac{2000/2000}{1 + 0{\cdot}005\text{D}} = \frac{1}{1 + 0{\cdot}005\text{D}}$$

For the d.c. motor the transfer function is

$$\frac{\theta_m}{E_g} = \frac{1/K_v}{\text{D}(1 + T'\,\text{D})}$$

where $T' = \dfrac{J'\,R_a}{K_v K_t}$.

Here J' is the effective moment of inertia of motor plus load referred to the motor shaft and R_a is the effective resistance of the armature circuit, including the output resistance of the generator.

Thus
$$J' = J_m + \frac{J_L}{N^2}$$

where
$$J_m = 10^{-2}\,\text{kg m}^2$$

$$N = 10$$

and
$$J_L = 1\,\text{kg m}^2$$

$$\therefore \qquad J' = 10^{-2} + \frac{1}{10^2}$$

$$\therefore \qquad J' = 2 \times 10^{-2}\,\text{kg m}^2$$

Also
$$R_a = R_{ag} + R_{am}$$

$$= 1 + 1$$

$$= 2\,\Omega$$

Finally, $K_v = 2$ V per rad/s and $K_t = 2$ N m/A.

$$\therefore \quad T' = \frac{J' R_a}{K_v K_t} = \frac{2 \times 10^{-2} \times 2}{2 \times 2}$$

$$= 10^{-2} \sec$$

The transfer function of the motor is

$$\frac{\theta_m}{E_g} = \frac{1/K_v}{D(1 + T' D)}$$

$$= \frac{0 \cdot 5}{D(1 + 0 \cdot 01 D)}$$

The transfer function of the gear-box is given by

$$\frac{\theta_o}{\theta_m} = \frac{1}{N} = \frac{1}{10}$$

Now overall open-loop transfer function is given by

$$\frac{\theta_o}{\epsilon} = \frac{V_e}{\epsilon} \times \frac{V_a}{V_e} \times \frac{E_g}{V_a} \times \frac{\theta_m}{E_g} \times \frac{\theta_o}{\theta_m}$$

$$= 10 \times 100 \times \frac{1}{1 + 0 \cdot 005 D} \times \frac{0 \cdot 5}{D(1 + 0 \cdot 01 D)} \times \frac{1}{10}$$

$$= \frac{50}{D(1 + 0 \cdot 005 D)(1 + 0 \cdot 01 D)}$$

(iii) The closed-loop transfer function θ_o/θ_i is given by

$$\frac{\theta_o}{\theta_i} = \frac{\theta_o/\epsilon}{1 + \theta_o/\epsilon} = \frac{50}{D(1 + 0 \cdot 005 D)(1 + 0 \cdot 01 D) + 50}$$

Hence the characteristic equation is

$$D(1 + 0 \cdot 005 D)(1 + 0 \cdot 01 D) + 50 = 0$$

$$\therefore \quad 5 \times 10^{-5} D^3 + 1 \cdot 5 \times 10^{-2} D^2 + D + 50 = 0$$

All the coefficients of the characteristic equation have the same sign, thus satisfying the first condition for closed-loop stability.
We also have

$$a_0 = 50$$

$$a_1 = 1$$

$$a_2 = 1 \cdot 5 \times 10^{-2}$$

and $$a_3 = 5 \times 10^{-5}$$

231

$$\therefore \qquad R_1 = a_1 = 1$$

$\therefore R_1$ is positive.

$$R_2 = \begin{vmatrix} a_1 & a_o \\ a_3 & a_2 \end{vmatrix}$$

$$= \begin{vmatrix} 1 & 50 \\ 5 \times 10^{-5} & 1 \cdot 5 \times 10^{-2} \end{vmatrix}$$

$$= 1 \cdot 25 \times 10^{-2}$$

$\therefore R_2$ is positive.

Hence the second condition for stability is satisfied and the system must therefore be stable on closed loop.

(iv) The velocity lag ϵ_{ss} is given by

$$\epsilon_{ss} = \frac{\omega_i}{K}$$

where ω_i = input velocity = 1 rev/min = $\dfrac{2\pi}{60}$ rad/s, and K = velocity error constant = 50 sec^{-1}.

$$\therefore \qquad \epsilon_{ss} = \frac{2\pi}{60 \times 50} \text{ rad}$$

$$= 0 \cdot 00209 \text{ rad}$$

9.7 Analysis of Multiloop Systems

Systems having more than one feedback loop are termed *multiloop systems*. In order to assess their general performance and stability it is necessary to determine the characteristic equation which involves setting up the overall closed-loop transfer function. This can of course be determined by the successive application of two rules which have already been introduced but which will be restated here for convenience.

Rule (i): The overall transfer function of several cascaded elements is the product of the transfer functions of the individual elements (see §9.3).

This rule can be extended to allow direct computation of the inverse transfer function (i.e. the reciprocal of the overall transfer function), i.e. *the overall inverse transfer function of several cascaded elements in the product of the inverse transfer functions of the individual elements.*

Rule (ii): The overall transfer function H of a feedback arrangement comprising elements of overall transfer function H_1 in the *forward path with elements of overall transfer function H_2 in the feedback path is given by*

$$H = \frac{H_1}{1 + H_1 H_2} \quad \text{(see §9.5.1)}$$

This rule is more compact when written in terms of reciprocal transfer functions, i.e.

$$H^{-1} = H_1^{-1} + H_2$$

These rules are used to reduce sub-loops to their simplest form and to finally convert a multiloop system to a single-loop system. The method will be illustrated by means of a worked example.

Worked Example

Determine the overall closed-loop transfer function of the multiloop system shown in Fig. 9.22.

Also find the characteristic equation for the system and determine the range of values of K for which it will be stable assuming the transfer functions below.

$$H_1 = (1 + 0.5D)/D; \quad H_2 = K/(1 + D); \quad H_3 = 1/\{D(1 + 0.1D)\};$$

$$H_4 = 2D; \quad H_5 = 3D^2$$

Solution

Now using rule (i) $\dfrac{z}{\theta_o} = H_2^{-1} H_3^{-1}$.

Then applying rule (ii) $\dfrac{y}{\theta_o} = H_2^{-1} H_3^{-1} + H_4$.

Again using rule (i) $\dfrac{x}{\theta_o} = H_1^{-1}\{H_2^{-1} H_3^{-1} + H_4\}$.

Then applying rule (ii) $\dfrac{\epsilon}{\theta_o} = H_1^{-1}\{H_2^{-1} H_3^{-1} + H_4\} + H_5$.

Final application of rule (ii) around the major loop gives

$$\frac{\theta_i}{\theta_o} = H_1^{-1}\{H_2^{-1} H_3^{-1} + H_4\} + H_5 + 1$$

$$= H_1^{-1} H_2^{-1} H_3^{-1} + H_1^{-1} H_4 + H_5 + 1$$

This is the overall inverse closed-loop transfer function, thus

$$\frac{\theta_o}{\theta_i} = \{H_1^{-1} H_2^{-1} H_3^{-1} + H_1^{-1} H_4 + H_5 + 1\}^{-1}$$

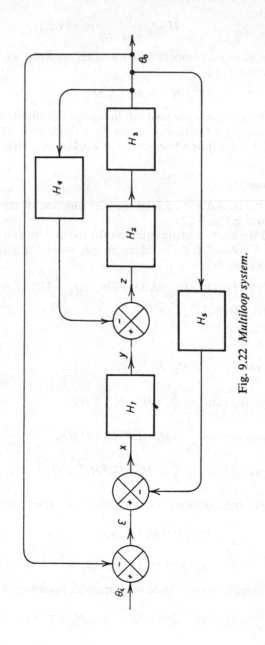

Fig. 9.22 *Multiloop system.*

Also $\dfrac{\theta_o}{\theta_i}(D) = \left\{ \dfrac{D^2(1 + D)(1 + 0{\cdot}1D)}{K(1 + 0{\cdot}5D)} + \dfrac{2D^2}{(1 + 0{\cdot}5D)} + 3D^2 + 1 \right\}^{-1}$

$\qquad = \left\{ \dfrac{\begin{array}{c} D^2(1 + D)(1 + 0{\cdot}1D) + 2KD^2 \\ + 3K(1 + 0{\cdot}5D)D^2 + K(1 + 0{\cdot}5D) \end{array}}{K(1 + 0{\cdot}5D)} \right\}^{-1}$

Thus

$$\{D^2(1 + D)(1 + 0{\cdot}1D) + 2KD^2 + 3K(1 + 0{\cdot}5D)D^2$$
$$+ K(1 + 0{\cdot}5D)\}\,\theta_o = K(1 + 0{\cdot}5D)\,\theta_i$$

The characteristic equation is thus

$$\{0{\cdot}1D^4 + (1{\cdot}1 + 1{\cdot}5K)D^3 + (1 + 5K)D^2 + 0{\cdot}5KD + K\} = 0$$

Let us now consider the various conditions for stability:

Condition (i): So long as $K > 0$ all coefficients will have same sign. The Routh determinants must be evaluated:

$$R_1 = 0{\cdot}5K$$

Condition (ii): $R_1 > 0$ so long as $K > 0$.

$$R_2 = \begin{vmatrix} a_1 & a_0 \\ a_3 & a_2 \end{vmatrix}$$

$$= \begin{vmatrix} 0{\cdot}5K & K \\ (1{\cdot}1 + 1{\cdot}5K) & (1 + 5K) \end{vmatrix}$$

$\therefore \qquad R_2 = 0{\cdot}5K(1 + 5K) - K(1{\cdot}1 + 1{\cdot}5K)$

$$= K(K - 0{\cdot}6)$$

Condition (iii): $R_2 > 0$ so long as $0 > K$ or $K > 0{\cdot}6$.

$$R_3 = \begin{vmatrix} a_1 & a_0 & 0 \\ a_3 & a_2 & a_1 \\ a_5 & a_4 & a_3 \end{vmatrix}$$

$$= \begin{vmatrix} 0{\cdot}5K & K & 0 \\ (1{\cdot}1 + 1{\cdot}5K) & (1 + 5K) & 0{\cdot}5K \\ 0 & 0{\cdot}1 & (1{\cdot}1 + 1{\cdot}5K) \end{vmatrix}$$

Expanding about bottom row gives

$$R_3 = -0{\cdot}1 \begin{vmatrix} 0{\cdot}5K & 0 \\ (1{\cdot}1 + 1{\cdot}5K) & 0{\cdot}5K \end{vmatrix}$$

$$+ (1{\cdot}1 + 1{\cdot}5K) \begin{vmatrix} 0{\cdot}5K & K \\ (1{\cdot}1 + 1{\cdot}5K) & 1 + 5K \end{vmatrix}$$

i.e. $R_3 = -0.025K^2 + (1.1 + 1.5K)\{0.5K(1 + 5K) - K(1.1 + 1.5K)\}$

$= K\{1.5K^2 + 0.175K - 0.66\}$

Condition (iv): $R_3 > 0$ for $K > 0.6075$, and for $0 > K > -0.724$.

We must inspect all four of the conditions to ensure that they are all satisfied. Inspection shows that all four are in fact satisfied for $K > 0.6075$; i.e. system will be stable for $K > 0.6075$.

9.8 Conclusion

The transfer function of an element has been defined and the method for its determination has been illustrated by considering a number of examples of elements in popular use. Methods have been described for determining the overall open- and closed-loop transfer functions of single and multiloop systems containing non-interacting and interacting elements. This has led to the classification of control systems according to their type number and to the concept of the error constant The manipulation of the closed-loop transfer function has also led to the formation of the characteristic equation from which the stability of a system may be assessed by application of the Routh-Hurwitz criterion.

EXAMPLES FOR SOLUTION

1. A type 1 control system with unity feedback has two exponential lags both having time constants of one second.
    (i) Determine the open-loop transfer function of the system in terms of the velocity error constant K and the operator D.
    (ii) Determine the characteristic equation of the system and use the Routh stability criterion to calculate the limiting value of K consistent with closed-loop stability.
2. (*a*) Derive an expression for the transfer function of a d.c. generator having a field winding of time constant T and d.c. voltage gain into open-circuit K.
    (*b*) Three identical d.c. generators each having time constant T and voltage gain K are connected in cascade. The first unit in the chain has its field winding supplied by an electronic amplifier which has a voltage gain μ and negligible output resistance. The arrangement is connected as a voltage regulator with 100% negative feedback.
    Using the Routh criterion or any other technique, determine the limiting value of μ consistent with stable operation. It may be assumed that the armature resistance of the generators is negligible.
3. Use the Routh criterion to determine the conditions which will ensure that a second-order system with integral control is stable.
4. A hydraulic servo is designed for the control of linear position x_0 of the slide of a machine tool in accordance with the electrical command voltage v_1. The output element is a hydraulic actuator with negligible load reaction. A feedback signal v_0 equal to 100 volts per metre of output motion is picked off by means of a potentiometer and compared with v_1; the error voltage $v_e = v_i - v_0$ is used to drive the input of an electronic amplifier of effectively infinite input and output resist-

ance. The output of the amplifier is connected to the field windings of a torque motor whose shaft is linked via a pinion and rack to a spool valve which controls the rate of flow of oil to the hydraulic actuator.

Further particulars of the system are:

Electronic Amplifier and Torque Motor
Transfer function of combination

$$\frac{x_v}{v}(D) = \frac{K}{D^2 + 80D + 2500}\text{ m/V},$$

where x_v is valve motion, and K is a constant.

Hydraulic Valve and Actuator

$$\frac{x_o}{x_v}(D) = \frac{20}{D}\text{ m/m}$$

(i) Draw a block diagram of the arrangement.

(ii) Find the overall open-loop and closed-loop transfer functions and determine the value of K which will just cause instability on closed loop.

5. A position control system consists of a field-controlled motor driving a load of inertia 1 kg m² through an ideal step-down velocity gear-box of ratio 20:1. The armature current of the motor is maintained constant and the field winding is supplied from an electronic amplifier which receives the error voltage at its input. The error detector is a mechanical differential with a potentiometer pick-off, the sensitivity being 100 V per radian of error.

Other parameters are:

Electronic Amplifier: gain into open-circuit 1000V/V; output resistance $2\,k\Omega$; input resistance effectively infinite.

Motor: resistance of field winding $2\,k\Omega$; inductance of field winding 2 H; moment of inertia of armature $2\cdot5 \times 10^{-3}$ kg m²; viscous friction 5×10^{-3} N m per rad/s of armature velocity; torque 2 N m/A field current.

(i) Draw a simplified circuit diagram and a block diagram of the system.

(ii) Determine the overall open-loop and closed-loop transfer functions.

(iii) Use the Routh criterion to prove that the system is stable on closed loop.

(iv) Determine the velocity lag for an input velocity of 10 rev/min.

6. Determine the closed-loop transfer function θ_o/θ_i of the system shown in Fig. 9.23.

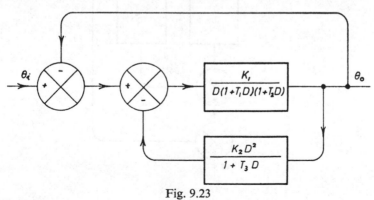

Fig. 9.23

7. Determine an expression for θ_o/θ_i for the system shown in Fig. 9.24.

237

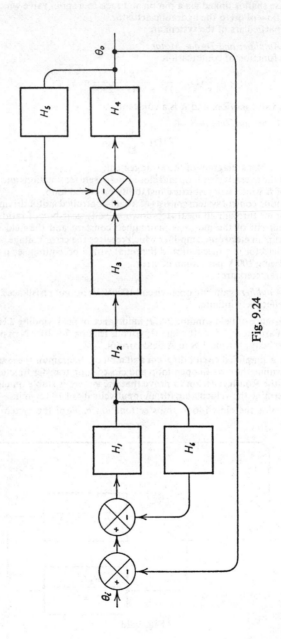

Fig. 9.24

Chapter Ten

Introduction To Frequency Response Methods

10.1 Introduction

The concept of frequency response testing has previously been considered in relation to the second-order servomechanism (§8.9). In these considerations the connections between transient and frequency response have been introduced. For higher order systems frequency response methods are extremely valuable for a number of reasons some of which are enumerated below:

(i) Even when the open-loop transfer function of a system is known precisely in analytical terms, direct design and adjustment of performance is extremely complex in the time domain. The effect of the variation of parameter values on the step response of a system is difficult to assess. However, the effect of variation of parameter values on the frequency response is relatively easy to assess. Design in the frequency domain is thus fairly simple; translation of the frequency response to the transient response where necessary may be performed either approximately using the second-order correlations given in §8.9.3 or more accurately by the method described in chapter 11 of reference 20 (the method described does, unfortunately, involve formidable labour and since the approximate method is so often successful it is recommended).

(ii) Again, when the open-loop transfer function of a system can be determined directly from the specifications of the hardware, the Routh-Hurwitz stability criterion can only be invoked to tell us whether or not the system will be stable on closed loop. It does not tell us either how stable the system will be or how to proceed with stabilization should this be necessary. In the frequency domain a different stability criterion is available, namely the Nyquist criterion, and this not only specifies the absolute stability of a system but also indicates the relative stability and provides implicitly information regarding procedures for stabilization.

(iii) In many instances it is not possible to use analysis in order to specify the transfer function of a system in advance. Frequently the control engineer is confronted with several pieces of hardware which are to be interconnected and made into a closed-loop system possessing certain specifications. Whilst the general form of the open-loop transfer function may sometimes be determined it is often the case that the parameters required to calculate the time constants and error coefficient are unknown. All the information required to compute a transfer function can be determined experimentally by means of a frequency response test. There are a number of pieces of equipment available commercially which make such tests quite easy to perform in practice.

The step-response test is also easy and quick to perform but the extraction of the transfer function from the step-response is an extremely laborious procedure. With the frequency response data extraction is simple.

(iv) Frequency response tests can be performed on open loop, thus systems which are unstable on closed loop can be tested just as easily as those which are stable because it is the existence of the feedback path which normally causes instability.

10.2 The Nyquist Diagram

When the error signal ϵ takes the form $\epsilon = \hat{\epsilon}\sin\omega t$, the output signal θ_o from a linear system has, in general, the form $\theta_o = \hat{\theta}_o\sin(\omega t + \phi)$; here $\hat{\epsilon}$ and $\hat{\theta}_o$ are the peak values of the error and output signals respectively, ω is the angular frequency, t is time and ϕ is a phase angle.

It is very convenient to represent these two signals as complex numbers on an Argand diagram as shown in Fig. 10.1.

It is more convenient still to 'normalize' this basic diagram to 'unity error'; that is to draw the vector θ_o/ϵ and then to consider the

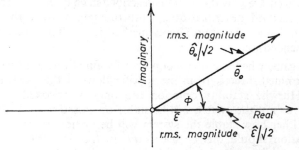

Fig. 10.1 *Vector representation of error ϵ and output θ_o.*

r.m.s. error signal to be of unit length and always lying along the positive real axis. Fig. 10.2 shows the revised vector diagram.

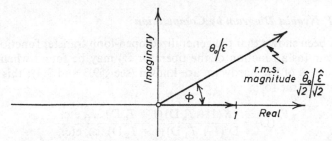

Fig. 10.2 *Normalized representation of* θ_o/ϵ.

It is standard practice to use r.m.s. values of signal quantities as opposed to peak values.

The 'open-loop frequency response' of a system may be represented by a series of such normalized 'vectors', each one at a different frequency as shown in Fig. 10.3. By joining the extremities of the

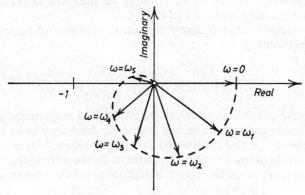

Fig. 10.3 *The frequency locus* θ_o/ϵ.

vectors we thus obtain a *frequency locus*. A diagram of this kind is usually called a **Nyquist diagram** and from it we may judge the absolute and relative stability of the system when the loop is closed.

10.3 Obtaining the Nyquist Diagram

The Nyquist diagram can be obtained in two ways:

(i) By computation when the open-loop transfer function is known.

241

(ii) By experiment when the open-loop transfer function is unknown.

10.3.1 Nyquist Diagram by Computation

It has been shown that the generalized open-loop transfer function of a system (as a function of the operator D) may be found when the parameters of the hardware are known (see §§9.3 and 9.4); this can be put into the form

$$\frac{\theta_o}{\epsilon}(D) = \frac{K(1 + T_a D)(1 + T_b D) \ldots, \text{etc.}}{D^n(1 + T_1 D)(1 + T_2 D) \ldots, \text{etc.}}$$

where K is an 'error constant', n is the number of pure integrations in the forward path, and T_a, T_b, T_1, T_2, etc. are the time constants. Systems with $n = 0$ are referred to as 'type 0', when $n = 1$, the system is 'type 1', and so on. In many practical systems a factor of the form $(k_1 D^2 + k_2 D + 1)$ may also appear in the denominator or the numerator of the transfer function. If the error signal is sinusoidal the generalized transfer function can be made to give the steady-state vector ratio θ_o/ϵ simply by substituting $j\omega$ wherever D occurs (the technique has been explained in §5.3.5).

Thus the open-loop frequency response may, in general, be described by the relationship

$$\frac{\theta_o}{\epsilon}(j\omega) = \frac{K(1 + j\omega T_a)(1 + j\omega T_b) \ldots, \text{etc.}}{(j\omega)^n(1 + j\omega T_1)(1 + j\omega T_2) \ldots, \text{etc.}}$$

It is quite possible to calculate the phases and magnitudes of such an expression for various values of angular frequency ω so long as the values of K, n and the time constants are known. Where possible it is advisable to use a digital computer to do the arithmetic; when a computer is not available it is advantageous to tabulate the arithmetic in order to save time and reduce the possibility of error.

The range of angular frequencies which must be covered in order to obtain a complete diagram depends on the values of the time constants and the number of integrations. The range required for most servomechanisms is for ω lying between 0·1 and 100 rad/s. These are usually extreme values and for many servomechanisms the interesting region (which is near where the frequency locus crosses the negative real axis) is between 1 and 10 rad/s. For process control systems the angular frequencies involved may be very much lower. The number of frequencies which need be used to obtain the locus should be such as to produce evenly-spaced vectors around the locus. The example below will serve as an introduction to this type of problem.

242

Worked Example

Draw the Nyquist diagram for a type 1 control system having two exponential lags in the forward path of time constants 0·2 sec and 0·05 sec respectively assuming the velocity error constant to be 10 sec^{-1}.

Solution

Now from the information provided the open-loop frequency response function is given by

$$\frac{\theta_o}{\epsilon}(j\omega) = \frac{10}{j\omega(1 + j\omega 0·2)(1 + j\omega 0·05)}$$

Trial will show that the important values of ω are between 0·5 and 20 rad/s. The arithmetic is tabulated and the key to the table is as below.

The phase angle of the function $\angle \theta_o/\epsilon$ is given by

$$\angle \theta_o/\epsilon = -(90 + \alpha + \beta) \text{ degrees}$$

where the constant 90° is due to $\angle j\omega$, and

$$\alpha = \angle(1 + j\omega 0·2) = \tan^{-1} 0·2\omega \text{ degrees}$$

and $$\beta = \angle(1 + j\omega 0·05) = \tan^{-1} 0·05\omega \text{ degrees}$$

The magnitude is given by

$$|\theta_o/\epsilon| = \frac{10}{\omega AB}$$

where $$\omega = |j\omega|$$

$$A = |1 + j\omega 0·2| = \sqrt{\{1 + (0·2\omega)^2\}}$$

$$B = |1 + j\omega 0·05| = \sqrt{\{1 + (0·05\omega)^2\}}$$

ω (rad/s)	α	β	$\angle \theta_o/\epsilon$	A	B	$\left\lvert\dfrac{\theta_o}{\epsilon}\right\rvert$
0·5	5·7°	1·4°	−97·1°	1·005	1·000	19·9
1·0	11·3°	2·9°	−104·2°	1·020	1·001	9·79
2·0	21·8°	5·7°	−117·5°	1·077	1·005	4·62
3·0	30·9°	8·5°	−129·4°	1·166	1·011	2·82
4·0	38·6°	11·3°	−139·9°	1·281	1·020	1·91
5·0	45·0°	14·0°	−149·0°	1·414	1·031	1·37
6·0	50·2°	16·7°	−156·9°	1·562	1·044	1·02
7·0	54·5°	19·3°	−163·8°	1·720	1·059	0·78
8·0	58·0°	21·8°	−169·8°	1·887	1·077	0·615
10·0	63·5°	26·6°	−180·1°	2·236	1·118	0·400
20·0	75·9°	45·0°	−210·9°	4·123	1·414	0·0858

The Nyquist diagram representing these results is shown in Fig. 10.4. The complete diagram is shown in Fig. 10.4 (*a*).

The magnitude θ_o/ϵ at any particular frequency is often also called the gain. An enlargement of the locus near the origin [Fig. 10.4 (*b*)] shows *gain crossover* which is the point on the locus where the gain is unity. The point on the locus where the phase is $-180°$ is called *phase crossover*.

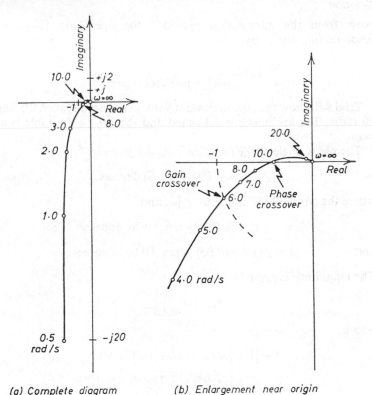

(a) Complete diagram   (b) Enlargement near origin

Fig. 10.4 *Nyquist diagram for* $\theta_o/\epsilon(j\omega) = 10/\{j\omega(1 + j\omega0\cdot2)(1 + j\omega0\cdot05)\}$.

10.3.2 Nyquist Diagram by Experiment

The majority of commercial test equipment is electronic or electro-mechanical and consists basically of a variable low frequency signal generator to excite the system and a phase-sensitive voltmeter to measure the steady-state response. Various firms in the U.K. supply complete sets which make the measurement possible. The devices which these firms market all possess advantages and disadvantages but they make both open- and closed-loop testing a fairly simple procedure.

The arrangement for open-loop testing is shown in Fig. 10.5.

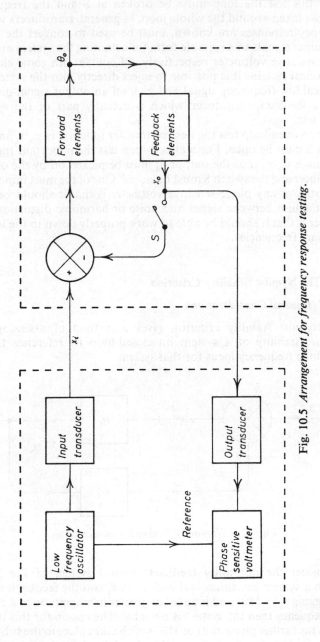

Fig. 10.5 *Arrangement for frequency response testing.*

245

For this test the loop must be broken at S and the frequency response taken around the whole loop. In general, transducers whose frequency responses are known, must be used to convert the input and output signals to a suitable form for actuating the system and the phase sensitive voltmeter respectively. Of course with some electro-mechanical systems it is possible to inject directly into the system an electrical low-frequency signal and pick off an output signal directly from a feedback transducer which is actually part of the system under test.

For an open-loop test the desired transfer function is x_o/x_i and the switch S must be open. For a closed-loop test the important transfer function is θ_o/x_i, thus the output θ_o must be picked off by the output transducer and the switch S must be closed. One of the most important properties of any phase-sensitive voltmeter is that it should be able to distinguish between signal and noise or harmonic distortion and another is that it should be able to work properly down to the lowest necessary frequencies.

10.4 The Nyquist Stability Criterion

10.4.1 General Considerations

The Nyquist stability criterion gives a method of assessing the absolute stability of a system on closed-loop by reference to the open-loop frequency locus for that system.

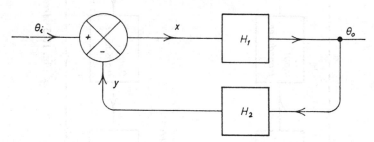

Fig. 10.6 *Non-unity feedback control system.*

Consider the non-unity feedback control system of Fig. 10.6. If such a system has sinusoidal excitation θ_i and the feedback signal y is lagging θ_i by 180° and is equal or greater in magnitude to it at any one frequency then the system is unstable. The reason for this is that due to the further phase shift of 180° which takes place in the subtracting device the signal reinforces the signal θ_i, thus causing an ever increasing build-up in the magnitude of oscillation. The Nyquist stability criterion[21] presents this fact in a rigorous mathematical form. Stability may therefore be assessed by viewing the frequency locus of the open-loop transfer function $H_1 H_2$ for the system in relation to the point of phase crossover and its proximity to the point $(-1, j0)$. Fig. 10.7 shows three open-loop frequency response loci.

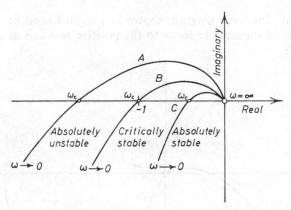

Fig. 10.7 *Illustrating the Nyquist criterion.*

We see that for locus C at an angular frequency ω_c the phase shift is $-180°$ but the gain is less than unity and thus oscillations will not build up on closed loop. The system is thus stable on closed loop.

For locus B at angular frequency ω_c the phase shift is $-180°$ and the gain is unity. Thus on closed loop the system will just be unstable. However, for locus A the gain crossover occurs for a gain well beyond unity and the system will be grossly unstable on closed loop.

10.4.2 *Method of Applying the Nyquist Criterion*

The common form of the Nyquist stability criterion involves one major assumption that is frequently valid in the simpler forms of control system, namely that the transfer function $H_1 H_2$ is by itself stable. When this assumption is valid the Nyquist criterion is applied as follows:

(i) Plot the open-loop frequency locus $H_1(j\omega) H_2(j\omega)$ for all values of ω from 0 to $+\infty$; when the zero frequency gain lies at infinity, the locus must be closed with a circular locus of infinite radius centred on the origin and moving clockwise from the positive real axis until it meets the frequency locus.

(ii) If the system is absolutely stable on closed-loop the complete frequency locus will not enclose the point $-1, j0$.

Now consider the worked example of §10.3.1 in which the frequency locus for a system having a transfer function

$$\frac{\theta_o}{\epsilon}(j\omega) = \frac{10}{j\omega(1 + j\omega0\cdot2)(1 + j\omega0\cdot05)}$$

is plotted. The locus diagram shown in Fig. 10.4 must be extended by means of the circular locus to the positive real axis as shown in Fig. 10.8.

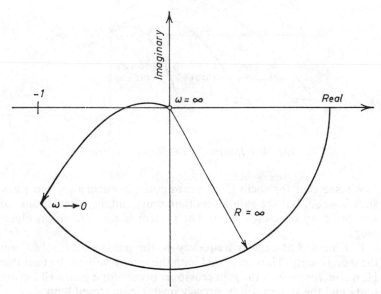

Fig. 10.8 *Nyquist diagram for* $10/\{j\omega(1 + j\omega0\cdot2)(1 + j\omega0\cdot05)\}$.

The point $(-1,j0)$ is not enclosed thus the system must be stable on closed-loop.

Let us investigate the effect of increasing the error coefficient from 10 to 50. The new Nyquist diagram is shown in Fig. 10.9.

The point $-1, j0$ is now enclosed and the system must thus be unstable on closed loop.

10.4.3 Comparison between Nyquist Criterion and Routh Criterion

It is of interest at this stage to compare the results given by the Nyquist criterion with those indicated by the Routh criterion (chapter 9) for the same transfer function.

248

Consider the transfer function

$$\frac{\theta_o}{\epsilon}(D) = \frac{K}{D(1 + 0 \cdot 2D)(1 + 0 \cdot 05D)}$$

Now

$$\frac{\theta_o}{\theta_i} = \frac{\theta_o/\epsilon}{1 + \theta_o/\epsilon} = \frac{K}{D(1 + 0 \cdot 2D)(1 + 0 \cdot 05D) + K}$$

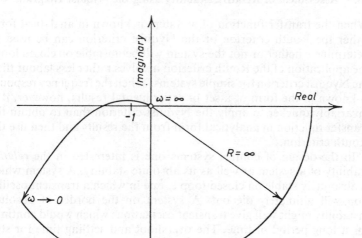

Fig. 10.9 *Nyquist diagram for* $50/\{j\omega(1 + j\omega 0 \cdot 2)(1 + j\omega 0 \cdot 05)\}$.

The characteristic equation is thus

$$D(1 + 0 \cdot 2D)(1 + 0 \cdot 05D) + K = 0$$

or

$$0 \cdot 01D^3 + 0 \cdot 25D^2 + D + K = 0$$

thus $a_3 = 0 \cdot 01$, $a_2 = 0 \cdot 25$, $a_1 = 1 \cdot 00$, and $a_0 = K$.

Hence, assuming that K is positive, the first condition of the Routh criterion that for closed-loop stability all coefficients must have the same sign is satisfied.

Also, $R_1 = a_1 = 1 \cdot 00$; therefore R_1 is positive.

$$R_2 = \begin{vmatrix} a_1 & a_0 \\ a_3 & a_2 \end{vmatrix}$$

$$= \begin{vmatrix} 1 & K \\ 0 \cdot 01 & 0 \cdot 25 \end{vmatrix}$$

$$= 0 \cdot 25 - 0 \cdot 01K$$

249

Thus for $K = 10$, R_2 is positive and the system must be stable on closed loop. For $K = 50$, however, R_2 is negative and the system must be unstable on closed loop. These findings are in accordance with the Nyquist criterion.

10.5 Assessment of Relative Stability using the Nyquist Diagram

When the transfer function of a system is known in analytical form either the Routh criterion or the Nyquist criterion can be used to determine whether or not the system will be unstable on closed loop; the application of the Routh criterion involves rather less labour than the Nyquist criterion for simple systems. When the frequency response is known in the form of a set of experimental results, however, it is invariably quicker to apply the Nyquist criterion than to obtain the transfer function in analytical form from the results and then use the Routh criterion.

In the design of control systems one is interested in the *relative* stability of a system as well as its absolute stability. A system which is absolutely stable on closed loop is one in which a transient oscillation will ultimately die out. A system on the border of absolute instability might well give transient oscillations which would continue for a long period of time. The overshoot and settling time for step inputs would both be excessive and the system would be useless for most practical purposes. A system thus has to be *relatively stable* in practice as well as absolutely stable. A relatively stable system is one in which the magnitude and duration of transient oscillations are not excessive. In systems other than those governed by first- and second-order differential equations it is usually a laborious process to determine by solution of the differential equations whether or not a system will be relatively stable. It is here where frequency response methods are most powerful. The Nyquist diagram gives methods of assessing both the absolute and the relative stability of a system.

Consider Fig. 10.10 which shows a typical open-loop frequency locus. Observation will show that the system is absolutely stable on closed loop. However, the relative stability depends on how near the frequency locus approaches the point $(-1, j0)$. When it is well away from this point it will be relatively stable. It can approach the locus in two ways. The first way is for the value of x to become near to unity and the second way is for the angle ϕ to become near zero. Thus for good relative stability x should not have a value near unity and ϕ should not have a value near zero. Control engineers often employ these concepts in order to assess relative stability and in this context they define *gain margin* and *phase margin* as practical measures of relative stability.

The *gain margin* is defined as the number of *decibels* by which the magnitude of the open-loop frequency response falls short of unity when the phase angle is 180°. Numerically the gain margin is $20\log_{10}(1/x)$ dB.

The phase margin is the angle by which the phase of the open-loop frequency response falls short of −180° when the modulus is unity. Referring to Fig. 10.10 the phase margin is ϕ.

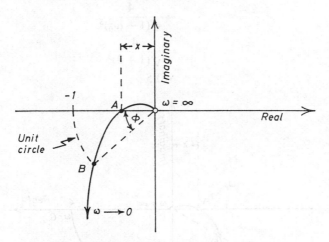

Fig. 10.10 *Typical open-loop frequency locus.*

A useful rule-of-thumb which is generally applicable to control systems is that for adequate closed-loop stability the gain margin should not be less than about 10 dB and the phase margin should not be less than about 50°. These values must of course only be used as working guides.

Worked Example

A type 0 control system has three exponential lags in the forward path each having a time constant of 1 sec; the error coefficient is 4. Determine whether or not the system will be stable on closed loop and discuss the relative stability.

Solution

The open-loop transfer function $H(j\omega) = 4/(1 + j\omega)^3$. The open-loop frequency response is sketched in Fig. 10.11.

A complete plot is quite unnecessary in this example because all the time constants are equal and thus at any particular frequency each lag contributes equally to both the gain and the phase.

Firstly the value of x must be found. The locus will cross the

251

negative real axis when the phase is $-180°$. Each lag must thus contribute $60°$ at the angular frequency ω_p, i.e.

$$\tan^{-1}\omega_p = 60°$$

$$\therefore \qquad \omega_p = \sqrt{3}\,\text{rad/s}$$

Now
$$x = |H(j\omega_p)|$$
$$= \frac{4}{\sqrt{(1 + \omega_p^2)^3}}$$
$$= \frac{4}{\sqrt{(1 + 3)^3}}$$
$$= 0.5$$

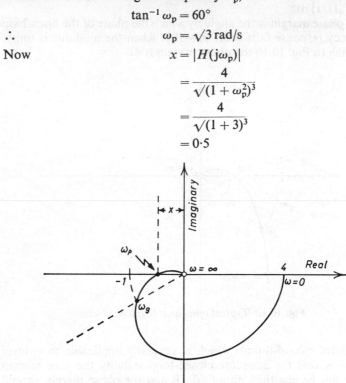

Fig. 10.11 *Frequency locus for worked example.*

Thus the frequency locus will not encircle the point $(-1, j0)$ and the system will be *absolutely stable* on closed loop.

The gain margin is $20\log_{10}(1/0.5)$, i.e. 6 dB.

The phase margin ϕ may be found when ω_g is known; ω_g is the angular frequency when the gain is unity; i.e.

$$|H(j\omega_g)| = 1 = \frac{4}{\sqrt{(1 + \omega_g^2)^3}}$$

$$\therefore \qquad 1 = \frac{16}{(1 + \omega_g^2)^3}$$

or
$$(1 + \omega_g^2)^3 = 16$$

$$\therefore \qquad 1 + \omega_g^2 = 2.52$$

$$\therefore \qquad \omega_g^2 = 1.52$$

$$\therefore \qquad \omega_g = 1.23\,\text{rad/s}$$

When ω is 1·23 rad/s each lag contributes a phase lag of 50·9°; hence total lag is 152·7° when the gain is unity. The phase margin ϕ is thus $180° - 152·7°$; i.e. $\phi = 27·3°$.

The gain margin of 6 dB is rather inadequate compared with the rule-of-thumb value of 10 dB. The phase margin of 27.3° is much less than the rule-of-thumb value of 50°. It may therefore be concluded that although the system is absolutely stable, its relative stability will be poor. That is to say its transient response will be very underdamped.

10.6 Analytical Determination of the Shapes of Frequency Loci

10.6.1 General

When the open-loop transfer function of a system is known it is possible to obtain much valuable information regarding the shape of the frequency locus by algebraic analysis rather than by the lengthy and laborious process of arithmetic computation. Even when arithmetic computation is necessary for design purposes it is often useful to use some elements of algebraic analysis prior to computation in order to assess the general shape and important frequency ranges.

The general shape of a frequency locus may usually be assessed simply by observing the open-loop transfer function

$$H(j\omega) = \frac{K(1 + j\omega T_a)(1 + j\omega T_b) \ldots, \text{etc.}}{(j\omega)^n (1 + j\omega T_1)(1 + j\omega T_2) \ldots, \text{etc.}}$$

The following rules can then be used to determine roughly the shape of the Nyquist diagram for positive values of frequency.

(i) The value of n governs the quadrant of the Nyquist diagram in which the frequency locus terminates for positive frequencies as the frequency tends to zero. For $n = 0$ the locus terminates on the positive real axis at K. For $n = 1$, the locus tends to infinity in the third quadrant, for $n = 2$ the locus tends to infinity in the second quadrant, for $n = 3$ the locus tends to infinity in the first quadrant (Fig. 10.12). This is only strictly true in the absence of leads.

(ii) For transfer functions representing physically realizable systems the total order of the denominator must always exceed the total order of the numerator. The frequency locus must thus always terminate at the origin as the frequency approaches infinity.

(iii) The value of K does not affect the general shape of the locus; it merely alters the scale of the plot.

(iv) In the absence of leading time constants the number of lagging time constants (T_1, T_2, etc.) is the total number of quadrants through which the locus must pass as the frequency moves from zero to infinity.

253

(v) The effect of leading time constants cannot be predicted so readily because it is their magnitude compared with those of the lagging time constants which controls the behaviour of the locus.

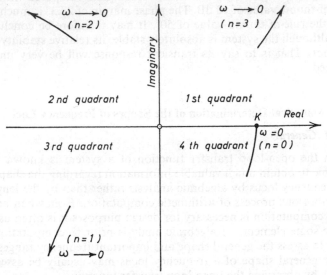

Fig. 10.12 *The effect on the frequency locus as $\omega \to 0$ of the type number n.*

Worked Example

Sketch a rough Nyquist diagram representing the transfer function $K/\{(j\omega)^2(1 + j\omega T_1)(1 + j\omega T_2)\}$.

Solution

Now $n = 2$, therefore locus tends to infinity in the second quadrant as $\omega \to 0$. As there are two lags the frequency locus must pass through

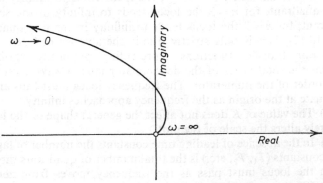

Fig. 10.13 *Frequency locus for $K/\{(j\omega)^2(1 + j\omega T_1)(1 + j\omega T_2)\}$.*

two quadrants before reaching the origin. The sketch is shown in Fig. 10.13.

10.6.2 Analytical Approach

Nyquist Diagram for a Type 1 System with Two Simple Lags

A great many position control systems used in practice are type 1 and very often there are two simple lags in the forward path. Such systems yield an open-loop transfer function of the form

$$H(j\omega) = \frac{K}{j\omega(1 + j\omega T_1)(1 + j\omega T_2)}$$

$$= \frac{-jK(1 - j\omega T_1)(1 - j\omega T_2)}{\omega(1 + \omega^2 T_1^2)(1 + \omega^2 T_2^2)}$$

$$= \frac{-K\omega(T_1 + T_2) - jK(1 - \omega^2 T_1 T_2)}{\omega(1 + \omega^2 T_1^2)(1 + \omega^2 T_2^2)}$$

If R is the real part of $H(j\omega)$ and I is the imaginary part, then

$$R = \frac{-K(T_1 + T_2)}{(1 + \omega^2 T_1^2)(1 + \omega^2 T_2^2)}$$

and

$$I = \frac{-K(1 - \omega^2 T_1 T_2)}{\omega(1 + \omega^2 T_1^2)(1 + \omega^2 T_2^2)}$$

as $\omega \to 0$, $R \to -K(T_1 + T_2)$, i.e. referring to Fig. 10.14, $a = -K(T_1 + T_2)$.

The value of ω for which I is zero gives the value of angular frequency for which the frequency locus crosses the real axis.

I is zero when $1 - \omega^2 T_1 T_2 = 0$, hence $\omega = 1/\sqrt{(T_1 T_2)}$.

Hence substituting this value of ω in the general equation for R will give b in Fig. 10.14, i.e.

$$b = \frac{-K(T_1 + T_2)}{(1 + T_1^2/T_1 T_2)(1 + T_2^2/T_1 T_2)}$$

$$= \frac{-KT_1 T_2}{T_1 + T_2}$$

Various useful pieces of information can be determined from the results of the above analysis:

(i) It is evident that so long as $b > -1$ the system will be absolutely stable on closed loop, i.e. the system will be absolutely stable so long as

$$\frac{KT_1 T_2}{T_1 + T_2} < 1$$

255

(ii) If K is increased until $\dfrac{KT_1T_2}{T_1+T_2} \geqslant 1$ the system will become unstable and will oscillate on closed loop with an angular frequency of $1/\sqrt{(T_1T_2)}$

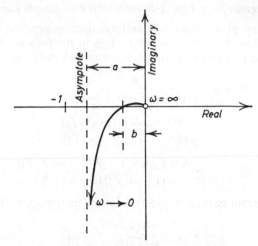

Fig. 10.14 *Nyquist diagram representing*
$\theta_o/\epsilon(j\omega) = K/\{j\omega(1+j\omega T_1)(1+j\omega T_2)\}.$

(iii) For a stable system the gain margin is equal to

$$20\log_{10}\left(\frac{T_1+T_2}{KT_1T_2}\right) \text{ decibels}$$

(iv) As $\omega \to 0$ the frequency locus approaches an asymptote parallel to the imaginary axis and distance $K(T_1+T_2)$ to the left of it.

A simple generalization makes this final observation applicable to any type 1 system.

$$H(j\omega) = \frac{K(1+j\omega T_a)(1+j\omega T_b)\dots, \text{etc.}}{j\omega(1+j\omega T_1)(1+j\omega T_2)\dots, \text{etc.}}$$

rationalizing gives

$$H(j\omega) = \frac{-jK(1+j\omega T_a)(1+j\omega T_b)\dots(1-j\omega T_1)(1-j\omega T_2)\dots}{\omega(1+\omega^2 T_1^2)(1+\omega^2 T_2^2)\dots}$$

Then the limit of the real part as $\omega \to 0$, is given by

$$a = K(T_a + T_b \dots - T_1 - T_2 \dots)$$

Thus for a type 1 system containing simple leads and lags, the frequency locus approaches, at very low frequencies, an asymptote parallel to the imaginary axis and specified by

$$a = K(T_a + T_b \ldots - T_1 - T_2)$$

Use of the asymptote can reduce the labour of computing the Nyquist diagram quite considerably.

Nyquist Diagram for a Type 1 System with a Quadratic Lag

An interesting form of transfer function given by some practical systems contains a *quadratic lag*. A quadratic lag has the form

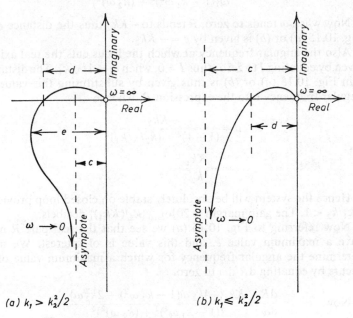

(a) $k_1 > k_2^2/2$ (b) $k_1 \leqslant k_2^2/2$

Fig. 10.15 *Nyquist diagram representing*
$H(j\omega) = K/[j\omega\{k_1(j\omega)^2 + k_2 j\omega + 1\}]$.

$1/\{k_1(j\omega)^2 + k_2 j\omega + 1\}$. A type 1 system containing just one quadratic lag has an open-loop transfer function given by

$$H(j\omega) = \frac{K}{j\omega\{k_1(j\omega)^2 + k_2 j\omega + 1\}}$$

The shape of the Nyquist diagram representing this transfer function can take two basic forms depending on the relative values k_1 and k_2 as shown in Fig. 10.15.

257

Simplifying the transfer yields

$$H(j\omega) = \frac{K}{j\omega\{(1 - k_1\omega^2) + jk_2\omega\}}$$

$$= \frac{-jK\{(1 - k_1\omega^2) - jk_2\omega\}}{\omega\{(1 - k_1\omega^2)^2 + (k_2\omega)^2\}}$$

If R is the real part of $H(j\omega)$ and I is the imaginary part, then

$$R = \frac{-Kk_2}{\{(1 - k_1\omega^2)^2 + (k_2\omega)^2\}}$$

and

$$I = \frac{-K(1 - k_1\omega^2)}{\omega\{(1 - k_1\omega^2)^2 + (k_2\omega)^2\}}$$

Now when ω tends to zero, R tends to $-Kk_2$ thus the distance c in Fig. 10.15 (*a*) or (*b*) is given by $c = -Kk_2$.

Also the angular frequency at which the locus cuts the real axis is given by equating I to zero; thus $I = 0$, when $\omega = 1/\sqrt{k_1}$. The distance d in Fig. 10.15 (*a*) or (*b*) is thus given by substituting this value of angular frequency into the expression R, whence

$$d = \frac{-Kk_2}{(1 - 1)^2 + (k_2/\sqrt{k_1})^2}$$

$$= -\frac{Kk_1}{k_2}$$

Hence the system will be absolutely stable on closed loop provided $Kk_1/k_2 < 1$. The gain margin is $20\log_{10}\{k_2/(Kk_1)\}$ decibels.

Now referring to Fig. 10.15 (*a*) we see that the real part R may have a maximum value e, and this value is of interest. We may determine the angular frequency for which a maximum value of R occurs by equating $dR/d\omega$ to zero.

Now

$$\frac{dR}{d\omega} = \frac{Kk_2\{-4k_1\omega(1 - k_1\omega^2) + 2k_2^2\omega\}}{\{(1 - k_1\omega^2)^2 + (k_2\omega)^2\}^2}$$

Hence for a maximum value of R,

$$-4k_1\omega(1 - k_1\omega^2) + 2k_2^2\omega = 0$$

It is of interest that $\omega = 0$ is one solution, as is $\omega = \infty$ (for which the denominator of $dR/d\omega$ becomes infinite), and these limiting cases have obvious physical implications when related to the shape of the frequency locus.

The solution required is given by

$$-4k_1 + 4k_1^2\omega^2 + 2k_2^2 = 0$$

i.e.

$$\omega = \sqrt{\{2k_1 - k_2^2)/(2k_1^2)\}}$$

It should be noted here that if $k_1 \leqslant k_2^2/2$, no separate maximum can occur because ω becomes zero or imaginary. This condition gives a frequency locus as shown in Fig. 10.15 (*b*).

If $k_1 > k_2^2/2$ then a separate maximum must occur at an angular frequency given by the above relationship, when the real part becomes

$$R = \frac{-Kk_2}{\{1 - k_1(2k_1 - k_2^2)/(2k_1^2)\}^2 + k_2^2(2k_1 - k_2^2)/(2k_1^2)}$$

This is the value of e in Fig. 10.15 (*a*), i.e.

$$e = \frac{-4k_1^2 K}{k_2(4k_1 - k_2^2)}$$

when $k_1 > k_2^2/2$.

Nyquist Diagram for a Type 2 System with a Simple Lag

A type 2 system with a simple lag has an open-loop transfer function given by

$$H(j\omega) = \frac{K}{(j\omega)^2 (1 + j\omega T)}$$

The locus tends to infinity in the second quadrant as $\omega \to 0$. The manner of the approach to infinity can be ascertained analytically. Rationalizing we have

$$H(j\omega) = \frac{-K(1 - j\omega T)}{\omega^2(1 + \omega^2 T^2)}$$

If R is the real part of $H(j\omega)$ and I is the imaginary part, then

$$R = \frac{-K}{\omega^2(1 + \omega^2 T^2)}$$

and

$$I = \frac{KT}{\omega(1 + \omega^2 T^2)}$$

As ω tends to zero both R and I tend to infinity. R approaches infinity faster than I.

But

$$I^2 = \frac{K^2 T^2}{\omega^2(1 + \omega^2 T^2)^2}$$

∴

$$\frac{I^2}{R} = \frac{-KT^2}{(1 + \omega^2 T^2)}$$

Thus as ω tends to zero I^2/R tends to $-KT^2$. Hence for small values of frequency the locus must asymptotically approach the curve given by $I^2/R = -KT^2$. This is the equation of a parabola and is more

259

easily recognized in the form $I^2 = -(KT^2)R$. The Nyquist diagram is as shown in Fig. 10.16.

Observation will show that when the circular arc of infinite radius is included the complete locus encloses the point $(-1, j0)$ and the system is thus unstable for all values of K. Such a system requires *compensation* to achieve stability (see chapter 11).

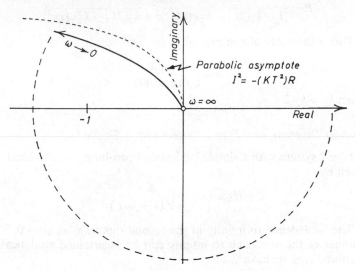

Fig. 10.16 *Nyquist diagram for* $H(j\omega) = K/\{(j\omega)^2(1 + j\omega T)\}$.

10.7 Summary of Loci Shapes

It is of considerable value to have available a list of Nyquist diagrams which are frequently encountered; such a list is shown in the table below. The circular arcs of infinite radius necessary to complete the diagrams for the purposes of stability assessment are also included.

10.8 Obtaining the Closed-loop Frequency Response from the Open-loop

It has been shown in §9.5.1 that for a unity feedback system

$$\frac{\theta_o}{\theta_i}(D) = \frac{\theta_o/\epsilon(D)}{1 + \theta_o/\epsilon(D)}$$

It hence follows that for a unity feedback system

$$\frac{\theta_o}{\theta_i}(j\omega) = \frac{\theta_o/\epsilon(j\omega)}{1 + \theta_o/\epsilon(j\omega)}$$

Transfer Function $H(j\omega)$	Complete Locus	Comments
1 $\dfrac{K}{1+j\omega T}$	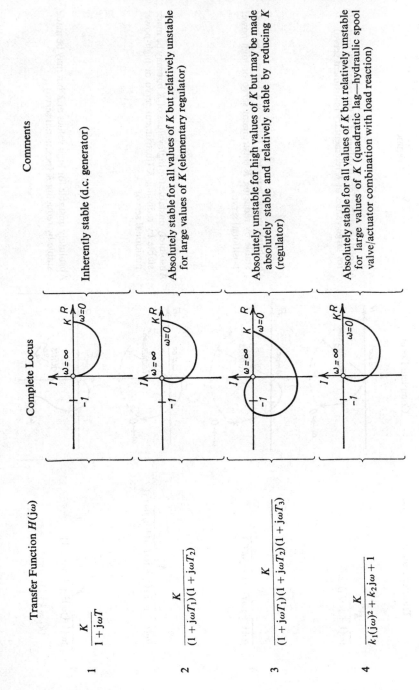	Inherently stable (d.c. generator)
2 $\dfrac{K}{(1+j\omega T_1)(1+j\omega T_2)}$		Absolutely stable for all values of K but relatively unstable for large values of K (elementary regulator)
3 $\dfrac{K}{(1+j\omega T_1)(1+j\omega T_2)(1+j\omega T_3)}$		Absolutely unstable for high values of K but may be made absolutely stable and relatively stable by reducing K (regulator)
4 $\dfrac{K}{k_1(j\omega)^2 + k_2 j\omega + 1}$		Absolutely stable for all values of K but relatively unstable for large values of K (quadratic lag—hydraulic spool valve/actuator combination with load reaction)

	Transfer Function $H(j\omega)$	Complete Locus	Comments
5	$\dfrac{K}{j\omega(1+j\omega T_1)}$		Absolutely stable for all values of K but relatively unstable for large values of K (elementary instrument servo)
6	$\dfrac{K}{j\omega(1+j\omega T_1)(1+j\omega T_2)}$		Absolutely unstable for high values of K but may be made stable by reducing K (instrument servo or high-power positional servo)
7	$\dfrac{K}{j\omega(1+j\omega1)(1+j\omega T_2)(1+j\omega T_3)}$		Absolutely unstable for high values of K but may be made stable by reducing K (instrument servo or high-power positional servo)
8	$\dfrac{K}{j\omega\{k_1(j\omega)^2+k_2j\omega+1\}}$ $(k_1 > k_2^2/2)$		Absolutely unstable for high values of K but may be made stable by reducing K (positional servo)

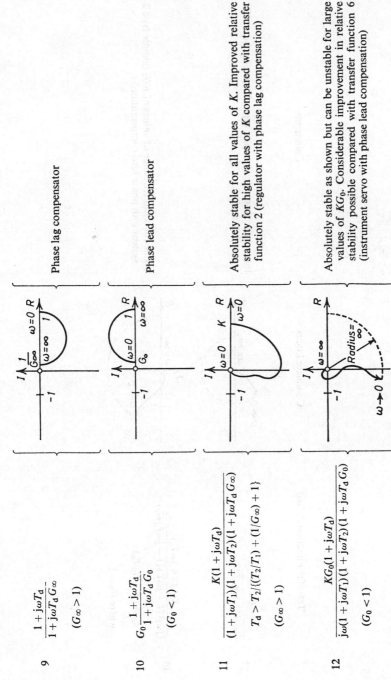

9 $\dfrac{1+j\omega T_d}{1+j\omega T_d G_\infty}$

$(G_\infty > 1)$

Phase lag compensator

10 $G_0\dfrac{1+j\omega T_d}{1+j\omega T_d G_0}$

$(G_0 < 1)$

Phase lead compensator

11 $\dfrac{K(1+j\omega T_d)}{(1+j\omega T_1)(1+j\omega T_2)(1+j\omega T_d G_\infty)}$

$T_d > T_2/\{(T_2/T_1)+(1/G_\infty)+1\}$

$(G_\infty > 1)$

Absolutely stable for all values of K. Improved relative stability for high values of K compared with transfer function 2 (regulator with phase lag compensation)

12 $\dfrac{KG_0(1+j\omega T_d)}{j\omega(1+j\omega T_1)(1+j\omega T_2)(1+j\omega T_d G_0)}$

$(G_0 < 1)$

Absolutely stable as shown but can be unstable for large values of KG_0. Considerable improvement in relative stability possible compared with transfer function 6 (instrument servo with phase lead compensation)

	Transfer Function $H(j\omega)$	Complete Locus	Comments
13	$\dfrac{K}{(j\omega)^2(1+j\omega T)}$	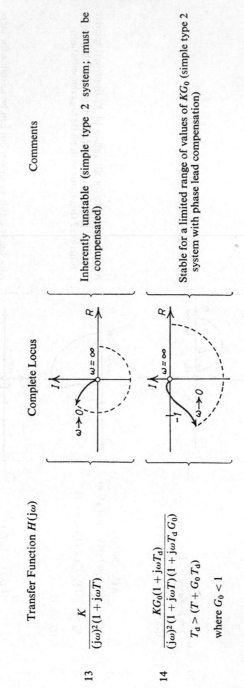	Inherently unstable (simple type 2 system; must be compensated)
14	$\dfrac{KG_0(1+j\omega T_d)}{(j\omega)^2(1+j\omega T)(1+j\omega T_d G_0)}$ $T_d > (T + G_0 T_d)$ where $G_0 < 1$		Stable for a limited range of values of KG_0 (simple type 2 system with phase lead compensation)

Referring to Fig. 10.17 it is seen that at any angular frequency ω, the numerator of the above expression is represented by the vector OP and the denominator is in fact the vector CP because

$$\overline{CP} + (-1) = \overline{OP}$$

$$\therefore \qquad \overline{CP} = 1 + \overline{OP}$$

Thus $$\frac{\theta_o}{\theta_i}(j\omega) = \frac{\overline{OP}}{\overline{CP}}$$

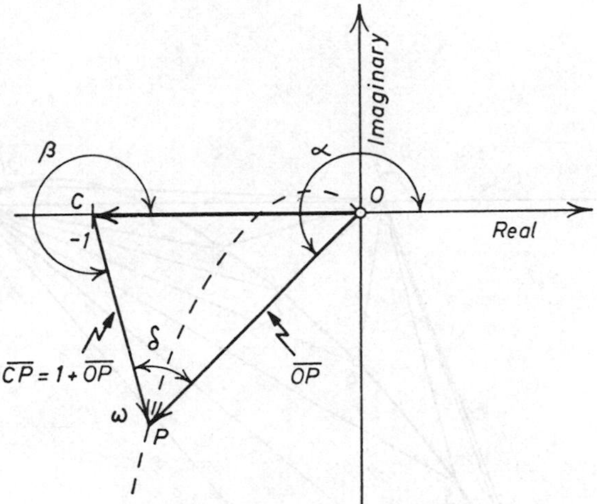

Fig. 10.17 *Vector relationships.*

Taking magnitudes and phases separately we thus have

$$\left|\frac{\theta_o}{\theta_i}(j\omega)\right| = \frac{|OP|}{|CP|}$$

and $$\angle\frac{\theta_o}{\theta_i}(j\omega) = \angle\overline{OP} - \angle\overline{CP}$$

$$= \alpha - \beta$$

$$= -\delta$$

These relationships give a rapid method of assessing and calculating the closed-loop response from the open-loop and it is particularly useful where the calculations are to be performed by hand. When a digital computer is available the programming is rather simpler if the vector $\overline{OP}$ is expressed as a complex number. A simple procedure can then be evolved to divide a given complex number by 1 plus the complex number. When the calculation is to be performed by hand however this procedure would be extremely laborious and the graphical technique is recommended.

265

Worked Example

The method will now be used to compute the closed-loop frequency response for the example of §10.3.1 in which

$$\frac{\theta_o}{\epsilon}(j\omega) = \frac{10}{j\omega(1+j\omega 0\cdot 2)(1+j\omega 0\cdot 05)}$$

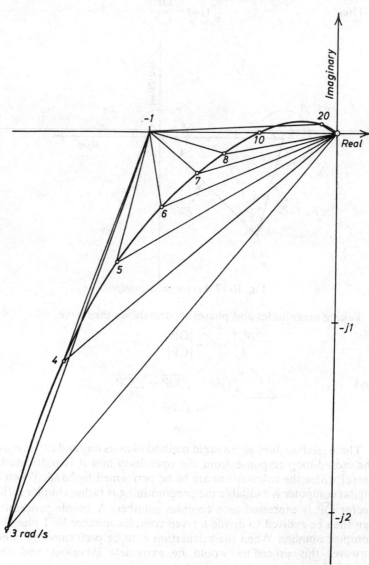

Fig. 10.18 *Determination of closed-loop frequency response.*

Solution

The Nyquist diagram is drawn in Fig. 10.18 and a table of values is shown below. This table has been made by measuring vector lengths and angles from the diagram and then by slide-rule calculation. The accuracy involved is thus not better than ±2%.

ω (rad/s)	$|OP|$	$|CP|$	δ (degrees)	$|\theta_o/\theta_i| = \dfrac{|OP|}{|CP|}$
20	0·086	0·925	215	0·093
10	0·400	0·600	180	0·667
8	0·615	0·400	153	1·54
7	0·780	0·330	123	2·36
6	1·02	0·400	75·0	2·55
5	1·37	0·720	45·0	1·90
4	1·91	1·30	30·0	1·46
3	2·82	2·22	20·0	1·27

The closed-loop frequency response so found may be represented in two ways. The first way is in a graph of $|\theta_o/\theta_i|$ versus ω as shown in Fig. 10.19.

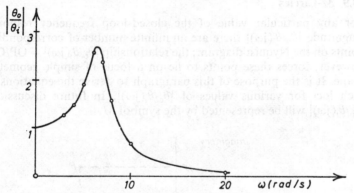

Fig. 10.19 *Closed-loop magnitude response.*

To obtain an accurate estimate of the peak magnitude it would be necessary to determine more values for angular frequencies lying between 6 and 7 rad/s.

The second way in which the closed-loop response can be represented is on a polar diagram as shown in Fig. 10.20.

A knowledge of the closed-loop frequency response is of importance because it enables us to use the second-order correlations between frequency response and transient response (as developed in chapter 8) to *predict* approximately the closed-loop transient response of the system. More important still, the simple connection between open- and closed-loop frequency response leads to a method of design which will ensure closed-loop stability and at the same time

267

allow us to assess the transient response. This method will be described in §10.10.

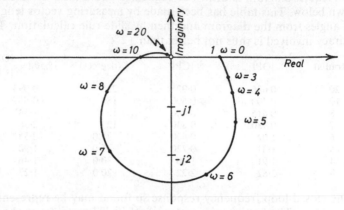

Fig. 10.20 *Closed-loop polar diagram.*

10.9 *M*-Circles

For any particular value of the closed-loop frequency response magnitude $|\theta_o/\theta_i(j\omega)|$ there are an infinite number of corresponding points on the Nyquist diagram; the relationship $|\theta_o/\theta_i(j\omega)| = OP/CP$, however, forces these points to lie on a locus of simple geometric shape. It is the purpose of this paragraph to derive the equations of such loci for various values of $|\theta_o/\theta_i(j\omega)|$. In future discussions $|\theta_o/\theta_i(j\omega)|$ will be represented by the symbol M.

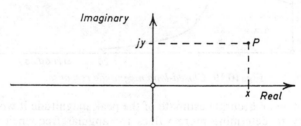

Fig. 10.21 *Defining a point P on the Nyquist diagram.*

Let P be any point on the Nyquist diagram defined by $x + jy$ (Fig. 10.21).

Thus the value of M is given by

$$M = \left| \frac{\theta_o}{\theta_i}(j\omega) \right|$$

$$= \left| \frac{\theta_o/\epsilon(j\omega)}{1 + \theta_o/\epsilon(j\omega)} \right|$$

268

Hence the value of M corresponding to the point P is given by

$$M = \left| \frac{x + jy}{1 + x + jy} \right|$$

$\therefore$

$$M = \frac{\sqrt{(x^2 + y^2)}}{\sqrt{\{(1 + x)^2 + y^2\}}}$$

or

$$M^2 = \frac{x^2 + y^2}{(1 + x)^2 + y^2}$$

Rearrangement gives

$$y^2 + \left\{ x + \frac{M^2}{M^2 - 1} \right\}^2 = \frac{M^2}{(M^2 - 1)^2}$$

This may be recognized as the equation for a circle with M as a parameter. The centre of the circle is

$$x_0 = - \frac{M^2}{M^2 - 1}$$

$$y_0 = 0$$

The radius of the circle is

$$r = \frac{M}{M^2 - 1}$$

The centres thus always lie on the real axis. The centres and radii are given in the table below for various values of M.

Magnitude M	Centre $\dfrac{M^2}{M^2 - 1}$	Radius $\dfrac{M}{M^2 - 1}$
0·3	+0·099	0·33
0·5	+0·333	0·67
0·7	+0·960	1·37
0·9	+4·26	4·74
1·0	∞	∞
1·1	−5·77	5·24
1·2	−3·27	2·73
1·3	−2·45	1·88
1·4	−2·04	1·46
1·5	−1·80	1·20
1·7	−1·53	0·90
1·9	−1·39	0·729
2·5	−1·19	0·476
3·00	−1·12	0·375
4·00	−1·07	0·266

A selection of *M*-circles are shown in Fig. 10.22.

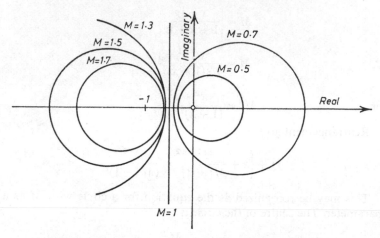

Fig. 10.22 *Loci of constant M on the Nyquist diagram.*

10.10 Use of the *M*-Circle in Design

10.10.1 Effect of the Error Constant K on the Closed-loop Performance

Variation of the error constant *K* merely adjusts the scale of the polar plot of the locus $\theta_o/\epsilon(j\omega)$. Take as example a system whose open-loop transfer is given by

$$\frac{\theta_o}{\epsilon}(j\omega) = \frac{K}{j\omega(1 + j\omega T_1)(1 + j\omega T_2)}$$

where T_1 and T_2 are fixed but *K* can be adjusted. A particular *M*-circle (for $M = M_1$) is superimposed on the open-loop frequency responses which are drawn for three different values of *K*, all of which give stable closed-loop operation. The closed-loop performances for the three different conditions are correlated with the corresponding open-loop Nyquist diagrams in Fig. 10.23.

In Fig. 10.23 (*a*) we note that $\theta_o/\epsilon(j\omega)$ does not intersect the M_1 circle, with the result that the resonant peak M_{pf} is less than M_1. However, Fig. 10.23 (*b*) shows the condition where *K* has been selected so that the locus $\theta_o/\epsilon(j\omega)$ just touches the M_1 circle. The resonant peak M_{pf} is thus exactly equal to M_1. The angular resonant frequency is ω_{rf}. In Fig. 10.23 (*c*) a value of *K* has been chosen so that the locus $\theta_o/\epsilon(j\omega)$ intersects the M_1 circle at two points at angular frequencies ω_1 and ω_2. The resonant peak M_{pf} must now be in excess of M_1.

270

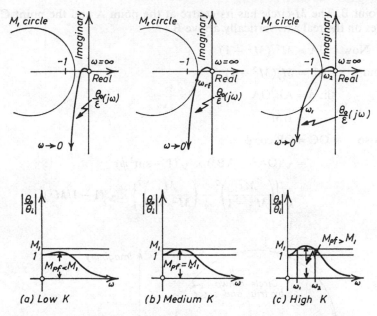

Fig. 10.23 *The effect of variation of K on the closed-loop performance.*

10.10.2 Selecting the Value of K to Give Adequate Relative Stability

A useful rule-of-thumb for design is that for adequate closed-loop stability M_{pf} should not be much more than 1·3. It is quite possible, however, to find the value of K which will give any desired value of M_{pf}. The method of finding the value of K which will give a specified value of M_{pf} is called *Brown's construction*. In order to develop this construction let us consider the geometry of the M-circle. In Fig. 10.24 a line is drawn from the origin to touch any given M-circle at a

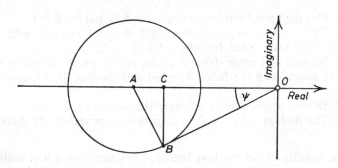

Fig. 10.24 *Geometry of the M-circle.*

point B. The M-circle has its centre at the point A and the point C lies on the real axis vertically above B.

Now $\quad OA = M^2/(M^2 - 1)$

and $\qquad AB = M/(M^2 - 1)$

$\therefore \qquad \sin \psi = AB/OA$

$\qquad\qquad\quad = 1/M$

Also $\qquad OC = OB \cos \psi$

$$= \sqrt{(OA^2 - AB^2)} \times \sqrt{(1 - \sin^2 \psi)}$$

$$= \sqrt{\left\{\left(\frac{M^2}{M^2 - 1}\right)^2 - \left(\frac{M}{M^2 - 1}\right)^2\right\}} \times \sqrt{(1 - 1/M^2)}$$

$$= 1$$

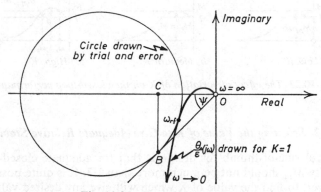

Fig. 10.25. *Brown's construction.*

Hence we may now evolve a simple construction which will yield the value of K necessary to give a specified M_{pf}. The steps in the construction are:

(1) Plot the open-loop frequency locus $\theta_o/\epsilon(j\omega)$ for $K = 1$.

(2) Draw a line to make an angle $\psi = \sin^{-1}(1/M_{pf})$ with the negative real axis. (Note, for $M_{pf} = 1\cdot3$, $\psi = 50\cdot2°$.)

(3) By trial and error draw a circle, centre on the negative real axis, to touch both the locus $\theta_o/\epsilon(j\omega)$ and the line drawn as in (2) above.

(4) Drop a perpendicular BC onto the negative real axis.

(5) The desired value of K is then the reciprocal of the distance OC.

The validity of the method becomes apparent when it is realized that we are simply forcing the circle to become the M_{pf} circle, firstly by specifying ψ and secondly by changing the value of K so as to make the distance OC become equal to unity.

The diagram also allows us to predict accurately the value of ω_{rf}, the angular resonant frequency on closed loop. Brown's construction thus gives a method of designing a system with good relative stability and predictable closed-loop frequency response. The approximate transient response can also be predicted using the second-order correlations derived in chapter 8.

Worked Example

A type 1 control system has two exponential lags in the forward path both having time constants of 1 sec. Use Brown's construction to determine the value of the error constant such that the peak magnitude of the closed-loop frequency response is 1·3. Predict the value of the angular resonant frequency and estimate the transient response using second-order correlations.

Solution

The transfer function is given by

$$\frac{\theta_o}{\epsilon}(j\omega) = \frac{K}{j\omega(1 + j\omega)^2}$$

The table below gives values of the open-loop frequency response for $K = 1$.

ω (rad/s)	$1 + \omega^2$	$\left\|\frac{\theta_o}{\epsilon}(j\omega)\right\| = \frac{1}{\omega(1 + \omega^2)}$	$\angle \frac{\theta_o}{\epsilon}(j\omega) = -(90° + 2\tan^{-1}\omega)$
0·3	1·09	3·06	−123·4°
0·4	1·16	2·16	−133·6°
0·5	1·25	1·60	−143·2°
0·7	1·49	0·96	−160·0°
1·0	2·00	0·50	−180·0°
1·2	2·44	0·34	−190·4°
1·5	3·25	0·20	−202·7°

The Nyquist diagram is shown in Fig. 10.26, together with the necessary construction.

The point C is $-2\cdot10 + j0$, hence the required value of K is $1/2\cdot10$, i.e. $K = 0\cdot476$ for $M_{pf} = 1\cdot3$.

The phase lag at the point of contact of the locus with the M-circle is about 139°.

$$\therefore \qquad -(90° + 2\tan^{-1}\omega_{rf}) = -139°$$

$$\therefore \qquad \tan^{-1}\omega_{rf} = 24\cdot5°$$

$$\therefore \qquad \omega_{rf} = 0\cdot456\,\text{rad/s}$$

273

Now using the second-order correlations developed in §8.9.3 we have for $M_{pf} = 1 \cdot 3$, $M_{pt} = 1 \cdot 228$. Thus the predicted peak overshoot is $22 \cdot 8 \%$.

Also for this condition

$$\omega_{rt} \simeq 1 \cdot 13 \, \omega_{rf}$$
$$\simeq 0 \cdot 515 \, \text{rad/s}$$

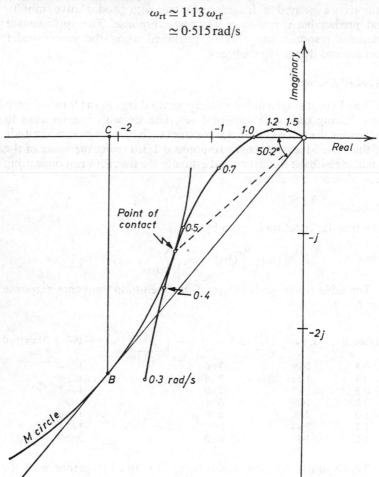

Fig. 10.26. *Brown's construction for worked example.*

Now the time to rise to the peak overshoot

$$= \frac{\pi}{\omega_{rt}}$$
$$\simeq \frac{\pi}{0 \cdot 515} \, \text{sec}$$
$$\simeq 6 \cdot 1 \, \text{sec}$$

A sketch of the estimated step response is shown in Fig. 10.27.

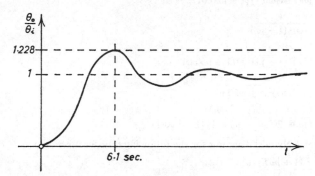

Fig. 10.27 *Estimated step-response for worked example.*

10.11 Conclusion

This chapter has attempted to show the way in which the open-loop frequency response may be used as a means of assessing the closed-loop performance of a control system. The theoretical and experimental procedures for plotting the Nyquist diagram of a given system and for determining the general shapes of vector loci have been explained. A simplified form of the Nyquist stability criterion applicable to systems which are stable on open loop has been described. The ideas of relative stability have been discussed together with the concepts of phase margin and gain margin which have been introduced as simple practical measures of relative stability.

The vector relationships between open- and closed-loop performance have led to a description of special loci known as M-circles. These circles have been used as a basis for the design of systems having adequate damping and for the accurate prediction of closed-loop frequency response and approximate prediction of transient response.

EXAMPLES FOR SOLUTION

1. Evaluate and plot on Nyquist diagrams frequency loci for the transfer functions given below. In each case state whether or not a system having such an open-loop transfer function would be absolutely stable on closed loop.

(i) $\dfrac{2}{(1 + j\omega 0 \cdot 1)}$

(ii) $\dfrac{5}{j\omega(1 + j\omega 0 \cdot 5)}$

(iii) $\dfrac{10(1 + j\omega)}{(1 + j\omega 0 \cdot 1)(1 + j\omega 0 \cdot 01)(1 + j\omega 0 \cdot 5)}$

275

(iv) $\dfrac{3}{j\omega(1 + j\omega 0\cdot 1)(1 + j\omega 0\cdot 01)}$

(v) $\dfrac{1}{(j\omega)^2(1 + j\omega)}$

(vi) $\dfrac{(1 + j\omega 0\cdot 5)}{(j\omega)^2(1 + j\omega 0\cdot 1)(1 + j\omega 0\cdot 01)}$

(vii) $\dfrac{2}{j\omega\{3(j\omega)^2 + j\omega + 1\}}$

(viii) $\dfrac{3(1 + j\omega 0\cdot 5)}{(j\omega)^2\{2(j\omega)^2 + j\omega + 1\}(1 + j\omega 0\cdot 1)}$

2. *Sketch* Nyquist diagrams for the following transfer functions:

(i) $\dfrac{K(1 + j\omega T)}{(j\omega)^3}$

(ii) $\dfrac{K(1 + j\omega T)}{(j\omega)^2 + j\omega + 1}$

(iii) $\dfrac{K}{j\omega(1 + j\omega T_1)(1 + j\omega T_2)(1 + j\omega T_3)}$

(iv) $\dfrac{K}{(j\omega)^2(1 + j\omega T_1)(1 + j\omega T_2)}$

(v) $\dfrac{K}{(1 + j\omega T)\{(j\omega)^2 + j\omega + 1\}}$

3. A type 1 control system with two exponential lags in the forward path both of 1 sec time constants has a velocity error constant of 1 $\sec^{-1}$. Determine the phase margin and gain margin and comment on the relative stability of the system on closed loop.

4. A type 1 control system with two exponential lags in the forward path of time constants 0·25 sec and 0·025 sec respectively has a velocity error constant of 10 $\sec^{-1}$. Draw a Nyquist diagram and determine the phase margin and gain margin. Comment on the relative stability of the system on closed loop.

5. (a) Explain in detail what is meant by a frequency response test and describe the principles of operation of any pieces of equipment which can be used to make such a test on an all-d.c. servomechanism.

(b) An open-loop frequency response test was performed on an all-d.c. servomechanism and a Nyquist diagram of the form shown in Fig. 10.28 was obtained. Deduce the open-loop transfer function of the system in terms of the operator $j\omega$.

6. A type 0 control system has three exponential lags in the forward path of time constants 1·0 sec, 0·1 sec and 0·01 sec respectively. The error constant is 100. Draw the Nyquist diagram for the system and determine whether or not it is stable on closed-loop. Comment on the relative stability if it is in fact absolutely stable.

7. A position control servomechanism consists of an armature-controlled d.c. motor fed from a d.c. generator which is driven at constant speed. The field of the generator is supplied from a d.c. amplifier, the input impedance of which is infinite. The error detector is a potentiometer bridge with a sensitivity of 2 V per radian. The particulars of the elements are as follows:

Motor: time constant 0·25 sec (this figure takes into account the armature resistance of the generator); generated e.m.f. per unit angular velocity is 38 V per rad/s.

Generator: inductance of field winding is 1·1 H; resistance of field winding is 10 Ω; generated e.m.f. is 2000 V per ampere of field current.

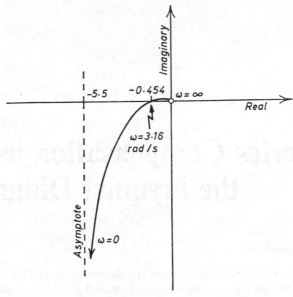

Fig. 10.28

Amplifier: gain on open circuit is 25 times; output resistance is 55 Ω; input resistance infinite.

(i) Draw a simplified circuit diagram for the system and also a block diagram.

(ii) Determine an expression for the open-loop transfer function of the system (as a function of $j\omega$).

(iii) Plot a Nyquist diagram and determine the gain and phase margins. Comment on the closed-loop stability of the system.

(iv) Determine by a series of geometric constructions a graph of the magnitude of the closed-loop frequency response versus the angular frequency.

8. Use Brown's construction to determine the values of K which will ensure that the maximum value of the magnitude of the closed-loop frequency response is equal to 1·3 in each of the following unity feedback systems:

(i) $\dfrac{\theta_o}{\epsilon}(j\omega) = \dfrac{K}{(1 + j\omega 0\cdot 1)(1 + j\omega 0\cdot 01)(1 + j\omega)}$

(ii) $\dfrac{\theta_o}{\epsilon}(j\omega) = \dfrac{K}{j\omega(1 + j\omega 0\cdot 5)(1 + j\omega 0\cdot 01)}$

(iii) $\dfrac{\theta_o}{\epsilon}(j\omega) = \dfrac{K(1 + j\omega 4)}{(j\omega)^2(1 + j\omega 0\cdot 25)^2}$

Also estimate the form of the closed-loop step response in each case.

277

Chapter Eleven

Series Compensation using the Nyquist Diagram

11.1 Introduction

It will have become evident from the discussion in §10.10 that for a given type 0 or type 1 system, when adequate closed-loop stability is the only design criterion, then this can always be achieved by adjustment of the error constant using Brown's construction. Normally the design specifications are very much more stringent and usually specify:

(*a*) A minimum value of error constant so as to achieve the desired degree of steady-state accuracy (frequently the basic system will be unstable with this error constant).

(*b*) A maximum or minimum rise time to a step input.

(*c*) Adequate stability (M_{pf} about 1·3).

It is usually a simple matter to calculate or measure the error coefficient of a control system and hence to determine whether or not the basic structure satisfies specification (*a*). The rise time, as specified by (*b*) is not itself a frequency domain parameter but may readily be related to the angular resonant frequency in the frequency domain (ω_{rf}) by assuming that the system response is approximately second order. The relevant equations relating rise time to ω_{rf} and M_{pf} have been developed in chapter 8. In some designs it may be necessary to decrease the rise time (where a fast transient response is required) whereas in others it may be necessary to lower the rise time to improve the signal-to-noise ratio. Specification (*c*) calling for adequate stability is a normal requisite for any control system.

It is often possible to bring the performance of a system within specification by placing in series with the main elements a 'compensating device' as shown in Fig. 11.1.

278

The nature of the compensating device which is chosen to bring the performance of a particular system within specification will depend on the nature of the error signal (i.e. whether it is electrical or mechanical, continuous or modulated, etc.) and on the performance of the uncompensated system. In pneumatic systems for process control, commercial controllers are constructed with inbuilt

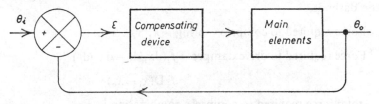

Fig. 11.1 *Series compensation.*

compensating characteristics (see chapter 14). In a mechanically or electrically signalled system it is usual to design a special network exactly matched to the needs of the system in order to achieve the required overall performance. Two of the most popular networks used for such work are called 'phase-lead' and 'phase-lag'. Both types may be made purely mechanical or purely electrical but the principles of the methods of specifying the characteristics of such devices are the same in both cases.

11.2 Analysis of Series-Compensating Devices

11.2.1 Mechanical Devices

The Mechanical Phase-lead Network

Mechanical compensating networks can be constructed of a combination of springs and dashpots (i.e. viscous dampers). Mechanical networks can be designed to operate on signals consisting of either rotational or rectilinear motion; Fig. 11.2 shows a network arranged

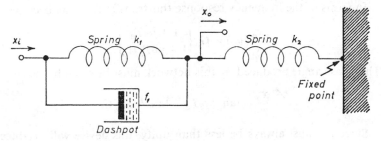

Fig. 11.2 *Mechanical phase-lead network.*

279

to produce 'phase-lead' on signals of rectilinear motion. The input signal has an instantaneous position x_i and the output has a position x_o. The transfer function x_o/x_i must first be determined.

The device has two springs of stiffnesses k_1 and k_2 respectively and a dashpot of viscous constant f_1.

The total force at the input is that necessary to compress spring k_1 amount $(x_i - x_o)$ and produce a relative velocity $dx_i/dt - dx_o/dt$ in the dashpot.

Force required to compress spring $= k_1(x_i - x_o)$.

Force required to drive damper $= f_1(dx_i/dt - dx_o/dt)$

$$= f_1 D(x_i - x_o)$$

$\therefore$ total force required to compress combination is

$$k_1(x_i - x_o) + f_1 D(x_i - x_o)$$

This force is transmitted to spring k_2 which is compressed an amount x_o. Thus

$$k_2 x_o = k_1(x_i - x_o) + f_1 D(x_i - x_o)$$

$\therefore \qquad x_o(k_2 + k_1 + f_1 D) = x_i(k_1 + f_1 D)$

$\therefore \qquad \dfrac{x_o}{x_i}(D) = \dfrac{k_1 + f_1 D}{k_2 + k_1 + f_1 D}$

If we define f_1/k_1 as a time constant T_d, then

$$\frac{x_o}{x_i}(D) = \frac{1 + T_d D}{\dfrac{k_2 + k_1}{k_1} + T_d D}$$

Also, let $k_1/(k_2 + k_1)$ be G_o, then

$$\frac{x_o}{x_i}(D) = G_o \left\{ \frac{1 + T_d D}{1 + G_o T_d D} \right\}$$

In terms of the frequency response this transfer function becomes

$$\frac{x_o}{x_i}(j\omega) = G_o \left\{ \frac{1 + j\omega T_d}{1 + j\omega T_d G_o} \right\}$$

The phase angle produced by this network must be given by

$$\angle \frac{x_o}{x_i} = \tan^{-1} \omega T_d - \tan^{-1} \omega T_d G_o$$

Since G_o must always be less than unity, this device will produce phase-leads at all frequencies from zero to infinity.

280

The Mechanical Phase-lag Network

A mechanical phase-lag network for rectilinear motion is shown in Fig. 11.3.

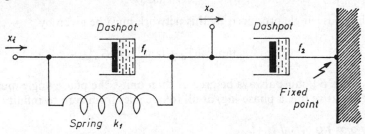

Fig. 11.3 *Mechanical phase-lag network.*

The total force at the input is that necessary to compress spring amount $x_i - x_o$ and produce a relative velocity $dx_i/dt - dx_o/dt$ in dashpot f_1.

Force required to compress spring $= k_1(x_i - x_o)$.

Force required to drive damper $= f_1(dx_i/dt - dx_o/dt)$

$$= f_1 D(x_i - x_o)$$

∴ total force required to compress combination is

$$k_1(x_i - x_o) + f_1 D(x_i - x_o)$$

This force is transmitted to dashpot f_2 which is driven at a velocity dx_o/dt, i.e.

$$f_2 Dx_o = k_1(x_i - x_o) + f_1 D(x_i - x_o)$$

∴

$$x_o\{k_1 + (f_1 + f_2) D\} = x_i(k_1 + f_1 D)$$

∴

$$\frac{x_o}{x_i}(D) = \frac{k_1 + f_1 D}{k_1 + (f_1 + f_2) D}$$

If we define f_1/k_1 as a time constant T_d, then

$$\frac{x_o}{x_i}(D) = \frac{1 + T_d D}{1 + \left\{\dfrac{f_1 + f_2}{f_1}\right\} T_d D}$$

Also, let $\dfrac{f_1 + f_2}{f_1} = G_\infty$, then

$$\frac{x_o}{x_i}(D) = \frac{1 + T_d D}{1 + G_\infty T_d D}$$

281

In terms of the frequency response this transfer function becomes

$$\frac{x_o}{x_i}(j\omega) = \frac{1 + j\omega T_d}{1 + j\omega T_d G_\infty}$$

The phase angle produced by this network must be given by

$$\angle \frac{x_o}{x_i} = \tan^{-1} \omega T_d - \tan^{-1} \omega T_d G_\infty$$

Since G_∞ must always be greater than unity, the phase angle must be negative (i.e. a phase-lag) at all frequencies from zero to infinity.

11.2.2 Electrical Devices

The Electrical Phase-lead Network

Electrical compensating networks can be constructed of a combination of capacitors and resistors. The phase-lead network is shown in Fig. 11.4.

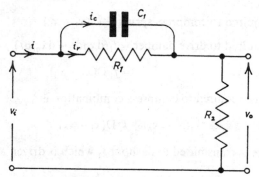

Fig. 11.4 *Electrical phase-lead network.*

The currents i_c and i_r through C_1 and R_1 respectively sum to give a total current which passes through R_2.

Thus
$$v_i - v_o = \frac{1}{C_1} \int i_c \, dt$$

$$= \frac{i_c}{C_1 D}$$

also
$$v_i - v_o = i_r R_1$$

$$\therefore \qquad i_c + i_r = (v_i - v_o)\left(\frac{1}{R_1} + C_1 D\right)$$

But
$$i_c + i_r = i$$

and
$$v_o = i R_2$$

282

$$\therefore \qquad \frac{v_o}{R_2} = (v_i - v_o)\left(\frac{1}{R_1} + C_1 D\right)$$

$$\therefore \qquad \frac{v_o}{v_i}(D) = \frac{\dfrac{1}{R_1} + C_1 D}{\dfrac{1}{R_2} + \dfrac{1}{R_1} + C_1 D}$$

If $R_1 C_1$ is defined as a time-constant T_d and $R_2/(R_1 + R_2)$ is represented by G_o, then

$$\frac{v_o}{v_i}(D) = G_o\left\{\frac{1 + T_d D}{1 + G_o T_d D}\right\}$$

This transfer function is identical in form to that derived for the mechanical phase-lead network of §11.2.1.

The Electrical Phase-lag Network

In the phase-lag network of Fig. 11.5 the current i is common to all the components.

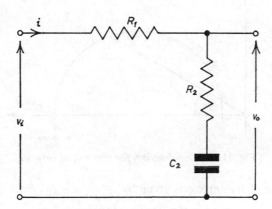

Fig. 11.5 *Electrical phase-lag network.*

Thus $\qquad\qquad v_i = iR_1 + iR_2 + i/C_2 D$

and $\qquad\qquad v_o = iR_2 + i/C_2 D$

$$\therefore \qquad \frac{v_o}{v_i}(D) = \frac{R_2 + (1/C_2 D)}{R_1 + R_2 + (1/C_2 D)}$$

Putting $T_d = C_2 R_2$ and $G_\infty = \dfrac{R_2 + R_1}{R_2}$, we have

$$\frac{v_o}{v_i}(D) = \frac{1 + T_d D}{1 + G_\infty T_d D}$$

283

11.2.3 The Polar Diagram

General

The design problem is, given a control system the performance of which is outside a certain specification, to choose a network (i.e. specify T_d and G_o or T_d and G_∞) which can be used to bring the system performance within the specification. To do this, graphical procedures must be developed whereby the choice can be made with minimum effort. One approach to this problem requires a knowledge of the geometry of the polar diagrams for these networks.

Polar Diagram for Phase-lead Network

Regardless whether the network is electrical or mechanical the transfer function H_a of a phase-lead network is given by

$$H_a(j\omega) = G_o \left\{ \frac{1 + j\omega T_d}{1 + j\omega G_o T_d} \right\}$$

The polar diagram for this is a semicircle as shown in Fig. 11.6.

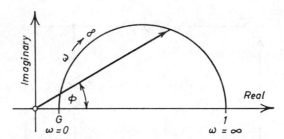

Fig. 11.6 *Polar diagram for phase-lead network.*

Now the phase angle ϕ is given by

$$\phi = \tan^{-1} \omega T_d - \tan^{-1} \omega G_o T_d$$

$$\therefore \qquad \frac{d\phi}{d\omega} = \frac{T_d}{1 + \omega^2 T_d^2} - \frac{G_o T_d}{1 + \omega^2 G_o^2 T_d^2}$$

and for a maximum value of ϕ, $d\phi/d\omega$ is zero

$$\therefore \qquad \frac{T_d}{1 + \omega^2 T_d^2} - \frac{G_o T_d}{1 + \omega^2 G_o^2 T_d^2} = 0$$

$$\therefore \qquad \omega^2 G_o T_d^2 (G_o - 1) = G_o - 1$$

$$\therefore \qquad \omega^2 G_o T_d^2 = 1$$

i.e. $$\omega = \frac{1}{T_d \sqrt{G_o}} \qquad (1)$$

284

This is the angular frequency at which the phase-lead has its maximum value ϕ_{max}

$$\therefore \qquad \phi_{max} = \tan^{-1} T_d \left\{ \frac{1}{T_d\sqrt{G_o}} \right\} - \tan^{-1}\sqrt{G_o}$$

$$\therefore \qquad \phi_{max} = \frac{\pi}{2} - 2\tan^{-1}\sqrt{G_o} \qquad (2)$$

The magnitude of H_a at this frequency is given by

$$|H_a(j\omega)| = G_o \left\{ \frac{\sqrt{\left(1 + \frac{1}{G_o}\right)}}{\sqrt{(1 + G_o)}} \right\}$$

$$= \sqrt{G_o} \qquad (3)$$

The formulae (1), (2) and (3) will be found useful in design.

Polar Diagram for Phase-lag Network

For both electrical and mechanical devices the transfer function H_b of a phase-lag network is given by

$$H_b(j\omega) = \frac{1 + j\omega T_d}{1 + j\omega G_\infty T_d}$$

The polar diagram for this is a semicircle as shown in Fig. 11.7.

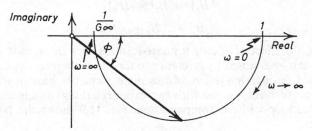

Fig. 11.7 *Polar diagram for phase-lag network.*

By a similar analysis to that given in §11.2.3 it may be shown that for a phase-lag network the maximum negative phase angle is given by

$$\phi_{max} = \frac{\pi}{2} - 2\tan^{-1}\sqrt{G_\infty}$$

and this occurs at an angular frequency

$$\omega = \frac{1}{T_d\sqrt{G_\infty}}$$

when the magnitude $|H_b(j\omega)|$ is $1/\sqrt{G_\infty}$.

11.3 The Effects of Cascaded Networks on the Performance of Control Systems

11.3.1 The Effect of Cascaded Phase-lead Networks

If the original system has an open-loop transfer function H_m then when a network of transfer function H_a is placed in cascade with

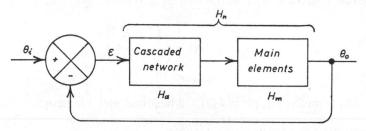

Fig. 11.8 *Cascaded network.*

the main elements, the new open-loop transfer function H_n is given by

$$H_n = H_a H_m$$

Taking magnitudes and phases separately we have

$$|H_n| = |H_a| \times |H_m|$$

and
$$\angle H_n = \angle H_a + \angle H_m$$

Thus, the effect of adding a phase-lead network in cascade with a system can be assessed by reference to the polar diagrams of the two devices. Consider a system whose main elements have a transfer function which is type one with two exponential lags and is unstable on closed loop without compensation. Fig. 11.9 shows the Nyquist diagram.

The effects are:

(i) High-frequency vectors are not appreciably attenuated nor phase shifted.

(ii) Medium-frequency vectors (i.e. those near phase crossover) are considerably advanced in phase and receive medium attenuation.

(iii) Low-frequency vectors are considerably attenuated but are not appreciably advanced in phase.

Various important points emerge from this discussion. Firstly it is noted that a system which is basically unstable can be made stable by using a cascaded phase-lead network. In itself this does not appear to be an advantage because this could have been achieved simply by reducing the gain. This will of course produce a system which has a

286

slower response and a greater steady-state error. **However, when the phase-lead network is introduced the speed of response is greater and the steady-state error reduced.**

The fact that the speed of response is greater becomes evident when considering the point of contact of the composite locus H_n with the maximum M-circle. This is certain to occur at a considerably higher angular frequency (near ω_M) than it would if stable performance

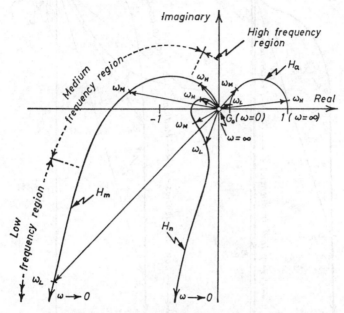

Fig. 11.9 *Showing the effect of phase lead.*

were achieved by gain reduction in which case the point of contact would then be near ω_L. Thus the resonant angular frequency and hence the speed of response must be greater with phase-lead compensation.

11.3.2 The Effect of Cascaded Phase-lag Networks

The effect of cascading a correctly designed phase-lag network of transfer function H_r with an unstable type 1 system of transfer function H_m can be observed by reference to Fig. 11.10 which is divided into several diagrams showing the effects over the various frequency ranges. Four frequency ranges must be considered. The effect on very low-frequency vectors (in the region of ω_{VL}) can be seen from the small-scale diagram of Fig. 11.10 (a). For low frequencies

287

(in the region of ω_L) and medium frequencies (in the region of ω_M) the effects can be observed by considering Fig. 11.10 (*b*). High-frequency vectors receive little phase-shift but considerable attenuation as shown in Fig. 11.10 (*c*).

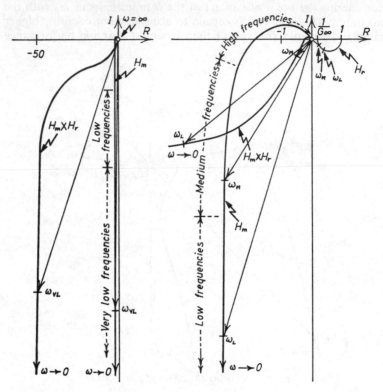

(a) Very low frequencies   (b)Low and medium frequencies

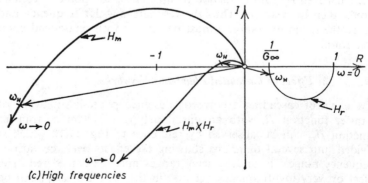

(c)High frequencies

Fig. 11.10 *Showing the effect of phase lag.*

The effects may thus be summarized as follows:

(i) Very low-frequency vectors receive little attenuation or phase shift.

(ii) Low-frequency vectors receive medium attenuation and considerable phase-shift.

(iii) Medium-frequency vectors receive considerable attenuation and some phase-shift.

(iv) High-frequency vectors receive considerable attenuation and negligible phase-shift.

It becomes evident that a type 1 system which is basically unstable can be made stable by using a cascaded phase-lag network. Whilst this could have been achieved by reducing gain the introduction of phase-lag compensation will have two other effects; firstly it will allow stabilization without reducing the error constant, and thus the compensated system will have a reduced steady-state error. Furthermore the resonant frequency and hence the speed of response is reduced; this may or may not be an advantage depending on the system. Where reduction of noise at the output is required it may be an advantage.

11.4 The Design of Cascaded Compensating Networks

11.4.1 The Design of Phase-lead Networks for the Improvement of Type 1 and Type 0 Systems

The problem is to design a phase-lead network required to improve the performance of a type 1 or type 0 system in which the error constant and resonant frequency are both too low to meet a given specification with the error constant adjusted for stable operation.

Let us assume that a system is to be designed with the following specifications:

(i) An error constant of *at least K'*.

(ii) A resonant angular frequency of *at least* ω_{rf}'.

(iii) Adequate damping ($M_{pf} \simeq 1\cdot3$).

Whilst it is not always possible to achieve a specified performance using one phase-lead network, fortunately in many situations it is possible. The recommended philosophy of design is to concentrate on bringing the resonant frequency within specification and then to see whether the resulting error constant is large enough. If it is not, the resonant frequency can be increased suitably and the network redesigned. Often this will yield a satisfactory solution; when it does not, it may be necessary to seek alternative methods of compensation.

The procedure for design is as follows:

(1) Draw the frequency locus of the uncompensated system $\theta_o/\epsilon(j\omega)$ for unity error constant. Draw the *M* circle for $M = 1\cdot3$ by

trial and error. Put in the true -1 point on the plot and determine the error constant (K_1 say) which would give the uncompensated system an M_{max} of 1·3.

(2) Mark on the M-circle the point of contact of the circle with the uncompensated frequency locus.

(3) The vector at ω'_{rf} on the uncompensated locus must be advanced in phase and increased in length to touch the M-circle at this point. The maximum angle of phase-lead required from the phase-lead network is thus determined; the parameters G_o and T_d and the error constant can then be determined.

The method can be illustrated by considering a type 1 system with two exponential lags.

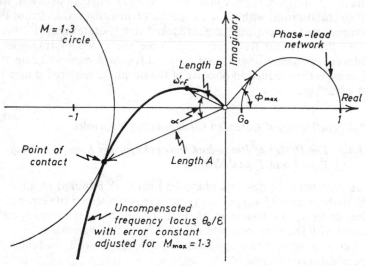

Fig. 11.11 *Illustrating design of phase-lead network.*

Fig. 11.11 shows the Nyquist diagram for the uncompensated system. Brown's construction is used to determine K_1 and the angle α is then measured from the diagram. The angle α is then made equal to ϕ_{max}. Then using the formulae developed in §11.2.3 we have

$$\alpha = \phi_{max} = \frac{\pi}{2} - 2\tan^{-1}\sqrt{G_o}$$

$$\therefore \qquad \tan^{-1}\sqrt{G_o} = \frac{\pi}{4} - \frac{\alpha}{2}$$

hence G_o may be found.

Also

$$\omega'_{rf} = \frac{1}{T_d\sqrt{G_o}}.$$

hence T_d may be found.

Now A and B are measured from the diagram; it is also known that the phase-lead network has a gain $\sqrt{G_o}$ at the angular frequency ω'_{rf}. In order that the gain is sufficient to make the new vector at ω'_{rf} touch the M-circle in the required position, the error constant must be adjusted by a factor F where

$$A = F(B \times \sqrt{G_o})$$

i.e.
$$F = \frac{A}{B\sqrt{G_o}}$$

The overall compensated transfer function is thus

$$\left(\frac{\theta_o}{\epsilon}\right)' = \frac{G_o K_1 F(1 + j\omega T_d)}{j\omega(1 + j\omega G_o T_d)(1 + j\omega T_1)(1 + j\omega T_2)}$$

The new error constant is thus $G_o K_1 F$.

If $G_o K_1 F$ is greater than K' (the original specified error constant) then the design is successful. If not the specified value of ω'_{rf} must be increased and the design repeated. Finally the whole locus should be plotted to make sure that the method has given the desired response.

Worked Example

A type 1 control system has two exponential lags in the forward path both having time constants of 1 sec. Design a phase-lead network which when connected in cascade with the system will produce the following specifications:

(i) Error constant of at least 1 sec^{-1}.
(ii) Resonant angular frequency ω'_{rf} of at least 1·5 rad/s.
(iii) M_{pf} between 1·2 and 1·4.

Solution

The open-loop transfer function of the uncompensated system is thus

$$\frac{\theta_o}{\epsilon} = \frac{K}{j\omega(1 + j\omega)^2}$$

We will design for an M_{pf} of 1·3.

The frequency locus is drawn for the uncompensated system in Fig. 10.26 and the value of the error coefficient K_1 which would give the uncompensated system an M_{max} of 1·3 has been determined in the worked example of §10.10.2. In this it was found that K_1 is 0·476. The relevant information related to this problem is shown in Fig. 11.12.

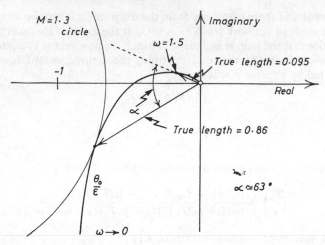

Fig. 11.12 *Nyquist diagram for $\theta_{\mathrm{o}}/\epsilon = 0.476/\{j\omega(1 + j\omega)^2\}$.*

The angle α is 63°, thus

$$\alpha = \phi_{\max} = \frac{\pi}{2} - 2\tan^{-1}\sqrt{G_{\mathrm{o}}}$$

$$\therefore \qquad \tan^{-1}\sqrt{G_{\mathrm{o}}} = \frac{90 - 63}{2} \text{ degrees}$$

$$\therefore \qquad \tan^{-1}\sqrt{G_{\mathrm{o}}} = 13\cdot5°$$

$$\therefore \qquad \sqrt{G_{\mathrm{o}}} = 0\cdot24$$

$$\therefore \qquad G_{\mathrm{o}} \simeq 0\cdot058$$

Also

$$\omega'_{\mathrm{rf}} = \frac{1}{T_{\mathrm{d}}\sqrt{G_{\mathrm{o}}}}$$

$$\therefore \qquad 1\cdot5 = \frac{1}{0\cdot24 T_{\mathrm{d}}}$$

$$\therefore \qquad T_{\mathrm{d}} = \frac{1}{0\cdot24 \times 1\cdot5}$$

$$\therefore \qquad T_{\mathrm{d}} \simeq 2\cdot78 \text{ sec}$$

The factor

$$F = \frac{A}{B\sqrt{G_{\mathrm{o}}}}$$

$$= \frac{0\cdot86}{0\cdot095 \times 0\cdot24}$$

$$\simeq 37\cdot8$$

The open-loop transfer function of the compensated system is thus

$$\left(\frac{\theta_o}{\epsilon}\right)' = \frac{G_o K_1 F(1 + j\omega 2 \cdot 78)}{j\omega(1 + j\omega)^2 (1 + j\omega 0 \cdot 161)}$$

The error constant K is given by

$$K = G_o K_1 F$$
$$= 0 \cdot 058 \times 0 \cdot 476 \times 37 \cdot 8$$
$$= 1 \cdot 04 \sec^{-1}$$

The error coefficient is thus within the specification of at least $1 \sec^{-1}$. The design must now be checked by drawing the Nyquist diagram for the compensated system. A table of values is given below.

ω (rad/s)	Open-loop Magnitude	Open-loop Angle	Closed-loop Magnitude
0·100	10·69	−86·81°	0·9905
0·200	5·718	−85·39°	0·9719
0·300	4·137	−86·34°	0·9581
0·400	3·345	−89·25°	0·9547
0·500	2·840	−93·46°	0·9616
0·600	2·467	−98·39°	0·9778
0·700	2·168	−103·6°	1·002
0·800	1·917	−108·9°	1·034
0·900	1·702	−114·0°	1·074
1·00	1·517	−118·9°	1·120
1·20	1·215	−128·0°	1·227
1·40	0·9838	−136·0°	1·325
1·60	0·8061	−143·1°	1·343
1·80	0·6679	−149·4°	1·226
2·00	0·5592	−154·9°	1·021
2·20	0·4729	−159·9°	0·8164
2·40	0·4034	−164·4°	0·6496
2·60	0·3470	−168·5°	0·5228
2·80	0·3006	−172·3°	0·4274
3·00	0·2622	−175·7°	0·3549
3·50	0·1911	−183·4°	0·2361
4·00	0·1436	−189·8°	0·1671

The Nyquist diagram for the compensated system is shown in Fig. 11.13. The resonant peak occurs at an angular frequency of about 1·5 rad/s and the corresponding value of M_{pf} is about 1·35. These values satisfy the specification and hence the design has been successful.

11.4.2 *The Design of Phase-lead Networks for the Stabilization of Type 2 Systems*

Type 2 systems are used in applications where velocity lags are intolerable. Such systems are inherently unstable and require compensation. Introduction of phase-lead compensation offers the possibility of stable operation. The method of design described for type 1 and type 0 systems is no longer applicable but must be modified as described below. It will be assumed that the system to be designed must have the following specifications:

(i) An error constant of *at least K'*.
(ii) A resonant angular frequency of *at least* ω'_{rf}.
(iii) Adequate damping ($M_{pf} = 1 \cdot 3$).

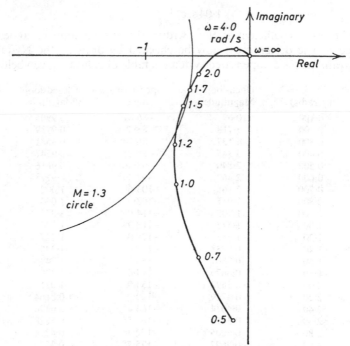

Fig. 11.13 *Nyquist diagram for compensated system.*

The recommended design procedure is as follows:

(1) Draw the open-loop frequency locus of the uncompensated system with the error constant set at unity.

(2) Draw the circle for $M = 1 \cdot 3$.

(3) Mark on the M-circle the expected point of contact of the compensated locus with the M-circle. This will be roughly where a circle of unity radius centred on the origin cuts the M-circle.

(4) The vector at ω'_{rf} on the uncompensated locus must be advanced in phase and adjusted in length to touch the M-circle at this point. The maximum angle of phase lead required from the phase-lead network is thus determined; the parameters G_o and T_d and the error constant can then be determined.

The method can be illustrated by considering a type 2 system with two exponential lags. The Nyquist diagram for the system is shown in Fig. 11.14.

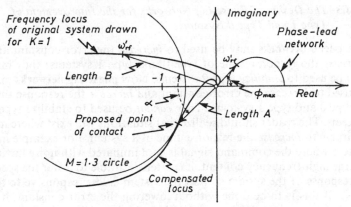

Fig. 11.14 *Compensation of a type 2 system.*

The angle α is measured and made equal to ϕ_{max} thus, i.e.

$$\alpha = \phi_{max} = \frac{\pi}{2} - 2\tan^{-1}\sqrt{G_o}$$

$\therefore$
$$\tan^{-1}\sqrt{G_o} = \frac{\pi}{4} - \frac{\alpha}{2}$$

$\therefore G_o$ may be found.

Also
$$\omega'_{rf} = \frac{1}{T_d\sqrt{G_o}}$$

hence T_d may be found.

Now A and B are measured from the diagram; it is also known that the phase-lead network has a gain $\sqrt{G_o}$ at the angular frequency ω'_{rf}. In order that the gain is correctly set so that the new vector at ω'_{rf} touches the M-circle, the error constant must be adjusted by a factor F where

$$A = F(B \times \sqrt{G_o})$$

i.e.
$$F = \frac{A}{B\sqrt{G_o}}$$

The overall compensated transfer function is thus

$$\left(\frac{\theta_o}{\epsilon}\right)' = \frac{G_o F(1 + j\omega T_d)}{(j\omega)^2 (1 + j\omega G_o T_d)(1 + j\omega T_1)(1 + j\omega T_2)}$$

If $G_o F$ is greater than K' (the original specified error constant) then the design is successful. If not the specified value of ω'_{rf} must be increased and the design repeated. Finally the whole locus should be plotted to make sure that the method has given the desired response.

11.4.3 The Design of Phase-lag Networks for the Improvement of Type 1 and Type 0 Systems

Phase-lead networks may be used to *increase* the error constant and *decrease* the response time of type 0 and type 1 systems: they may also be used to *stabilize* type 2 systems. Now **phase-lag networks** may be used to *increase* the error constant and *increase* the response time of type 0 and type 1 systems. They *cannot* be used to stabilize type 2 systems. The reader should realize that situations will exist where it is desirable to *increase* the response time of a system. For example in a system where the command signal is contaminated with noise having a large high-frequency content, it is often desirable to lower the speed of response of the system so that the system is less responsive to the noise. If this is to be done without lowering the error constant, it is usually convenient to introduce phase-lag compensation. Let us assume that a type 0 or type 1 system is to be designed with the following specifications:

(i) An error constant of at least K'.
(ii) A resonant angular frequency of *at most* ω'_{rf}.
(iii) Adequate damping ($M_{pf} = 1 \cdot 3$).

The design procedure is as follows:

(1) Draw the open-loop frequency locus for the system using an error constant of K' and draw in the circle for $M = 1 \cdot 3$.

(2) Mark on the M-circle the point at which the compensated frequency locus is most likely to touch it. This will be roughly where a circle of unity radius centred on the origin cuts the M-circle.

(3) Measure the angle α between the vector joining the origin to the new point of contact with the M-circle and the vector on the uncompensated locus at ω'_{rf}.

(4) Measure the length of the vector at ω'_{rf}; this vector is to be attenuated by *approximately* $1/G_\infty$ and phase retarded by the angle α. Calculate G_∞ and hence T_d using this information.

The method will be illustrated by considering an unstable type 1 system with two exponential lags. The open-loop frequency locus θ_o/ϵ for such a system is shown in Fig. 11.15.

The design method relies on the approximation that the gain of the phase-lag network is $1/G_\infty$ when the angular frequency is ω'_{rf}. This approximation is quite good, however, and may well yield a solution after one trial.

Thus we make $G_\infty = A$. Then

$$\alpha = \tan^{-1} G_\infty \omega'_{rf} T_d - \tan^{-1} \omega'_{rf} T_d$$

or $\qquad \alpha = \tan^{-1} A\omega'_{rf} T_d - \tan^{-1} \omega'_{rf} T_d$

since α, A and ω'_{rf} are known, T_d may be found.

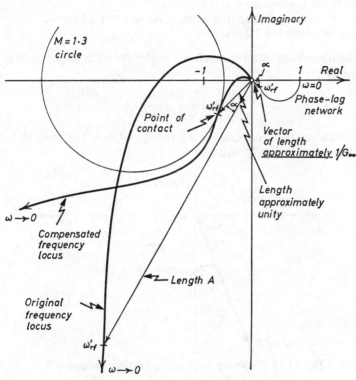

Fig. 11.15 *Showing design of phase-lag network.*

The relevant solution of this equation gives

$$T_d = \frac{(A-1) + \sqrt{\{(A-1)^2 - 4A\tan^2\alpha\}}}{2\omega'_{rf} A \tan\alpha}$$

The new overall transfer function will have the form

$$\left(\frac{\theta_o}{\epsilon}\right)' = \frac{K'(1 + j\omega T_d)}{j\omega(1 + j\omega T_1)(1 + j\omega T_2)(1 + j\omega T_d G_\infty)}$$

The new locus should finally be plotted out to check that the design has been successful.

297

Worked Example

A type 1 control system has two exponential lags in the forward path
both having time constants of 1 sec. Design a phase-lag network
which when connected in cascade with the system will produce the
following overall specifications:

(i) Error coefficient of at least 10 sec^{-1}.
(ii) Resonant angular frequency ω'_{rf} of at most 0·2 rad/s.
(iii) M_{pf} between 1·2 and 1·4.

The open-loop transfer function for the uncompensated system is
given by

$$\frac{\theta_o}{\epsilon}(j\omega) = \frac{10}{j\omega(1+j\omega)^2}$$

For an angular frequency of 0·2 rad/s, $\angle\theta_o/\epsilon$ is 113° and $|\theta_o/\epsilon|$ is
48. Hence we make G_∞ equal to 48.

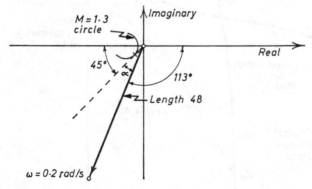

Fig. 11.16 *Phase-lag compensation for worked example.*

Also, as seen from Fig. 11.16, the angle α is $180° - 45° - 113°$, i.e.

$$\alpha = 22°$$

Now the angle of lag ϕ produced by a phase-lag network is given
by

$$\phi = \tan^{-1}\omega T_d - \tan^{-1}\omega T_d G_\infty$$

This angle is negative, hence making $\phi = -\alpha$ at an angular frequency of 0·2 rad/s we have

$$\alpha = \tan^{-1}\omega T_d G_\infty - \tan^{-1}\omega T_d$$

or $\qquad 22° = \tan^{-1}(0·2 \times T_d \times 48) - \tan^{-1}(0·2T_d)$

298

Now tan $22° = 0.404$, hence

$$T_d = \frac{47 + \sqrt{(47^2 - 4 \times 0.404^2 \times 48)}}{2 \times 0.2 \times 48 \times 0.404}$$

$$\therefore \qquad T_d = 12.1 \text{ sec}$$

The design must now be checked using a Nyquist diagram. The compensated system has an open-loop transfer function $(\theta_o/\epsilon)'$ given by

$$\left(\frac{\theta_o}{\epsilon}\right)' = \frac{10}{j\omega(1 + j\omega)^2} \times \frac{1 + j12.1\omega}{1 + j581\omega}$$

The magnitudes and phases of this transfer function are shown in the table below.

ω (rad/s)	Open-loop Magnitude	Open-loop Angle	Closed-loop Magnitude
0.07	4.79	$-146.8°$	1.20
0.10	2.73	$-139.9°$	1.33
0.12	2.07	$-137.8°$	1.38
0.15	1.55	$-135.3°$	1.41
0.18	1.23	$-134.4°$	1.37
0.22	1.21	$-135.0°$	1.28
0.27	0.75	$-137.2°$	1.10
0.33	0.58	$-140.6°$	0.88
0.39	0.47	$-143.7°$	0.70
0.68	0.21	$-166.0°$	0.26
1.0	0.10	$-184.6°$	0.12

The Nyquist diagram is shown in Fig. 11.17.

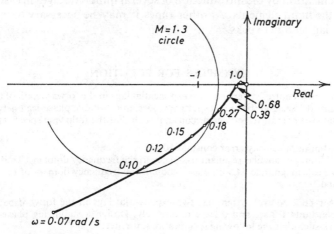

Fig. 11.17 *Nyquist diagram for phase-lag compensated system.*

The value of ω_{rf} is about 0·14 rad/s and the value of M_{pf} is about 1·4. The compensated system is thus within specification.

11.5 Conclusion

In order to bring the performance of a system within specification it is usually necessary to do more than simply make it stable; to stabilize a system of type lower than 2 involves no more than adjustment of gain.

In type 0 or type 1 systems it is often found that without compensation, when the error constant has been set up for adequate damping, using Brown's construction the performance is outside specification on two counts:

(i) The angular resonant frequency ω_{rf} is either too high or too low to give the desired transient response.

(ii) The error constant is too low.

It has been shown in this chapter how in many cases cascaded phase-lead networks may be used to increase ω_{rf} and the error constant without impairing system stability. It has also been shown that cascaded phase-lag networks may be used to decrease ω_{rf} and increase the error constant, again without impairing stability.

Type 2 systems, whilst inherently unstable can be made stable by the introduction of cascaded phase-lead networks.

This chapter has introduced routine methods of synthesizing phase-lead and phase-lag networks for the compensation of systems. Some systems cannot be brought within specification by means of single phase-lead or phase-lag networks. Sometimes it is possible to satisfy a specification by the introduction of several buffered stages in cascade with the main elements. At other times it may be necessary to introduce lag-lead networks.[22]

EXAMPLES FOR SOLUTION

1. A type 1 control system has two exponential lags in the forward path of time-constants 0·2 sec and 0·05 sec respectively. Design a suitable phase-lead network and state the overall velocity error constant such that the following specifications are met:

(i) Minimum velocity error constant 10 sec^{-1}.

(ii) Minimum angular resonant frequency in the frequency domain 10 rad/s.

(iii) Peak magnitude M_{pf} on closed-loop in the frequency domain of between 1·25 and 1·35.

2. A type 2 control system has two exponential lags in the forward path of time constants 1·0 sec and 0·1 sec respectively. Design a stabilizing phase-lead network such that the following specifications are met:

(i) Minimum acceleration error constant 0·04 sec^{-2}.

(ii) Minimum angular resonant frequency in the frequency domain of at least 0·5 rad/s.

(iii) Peak magnitude on closed-loop $M_{pf} = 1·3 \pm 10\%$.

3. A type 0 system has three exponential lags having time constants of 0·1 sec, 0·3 sec and 1 sec respectively. Design a phase-lag network which when connected in cascade with the main elements will give the following specifications:

(i) Error constant at least 100.

(ii) Angular resonant frequency $\omega_{rf} = 2·5$ rad/s $\pm 10\%$.

(iii) Peak magnitude on closed-loop $M_{pf} = 1·3 \pm 10\%$.

Chapter Twelve

Parallel Compensation using the inverse Nyquist Diagram

12.1 Introduction

Series compensation, as described in chapter 11, provides a potent and economical method of bringing the performance of a system within specification; there are, however, many occasions, where, for various reasons, parallel compensation is more useful. This involves the use of auxiliary feedback. The method of compensation chosen for any particular application will depend upon various factors, some of which are:

(*a*) The physical nature of the system. In electrically operated control systems usually either type is possible but in a specific system one type may be more practical. In a hydraulic, pneumatic, or mechanical system a suitable device for series (or parallel) compensation may not exist.

(*b*) The type of carrier. The most suitable form of compensation will depend on whether the error signal is modulated or not.

(*c*) Economic factors. In many cases either series or parallel compensation might be practically feasible; however, one method might require more expensive equipment than the other. Furthermore there will be some systems in which a combination of series and parallel compensation provide the best solution.

The objects of this chapter are to show how parallel compensation may be used to bring the performance of a system within specification and to describe methods of synthesizing the parameters of the compensating devices. It will be shown that the inverse Nyquist diagram offers the simplest methods of synthesis.

12.2 Basic Analysis of a System with Parallel Compensation

A simple feedback system is shown in Fig. 12.1 (*a*); in Fig. 12.1 (*b*) an extra parallel element of transfer function H_2 has been added to provide auxiliary feedback signals.

Parallel Compensation using the inverse Nyquist Diagram

The open-loop transfer function of the basic system is H_1. The open-loop transfer function of the system with the extra element is given by

$$\frac{\theta_o}{\epsilon} = \frac{H_1}{1 + H_1 H_2}$$

(see §9.5.1).

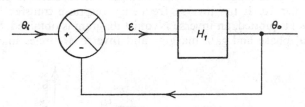

(a) Simple feedback system.

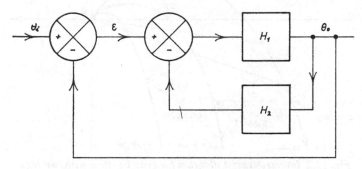

(b) System with extra parallel element.

Fig. 12.1 *Defining parallel compensation.*

Now if we write down the reciprocal of this transfer function we have

$$\frac{\epsilon}{\theta_o} = \frac{1 + H_1 H_2}{H_1}$$

$\therefore$
$$\frac{\epsilon}{\theta_o} = H_1^{-1} + H_2 \tag{1}$$

The reciprocal of a transfer function is usually called the *inverse transfer function*. Equation (1) above represents the basis of synthesis of the parallel compensating device. It means that the inverse open-loop transfer function of the system with the extra parallel element is equal to the inverse open-loop transfer function of the simple system added to the actual transfer function of the parallel device. If the frequency response is used, the inverse transfer function H_1^{-1} can be represented by a frequency locus on the complex plane. The effect of

303

a transfer function H_2 can then be determined using a point by point vector addition of two loci.

12.3 Inverse Nyquist Diagrams

If a frequency response transfer function $H(j\omega)$ is plotted as a locus on the Argand diagram, a Nyquist diagram is produced as explained in chapter 10. If the inverse frequency response transfer function $H^{-1}(j\omega)$ is plotted, an inverse Nyquist diagram is obtained. Stability criteria, phase and gain margins and inverse M-circles may all be

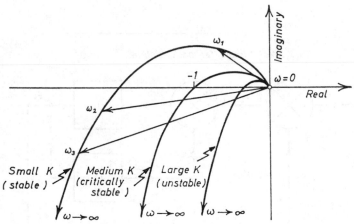

Fig. 12.2 *Inverse Nyquist diagram for type* 1 *system with two lags.*

used to aid synthesis. Inverse Nyquist diagrams are as simple to construct as Nyquist diagrams. Consider a type 1 system with two exponential lags; the open-loop transfer function $\theta_o/\epsilon(j\omega)$ for such a system is given by

$$\frac{\theta_o}{\epsilon}(j\omega) = \frac{K}{j\omega(1 + j\omega T_1)(1 + j\omega T_2)}$$

hence

$$\frac{\epsilon}{\theta_o}(j\omega) = \frac{j\omega(1 + j\omega T_1)(1 + j\omega T_2)}{K}$$

The magnitude and phase of $\epsilon/\theta(j\omega)$ can be determined for various values of ω using:

$$\left|\frac{\epsilon}{\theta_o}(j\omega)\right| = \frac{\omega\sqrt{\{1 + (\omega T_1)^2\}}\sqrt{\{1 + (\omega T_2)^2\}}}{K}$$

and

$$\angle\frac{\epsilon}{\theta_o}(j\omega) = +90° + \tan^{-1}\omega T_1 + \tan^{-1}\omega T_2$$

304

Inverse Nyquist diagrams are shown for this system in Fig. 12.2. Three frequency loci are drawn for three values of K. On the inverse diagram absolute stability is denoted by the *enclosure* of the point $(-1, j0)$ by the frequency locus. Thus for large values of K, it is seen that the locus does not enclose the -1 point and the system is thus absolutely unstable. Use may be made of phase margin and gain margin as shown in Fig. 12.3.

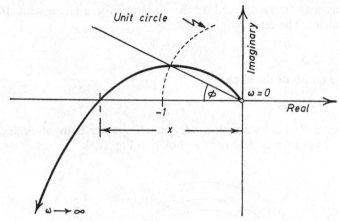

Fig. 12.3 *Phase margin and gain margin on the inverse Nyquist diagram.*

The phase margin is the angle ϕ and the gain margin expressed in dB is $20\log_{10} x$.

12.4 Inverse M-Circles

The M-circle proved to be of considerable use in the design of series compensating devices. Inverse M-circles are of equal value in the design of parallel compensating devices.

Consider any point on the inverse Nyquist diagram defined by $x + jy$.

Now
$$M = \left| \frac{\theta_o}{\theta_i}(j\omega) \right|$$

But
$$\frac{\theta_o}{\theta_i} = \frac{\theta_o}{\epsilon + \theta_o} = \frac{1}{\epsilon/\theta_o + 1}$$

∴
$$M = \left| \frac{1}{\epsilon/\theta_o(j\omega) + 1} \right|$$

$$= \left| \frac{1}{x + jy + 1} \right|$$

305

$$\therefore \qquad M = \frac{1}{\sqrt{\{(x+1)^2 + y^2\}}}$$

or
$$M^2 = \frac{1}{(x+1)^2 + y^2}$$

rearrangement gives
$$y^2 + (x+1)^2 = \frac{1}{M^2}$$

This may be recognized as the equation for a circle with M as parameter. The centre of the circle is

$$x_o = -1$$
$$y_o = 0$$

The radius of the circle is

$$r = \frac{1}{M}$$

Inverse M-circles are thus very much simpler than M-circles. A selection of inverse M-circles is shown in Fig. 12.4.

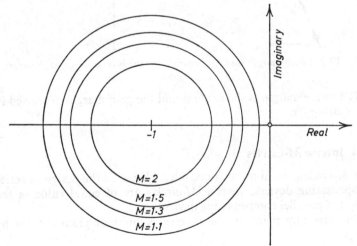

Fig. 12.4 *Inverse M-circles.*

12.5 The Effects of Typical Parallel Compensating Elements on Inverse Loci

12.5.1 *General*

Some typical parallel compensating arrangements involve the use of:

(i) Auxiliary velocity (rate) feedback using, for example, tacho-generators (transfer function $k_s j\omega$).

306

(ii) Auxiliary 'transient velocity feedback' using, for example, resistance–capacitance coupled tachogenerators [transfer function $k_s T(j\omega)^2/(1 + j\omega T)$].

(iii) Auxiliary acceleration feedback using accelerometers (transfer function $k_a(j\omega)^2$).

Auxiliary feedback may often be used to bring a system within specification and this section will be devoted to investigating exactly what effects such feedback will have.

12.5.2 The Effect of Auxiliary Velocity (Rate) Feedback

Take as example an unstable type 1 system with two lags. Thus

$$H_1^{-1} = \frac{j\omega(1 + j\omega T_1)(1 + j\omega T_2)}{K}$$

and for a tachogenerator

$$H_2 = k_s j\omega$$

The inverse Nyquist diagram is shown in Fig. 12.5.

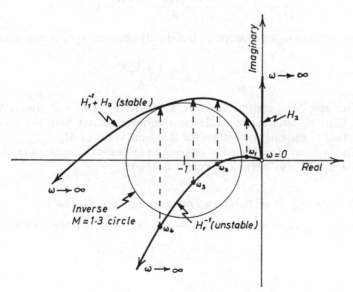

Fig. 12.5 *Effect of auxiliary velocity feedback.*

Provided that k_s is large enough, the combined locus $H_1^{-1} + H_2$ can be made to enclose the point -1. Thus an unstable system can be made stable by this means. However, if stability were the only criterion, as has been explained previously, this could be achieved by lowering the value of K. More important, velocity feedback, allows us to increase the angular resonant frequency ω_{rf}. If the system were stabilized by reducing K, the value of ω_{rf} would be approximately ω_1 If velocity feedback were used a higher value ω_4 could be achieved. The effect on the error constant can be determined by a simple analysis.

In D-form

$$H_1^{-1} + H_2 = \frac{D(1 + DT_1)(1 + DT_2)}{K} + k_s D$$

Thus for the compensated system

$$\frac{\epsilon}{\theta_o} = \frac{D(1 + DT_1)(1 + DT_2)}{K} + k_s D$$

But

$$\frac{\epsilon}{\theta_o} = \frac{\epsilon}{\theta_i - \epsilon}$$

$\therefore$

$$\frac{\epsilon}{\theta_i - \epsilon} = \frac{D(1 + DT_1)(1 + DT_2)}{K} + k_s D$$

$\therefore$

$$\frac{\epsilon}{D(\theta_i - \epsilon)} = \frac{(1 + DT_1)(1 + DT_2)}{K} + k_s$$

For a ramp input of slope ω_i the steady-state error ϵ_{ss} is thus given by

$$\frac{\epsilon_{ss}}{\omega_i} = \frac{1}{K} + k_s = \frac{1 + k_s K}{K}$$

The new error constant is thus $K/(1 + k_s K)$. This will always be less than K, but can be made considerably greater than the error constant of the original system for the same value of M_{pf}.

Thus velocity feedback can be used to increase the value of ω_{rf} for a system and also increase the error constant.

12.5.3 The Effect of Auxiliary Transient Velocity Feedback

Considering again an unstable type 1 system with two lags, we have

$$H_1^{-1} = \frac{j\omega(1 + j\omega T_1)(1 + j\omega T_2)}{K}$$

$$H_2 = \frac{k_s T(j\omega)^2}{1 + j\omega T}$$

The inverse Nyquist diagram is shown in Fig. 12.6.

It is evident that apart from stabilizing an unstable system, auxiliary transient velocity feedback has the effect of increasing the resonant frequency. The effect of transient velocity feedback on the error constant can be readily determined.

In D-form

$$H_1^{-1} + H_2 = \frac{D(1 + DT_1)(1 + DT_2)}{K} + \frac{Tk_s D^2}{1 + DT}$$

Thus for the compensated system

$$\frac{\epsilon}{\theta_o} = \frac{D(1 + DT_1)(1 + DT_2)}{K} + \frac{Tk_s D^2}{1 + DT}$$

$$\therefore \qquad \frac{\epsilon}{\theta_i - \epsilon} = \frac{D(1 + DT_1)(1 + DT_2)}{K} + \frac{Tk_s D^2}{1 + DT}$$

or $\qquad \dfrac{\epsilon}{D(\theta_i - \epsilon)} = \dfrac{(1 + DT_1)(1 + DT_2)}{K} + \dfrac{Tk_s D}{1 + DT}$

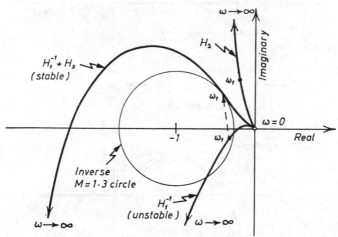

Fig. 12.6 *Effect of auxiliary transient velocity feedback.*

For a ramp input of slope ω_i

$$\frac{\epsilon_{ss}}{\omega_i} = \frac{1}{K}$$

The error constant is thus K, which can be made considerably greater than the error constant of the uncompensated system for the same M_{pf}.

Transient velocity feedback can thus be used to increase the resonant frequency and the error constant of a given system.

12.5.4 *The Effects of Auxiliary Acceleration Feedback*

The transfer function representing auxiliary acceleration feedback is given by

$$H_2 = \pm k_a(j\omega)^2$$

309

When the auxiliary feedback is negative or 'degenerative' the positive sign applies but when the auxiliary feedback is positive or 'regenerative' the negative sign applies. The effect of acceleration feedback is to shift the points on the original locus to the left or right an amount proportional to frequency squared.

Negative acceleration feedback may be used to stabilize an absolutely unstable type 0 or type 1 system. The relative stability so

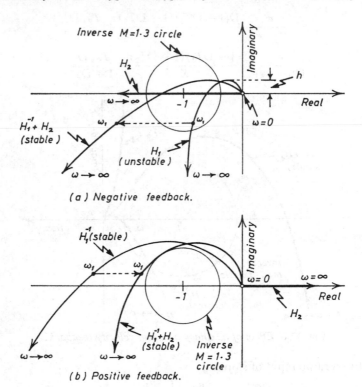

Fig. 12.7 *Effect of auxiliary acceleration feedback.*

achieved will rarely be adequate in practice however because the phase margin will almost invariably be inadequate. Adequate relative stability can only be achieved on the rare occasions when the height h in Fig. 12.7 (a) is equal to the radius of a suitable inverse M-circle (e.g. $M = 1\cdot3$).

However, it is also possible to make use of the right shift imposed by positive acceleration feedback. It is usually possible to obtain a slightly higher resonant frequency for the same relative stability by lowering the error constant and adding positive acceleration feedback [Fig. 12.7 (b)].

In general pure acceleration feedback is not as useful as either velocity feedback or transient velocity feedback. Acceleration feedback in combination with velocity feedback can be of considerable use however.

12.6 Design of Parallel Compensated Systems

12.6.1 Compensation of Type 0 and Type 1 Systems using Auxiliary Velocity (Rate) Feedback

In systems where with the error constant adjusted for adequate stability it is found that the angular resonant frequency is lower than specified and the error constant is also lower, it is frequently possible to bring the performance within specification by using auxiliary negative velocity feedback. The design philosophy is to bring the resonant frequency within specification, whilst maintaining adequate stability ($M_{pf} = 1\cdot3$) and then to test whether the error constant is also within specification; if not the specification for the resonant frequency is then arbitrarily raised and a further trial made. A design procedure which will achieve a rapid approximate solution is as follows:

(1) Draw in the relevant inverse circle for the specified value of M_{pf}.

(2) Mark on this circle the proposed point of contact with the inverse locus of the compensated system. Experience helps with this but when M_{pf} is $1\cdot3$, to a first approximation the point of contact is directly above the point $(-1\cdot4, j0)$. In general suppose that the real co-ordinate of the point of contact is x.

(3) Determine an expression for the real part of the inverse frequency locus in terms of the angular frequency ω and a variable error constant K. Substitute in this expression the value of the specified angular resonant frequency ω'_{rf} and hence determine the value of K such that the numerical value of the expression for the real part of the inverse transfer function is equal to x.

(4) The exact position of the point on the inverse frequency locus at the frequency ω'_{rf} is then found. Let this lie a distance h below the proposed point of contact with the M-circle. The value of the tacho-generator constant k_s can now be calculated, because $h = k_s \omega'_{rf}$.

(5) The overall error constant is calculated. (For a type 1 system this is $K/(1 + k_s K)$.) If the overall error constant is within specification, the complete uncompensated locus is drawn and from it the complete compensated locus is determined. The compensated locus should possess a clean tangency with the M-circle at the desired frequency. Usually there are tolerance limits on the specification and if the performance is within these limits the initial design is successful.

If the error constant is too low, however, the value of ω'_{rf} can be raised and a second trial made.

The above method of design will be illustrated by considering a type 1 system with two exponential lags. Fig. 12.8 shows the relevant constructions.

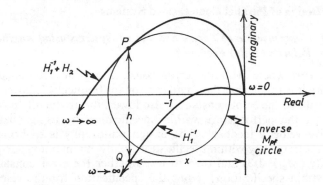

Fig. 12.8 *Design using auxiliary velocity feedback.*

The inverse M-circle for the specified value of M_{pf} is drawn and the point P marked on. The inverse transfer function of the original system H_1^{-1} is given by

$$H_1^{-1} = \frac{j\omega(1 + j\omega T_1)(1 + j\omega T_2)}{K}$$

The real part of H_1^{-1} is $-\dfrac{\omega^2(T_1 + T_2)}{K}$

Hence $$x = \frac{(\omega'_{rf})^2(T_1 + T_2)}{K}$$

or $$K = \frac{(\omega'_{rf})^2(T_1 + T_2)}{x}$$

The exact position of the point Q may now be found by determining the imaginary part of H_1^{-1} for this value of K at the angular frequency ω'_{rf}. Thus the distance h can be determined. Then the tacho constant k_s can be found from

$$h = k_s \omega'_{rf}$$

i.e. $$k_s = h/\omega'_{rf}$$

The overall velocity error constant $K/(1 + k_s K)$ is now calculated. If this is within specification, the original inverse frequency locus is computed and drawn. The inverse locus of the compensated system can then be rapidly constructed and checked for a clean tangency with the M-circle at ω'_{rf}.

Worked Example

A type 1 system has two exponential lags both having time constants of 1 sec. Design a parallel compensated system using rate feedback which will have the following specifications:

(i) Error constant of at least 1 sec^{-1}.
(ii) Resonant angular frequency ω'_{rf} of between 3·0 and 4·0 rad/s.
(iii) M_{pf} between 1·25 and 1·35.

Solution

The inverse open-loop transfer function H_1^{-1} is given by

$$H_1^{-1} = \frac{j\omega(1 + j\omega)^2}{K}$$

Using $M_{pf} = 1·3$, the point of contact of the inverse compensated locus will lie approximately above the point $(-1·4, j0)$.

The real part of H_1^{-1} is $-2\omega^2/K$, thus for a nominal resonant angular frequency of 3·5 rad/s, we have

$$1·4 = \frac{2 \times 3·5^2}{K}$$

$\therefore$
$$K = \frac{2 \times 3·5^2}{1·4}$$

i.e. $\qquad\qquad K = 17·5 \, \text{sec}^{-1}$

The distance h can now be determined. The height of the point of contact above the negative real axis is approximately 0·657. The value of the imaginary part of H_1^{-1} is $\omega(1 - \omega^2 T^2)/K$, thus at $\omega = 3·5$, this is $3·5(1 - 3·5^2)/17·5$, i.e. $-2·25$.

Hence $\qquad\qquad h = 0·657 + 2·25$

$\qquad\qquad\qquad = 2·907$

Now $\qquad\qquad h = k_s \omega'_{rf}$

$\therefore \qquad\qquad 2·907 = k_s \times 3·5$

$\therefore \qquad\qquad k_s = \frac{2·907}{3·5}$

i.e. $\qquad\qquad k_s = 0·83 \, \text{sec}$

Now the error constant is $K/(1 + k_s K)$ which is

$$17·5/(1 + 0·83 \times 17·5)$$

i.e. error constant $= 1·13 \, \text{sec}^{-1}$.

The error constant is thus within the specification.

The complete inverse locus for H_1^{-1} will now be determined.

$$H_1^{-1} = \frac{j\omega(1 + j\omega)^2}{K}$$

Angular Frequency ω (rad/s)	H_1^{-1} Magnitude	Angle	Auxiliary Rate Feedback $k_s\omega$
1·0	0·114	180·0°	0·830
1·2	0·168	190·4°	0·998
1·4	0·237	198·9°	1·16
1·8	0·436	211·9°	1·49
2·0	0·571	216·9°	1·66
2·6	1·150	227·9°	2·16
3·0	1·715	233·1°	2·49
3·5	2·640	238·1°	2·91
3·7	3·120	239·8°	3·07
4·0	3·880	241·9°	3·32
4·5	5·460	244·9°	3·74

The inverse Nyquist diagrams for the uncompensated system and the compensated system are plotted in Fig. 12.9.

The angular resonant frequency is about 3·7 rad/s but the value of M_{pf} is about 1·47. The first trial has not been completely successful because M_{pf} should lie between 1·25 and 1·35.

A complete redesign is, however, unnecessary as it is possible to raise the locus by a small increase in k_s.

At $\omega = 3·7$ rad/s, distance of uncompensated locus below apparent point of tangency with inverse M-circle is about 3·2. Thus a new value of k_s is given by

$$3·2 = 3·7k_s$$

$$\therefore \qquad k_s = \frac{3·2}{3·7} = 0·865$$

The new table of values for the auxiliary rate feedback is given below.

ω (rad/s)	$k_s\omega$
1·0	0·865
1·2	1·04
1·4	1·21
1·8	1·56
2·0	1·73
2·6	2·25
3·0	2·60
3·5	3·03
3·7	3·20
4·0	3·46
4·5	3·90

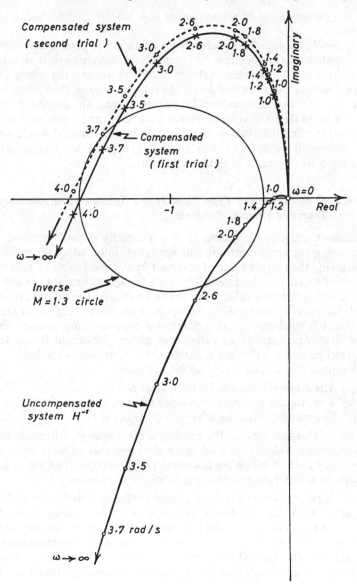

Fig. 12.9 *Inverse Nyquist diagram for system compensated by velocity feedback.*

The compensated locus for the second trial is also shown in Fig. 12.9. The value of M_{pf} is now about 1·33 and ω_{rf} is about 3·8 rad/s. The new value of the error constant is $17·5/(1 + 0·865 \times 17·5)$, i.e. error constant $= 1·09$ sec^{-1}.

The performance of the system is now within specification on all counts.

It should be noted that velocity feedback is not particularly useful in the stabilization of type 2 systems. Such systems are used when velocity lag is intolerable. Velocity feedback around the whole of a type 2 system would in fact lower the type number of the system and velocity lag would therefore be reintroduced. An expedient here would be to feed the velocity signal back into the system at a point beyond the first integration. Stabilization by this method would only be successful in systems which already contain very substantial leading time constants in the forward path.

12.6.2 Compensation of Type 0 and Type 1 Systems using Auxiliary Transient Velocity Feedback

Transient velocity feedback is a particularly potent method of increasing the error constant and yet maintaining adequate stability and giving the correct value of resonant frequency. In this respect it is superior to velocity feedback for which the error constant cannot be set at any minimum value once the resonant frequency and relative stability have been specified. As has been shown in §12.5.3 the error constant is unaltered by this particular compensating arrangement and so can be fixed at an early stage during the design in the sure knowledge that it will remain at that value after compensation.

Suppose that a system is specified as follows:

(*a*) The error constant must be at least K'.
(*b*) The angular resonant frequency must be at least ω'_{rf}.
(*c*) The stability must be adequate (e.g. $M_{pf} = 1 \cdot 3$).

Let us also assume that the uncompensated system, when adjusted for adequate stability, has an error constant and angular resonant frequency both of which are lower than that specified. The method of design to achieve the specified performance is as below:

(i) Draw in the relevant inverse circle for the specified value of M_{pf}.

(ii) Mark on this circle the proposed point of contact of inverse locus with the inverse M-circle. Experience helps with this, but when M_{pf} is $1 \cdot 3$, to a first approximation the point of contact is above the point $(-0 \cdot 6, j0)$; this will be referred to as point P. (*Note that the likely point of contact is different from that for systems compensated with velocity feedback.*)

(iii) Calculate the magnitude and phase of the inverse transfer function of the uncompensated system for the angular frequency ω'_{rf} based on an error constant equal to K'. Plot this point (which will be called Q) on the polar diagram.

For compensation to be possible with this value of error constant, Q must lie below P and to the right of it.

If Q lies to the left of P, the error constant may be raised arbitrarily until it lies a little to the right.

(iv) Join P to Q and find the angle ϕ which this line makes with the real axis (see Fig. 12.10) and measure the length A of the line.

The transfer function H_2 of the parallel compensator is given by

$$H_2 = \frac{k_s T(j\omega)^2}{1 + j\omega T}$$

The phase angle ϕ is thus given by

$$\phi = 180° - \tan^{-1} \omega'_{rf} T$$

$$\therefore \qquad \tan^{-1} \omega'_{rf} T = 180° - \phi$$

From this the time constant T can be calculated.

Finally the value of A can be used to find k_s because

$$A = \frac{k_s T(\omega'_{rf})^2}{\sqrt{\{1 + (\omega'_{rf} T)^2\}}}$$

It only remains to check whether the design has been successful. The complete loci for H_1^{-1} and H_2 are computed and the inverse locus for the compensated system $H_1^{-1} + H_2$ is determined by vector addition for each frequency. This should possess a clean tangency with the M-circle at the desired frequency. If it does not, slight adjustments can be made to k_s and/or T on a trial and error basis until this condition is reached.

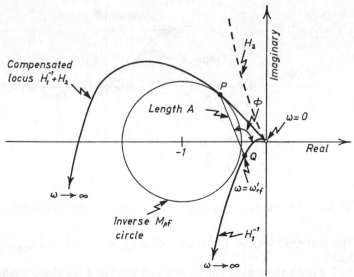

Fig. 12.10 *Compensation using transient velocity feedback.*

317

The method which has been described above is illustrated in Fig. 12.10 where the uncompensated system is type 1 with two exponential lags.

Worked Example

A type 1 system has two exponential lags in the forward path of time constants 0·2 sec and 0·5 sec respectively. Design a parallel compensated arrangement using transient velocity feedback in order that the system shall have the following specifications:

(i) An error constant of at least 100 sec^{-1}.

(ii) An angular resonant frequency in the frequency domain lying between 1·8 and 2·2 rad/s.

(iii) Adequate stability with M_{pf} lying between 1·2 and 1·4.

Solution

The open-loop inverse transfer function H_I^{-1} of the uncompensated system for the specified error constant is given by

$$H_I^{-1} = \{j\omega(1 + j\omega 0·2)(1 + j\omega 0·5)\}/100$$

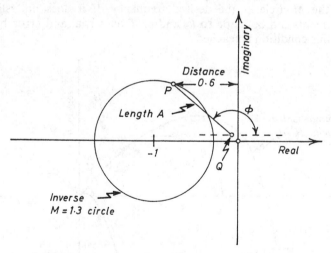

Fig. 12.11 *Illustrating design of transient velocity feedback arrangement.*

The first trial will be aimed at obtaining $M_{pf} = 1·3$ and $\omega'_{rf} = 2·0$ rad/s.

At 2·0 rad/s the magnitude of H_I^{-1} is 0·0305 and the phase angle is +156·8°. Fig. 12.11 illustrates the first stage of the design.

Now the length $A = 0.86$ and the angle $\phi = 131.5°$.

$$\therefore \quad \omega'_{rf}T = \tan(180° - 131.5°)$$

$$= 1.13$$

$$\therefore \quad T = \frac{1.13}{2}$$

$$= 0.565 \text{ sec}$$

But
$$k_s = \frac{A\sqrt{\{1 + (\omega'_{rf}T)^2\}}}{T(\omega'_{rf})^2}$$

$$= \frac{0.86\sqrt{(1 + 1.275)}}{2.26} = 0.573 \text{ sec}$$

Thus
$$H_2 = \frac{k_s\, T(j\omega)^2}{1 + j\omega T}$$

$$= \frac{0.573 \times 0.565(j\omega)^2}{1 + j\omega 0.565}$$

$$= \frac{-0.324\omega^2}{1 + j\omega 0.565}$$

$$= \frac{-0.324\omega^2(1 - j\omega 0.565)}{1 + (\omega 0.565)^2}$$

$$= \frac{-0.324\omega^2}{1 + 0.319\omega^2} + \frac{j\omega^3\, 0.183}{1 + 0.319\omega^2}$$

A table of values of H_1^{-1} and H_2 is shown below. H_2 has been calculated in terms of its real and imaginary parts, rather than its magnitude and phase, so as to achieve better precision in the construction of the compensated locus.

Angular Frequency ω (rad/s)	H_1^{-1}		H_2	
	Magnitude	Phase	Real	Imaginary
1·0	0·0114	127·9°	−0·246	0·139
1·6	0·0216	146·4°	−0·456	0·414
1·8	0·0257	151·8°	−0·515	0·525
2·0	0·0305	156·8°	−0·570	0·645
2·2	0·0358	161·5°	−0·616	0·766
2·6	0·0480	169·9°	−0·694	1·020
2·8	0·0553	173·9°	−0·725	1·148
3·0	0·0630	177·3°	−0·752	1·275

Fig. 12.12 shows the low-frequency section of the compensated locus, indicating that M_{pf} is approximately 1·5 and the angular resonant frequency ω'_{rf} is approximately 1·5 rad/s.

The first design has thus failed to bring the system within specification and another trial is needed. However, the first trial has indicated how we may best proceed in the second. The value of M_{pf} is too high and the value of ω'_{rf} is too low. Thus if we now use the same design technique but artificially lower the value of M_{pf} used and artificially raise the value of ω'_{rf} used it is possible that our second design may be more successful. Taking $M_{pf} = 1\cdot1$ and $\omega'_{rf} = 3$ rad/s leads to $A = 0\cdot98$ and $\phi = 123°$.

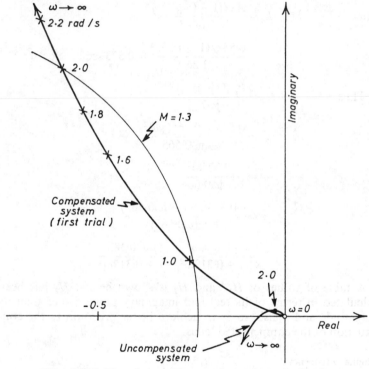

Fig. 12.12 *First design using transient velocity feedback.*

From these we obtain $T = 0\cdot514$ sec and $k_s = 0\cdot39$ sec, giving a transfer function

$$H_2 = \frac{0\cdot39 \times 0\cdot514(j\omega)^2}{1 + j\omega0\cdot514}$$

Another table of values of H_1^{-1} and H_2 is shown below.

The uncompensated and compensated inverse frequency loci are shown in Fig. 12.13.

The closed-loop frequency response can be determined by measuring the distances of each point on the compensated inverse frequency

Angular Frequency ω (rad/s)	H_1^{-1} Magnitude	Phase	H_2 Real	Imaginary
1·0	0·0114	127·9°	−0·158	0·081
1·6	0·0216	146·4°	−0·307	0·252
2·0	0·0305	156·8°	−0·392	0·403
2·6	0·0480	169·9°	−0·485	0·646
3·0	0·0630	177·3°	−0·535	0·824
3·5	0·0860	185·2°	−0·580	1·04
4·0	0·144	192·1°	−0·625	1·28
5·0	0·190	203·2°	−0·660	1·69
6·0	0·297	211·8°	−0·688	2·12
7·0	0·439	218·5°	−0·705	2·54
8·0	0·622	224·0°	−0·715	2·94
10·0	1·14	232·1°	−0·730	3·75
12·0	1·90	237·9°	−0·740	4·55
14·0	2·92	242·2°	−0·745	5·35
16·0	4·34	245·5°	−0·748	6·15
18·0	6·70	248·1°	−0·752	6·95

locus from the point $-1, j0$. This gives the values of $\theta_i/\theta_o(j\omega)$ for each frequency; the magnitude of the closed-loop frequency response can then be calculated by taking the reciprocals of each of these. The table below gives the values of the closed-loop magnitudes calculated in this way.

Angular Frequency ω (rad/s)	Magnitude $\left\lvert \dfrac{\theta_i}{\theta_o}(j\omega) \right\rvert$	Magnitude $\left\lvert \dfrac{\theta_o}{\theta_i}(j\omega) \right\rvert$
1·0	0·82	1·22
1·6	0·73	1·37
2·0	0·72	1·39
2·6	0·82	1·22
3·0	0·93	1·075
3·5	1·08	0·925
4·0	1·28	0·780
5·0	1·63	0·613
6·0	1·98	0·505
7·0	2·28	0·438
8·0	2·52	0·396
10·0	2·84	0·352
12·0	3·02	0·331
14·0	3·00	0·333
16·0	2·70	0·370
18·0	2·38	0·420

Fig. 12.14 shows a graph of the magnitude of the closed-loop frequency response versus angular frequency for the compensated system.

The maximum magnitude M_{pf} is about 1·4 and occurs at an angular frequency of about 1·9 rad/s. There is a slight double humping effect at an angular frequency of about 19 rad/s but the second hump is

321

well attenuated and is unlikely to affect the transient response very greatly. The second design is just within specification and satisfactorily solves the problem.

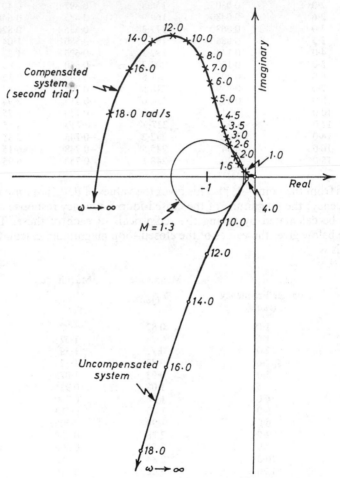

Fig. 12.13 *Second design using transient velocity feedback.*

12.6.3 Compensation of Type 0 and Type 1 Systems using Auxiliary Acceleration Feedback

As explained in §12.5.1, acceleration feedback may be used in two ways:

(a) Negative acceleration feedback; this will stabilize and lower the resonant frequency of some systems. The method is strictly limited in application and there is no point in developing a design procedure for it. For negative acceleration feedback the transfer function of the compensating element is given by $H_2 = + k_a(j\omega)^2$.

(b) Positive acceleration feedback: this will increase the resonant frequency of a system in which the error constant is already lower than or equal to that necessary to give adequate damping. A simple design method will be described. For positive acceleration feedback the transfer function of the compensating element is given by $H_2 = - k_a(j\omega)^2$.

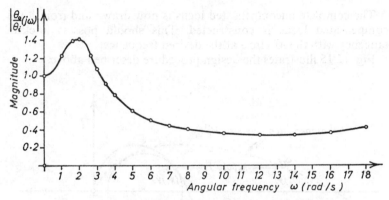

Fig. 12.14 *Closed-loop frequency response of compensated system.*

Suppose a system specification demands the following:

(i) A resonant frequency ω'_{rf} (greater than ω_{rf}, the resonant frequency achievable by simple gain adjustment).
(ii) A minimum value of error constant K'.
(iii) Adequate stability with a quoted value of M_{pf}.

A suitable design procedure is as follows:

(1) Determine the phase angle of the inverse transfer function at ω'_{rf}. This must be less than $180°$ for design to be possible.
(2) Draw in the relevant inverse circle for the specified value of M_{pf}.
(3) Mark on this circle the proposed point of contact with the inverse locus of the compensated system. Experience helps with this, but when M_{pf} is $1\cdot3$, to a first approximation the point of contact is directly above the point $(-1\cdot4, j0)$. In general suppose that the point of contact is P given by (x, jy).
(4) Determine an expression for the imaginary part of the inverse frequency locus in terms of the angular frequency ω and a variable error constant K. Substitute in this expression the value of the specified

323

angular resonant frequency ω'_{rf} and hence determine the value of K such that the numerical value of the expression for the imaginary part of inverse transfer function is equal to y. The value of K must be equal to or greater than K' the specified error constant otherwise the specification cannot be met using the method.

(5) Determine the real part of the inverse transfer function at ω'_{rf} using the value of K found in (4). Let this have a value r. Then the required right shift of the inverse frequency locus can be achieved by making

$$k_a (\omega'_{rf})^2 = x - r \quad \text{(a positive distance)}$$

The complete uncompensated locus is now drawn and from it the compensated locus is constructed. This should possess a clean tangency with the M-circle at the desired frequency.

Fig. 12.15 illustrates the design procedure described above.

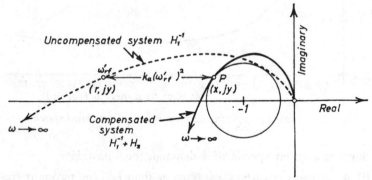

Fig. 12.15 *Illustrating parallel compensation using positive acceleration feedback.*

Worked Example

A type 1 system has two exponential lags in the forward path of time constants 0·2 sec and 0·05 sec respectively. Design a parallel compensated system using positive auxiliary acceleration feedback which will have the following specifications.

    (i) Error constant of at least 4 sec^{-1}.
    (ii) Resonant angular frequency ω'_{rf} of between 7·5 and 8·5 rad/s.
    (iii) M_{pf} between 1·25 and 1·35.

Solution

The design will be based on a nominal value of $\omega'_{rf} = 8$ rad/s and a nominal value of $M_{pf} = 1·3$.

324

The inverse transfer function of the uncompensated system is given by

$$H_1^{-1} = \frac{j\omega(1 + j\omega 0\cdot 2)(1 + j\omega 0\cdot 05)}{K}$$

At an angular frequency of $8\cdot 0$ rad/s, the phase angle is given by

$$\angle H_1^{-1} = 90° + \tan^{-1} 1\cdot 6 + \tan^{-1} 0\cdot 40$$

$$= 90° + 58° + 21\cdot 8°$$

$$= 169\cdot 8°$$

Since this is less than $180°$, the design may proceed.

The imaginary part of the inverse transfer function is

$$\frac{\omega(1 - 0\cdot 01\omega^2)}{K}$$

The proposed point of contact is $(-1\cdot 4, j0\cdot 657)$, thus at $\omega = 8\cdot 0$ rad/s

$$\frac{8(1 - 0\cdot 01 \times 64)}{K} = 0\cdot 657$$

from which $K = 4\cdot 38$ sec^{-1}. This is within the specification of $4\cdot 0$ sec^{-1}.

The real part of H_1^{-1} is

$$\frac{-0\cdot 25\omega^2}{K} = \frac{-0\cdot 25\omega^2}{4\cdot 38}$$

At $\omega = 8$ rad/s, the real part of H_1^{-1} becomes

$$r = \frac{-0\cdot 25 \times 64}{4\cdot 38} = -3\cdot 65$$

Now $$x = -1\cdot 4$$

$\therefore$ $$k_a(\omega'_{rf})^2 = x - r$$

$$= -1\cdot 4 - (-3\cdot 65)$$

$$= 2\cdot 25$$

$\therefore$ since $$\omega'_{rf} = 8\,\text{rad/s}$$

$$k_a = \frac{2\cdot 25}{64}$$

$$= 0\cdot 0352 \text{ sec}^{-2}$$

Thus $$H_2 = -0\cdot 0352(j\omega)^2$$

325

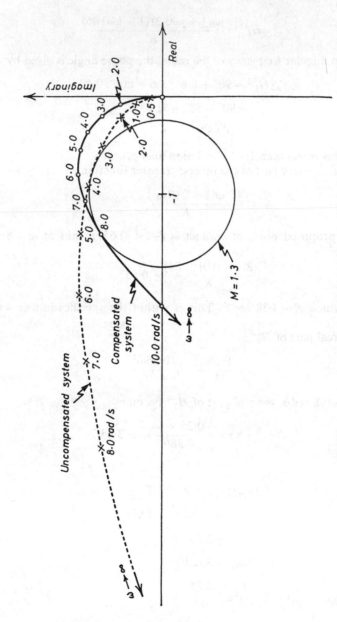

Fig. 12.16 *Inverse frequency loci for system compensated by positive acceleration feedback*

The table below gives values of H_1^{-1} and the magnitudes of H_2.

Angular Frequency ω (rad/s)	H_1^{-1} Magnitude	Phase	Magnitude of H_2
0·5	0·115	97·1°	0·00870
1·0	0·228	104·2°	0·0352
2·0	0·485	117·5°	0·141
3·0	0·809	129·4°	0·317
4·0	1·19	139·9°	0·564
5·0	1·66	149·0°	0·870
6·0	2·24	156·9°	1·27
7·0	2·86	163·8°	1·73
8·0	3·71	169·8°	2·26
10·0	5·71	180·1°	3·52

The uncompensated and compensated inverse frequency loci are plotted in Fig. 12.16. The clean tangency at $\omega = 8$ rad/s with the inverse $M = 1\cdot3$ circle shows that the design has been successful.

12.7 Conclusion

This chapter has shown how the performance of systems may be brought within specification by using parallel compensation. Methods of design have been described for systems requiring compensation by means of auxiliary velocity (rate) feedback, transient velocity feedback and acceleration feedback. The methods described have made use of inverse frequency loci and have been used to yield design solutions for various numerical examples.

In some cases parallel compensation will alone solve the design problem, whereas in many others a combination of series and parallel compensation is necessary to achieve a solution.

The methods discussed have been limited to the compensation of type 0 and type 1 systems. In type 2 systems, other problems are introduced. For instance it is pointless using velocity feedback to compensate a type 2 system, for although stabilization may be possible, the type number of the system will be reduced. The problems associated with the parallel compensation of type 2 systems are not in the least difficult but are omitted from this text because of lack of space.

EXAMPLES FOR SOLUTION

(Assume all systems to have a main feedback of unity.)

1. A type 1 system has two exponential lags in the forward path having time constants 0·1 sec and 0·01 sec respectively. Design a parallel compensated system using velocity (rate) feedback which will have the following specifications:

(i) Error constant of at least 30 sec^{-1}.

(ii) Resonant angular frequency in the frequency domain of between 45 and 55 rad/s.

(iii) M_{pf} lying between 1·2 and 1·4.

2. A type 0 system has three exponential lags in the forward path having time constants 1·0 sec 0·1 sec and 0·01 sec respectively. Design a parallel compensated system using transient velocity feedback which will have the following specifications:

(i) Error constant of at least 100.

(ii) Resonant angular frequency in the frequency domain of between 2·0 and 3·0 rad/s.

(iii) M_{pf} lying between 1·15 and 1·45.

3. A type 1 system has two exponential lags in the forward path having time constants of 1 sec. Design a parallel compensated system using acceleration feedback which will have the following specifications:

(i) Error constant of at least 0·4 sec⁻¹.

(ii) Resonant angular frequency in the frequency domain of between 0·75 rad/s and 0·85 rad/s.

(iii) M_{pf} lying between 1·25 and 1·35.

Chapter Thirteen

Logarithmic Representation of Frequency Response Functions

13.1 Introduction

In chapters 10 and 11 it is shown how frequency response functions can be represented on Nyquist diagrams. This method will yield very satisfactory results when properly applied. The calculation of gain for each frequency puts limitations on the speed at which the method can be applied unless there is immediate access to a computer. Analysis and design of systems, particularly those in which *series compensation* is used, can be achieved more rapidly by employing a co-ordinate representation of open-loop frequency responses using logarithmic scales. In such representations the modulus of the open-loop transfer function, expressed in decibels, i.e. $20\log_{10}\left|\dfrac{\theta_o}{\epsilon}\right|$, and the phase of the open-loop transfer function, i.e. $\angle\dfrac{\theta_o}{\epsilon}$, are plotted as separate ordinates on a linear scale against frequency (or more often angular frequency) plotted as a common abscissa. The frequency axis is normally logarithmic to a base of ten along which equal intervals correspond to a frequency ratio of 10:1 or a *decade*.

These graphs are called Bode diagrams and the advantages of using them are:

(*a*) The graphs associated with commonly encountered transfer functions are easily determined, particularly when straight line approximations (as explained subsequently) are used.

(*b*) The multiplication and division of transfer functions, which are particularly tedious on the Nyquist diagram, are simplified. Multiplication of moduli expressed in decibels involves only addition,

329

whilst division is replaced by subtraction. Phase angles are also added for multiplication and subtracted for division.

(*c*) The phase is related to the slope of the log-modulus characteristic (Bode's theorem).

(*d*) The design of series compensated systems is more rapid.

(*e*) They may be used in the analysis of experimental results for the accurate determination of the constants of a system.

13.2 Graphs of Commonly Encountered Functions

13.2.1 Basic Functions

The forms of the commonly encountered factors in transfer functions are $(j\omega)$, $(1 + j\omega T)$ and $\{k_1(j\omega)^2 + k_2(j\omega) + 1\}$; they may occur in

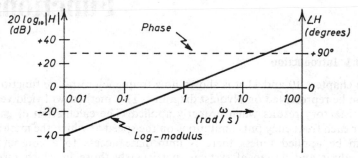

Fig. 13.1 *Bode diagram for $H(j\omega) = j\omega$.*

the denominator or numerator of expressions and may be raised to integral powers.

(*i*) $H(j\omega) = j\omega$

Now

$$20 \log_{10} |H(j\omega)| = 20 \log_{10} \omega$$

The table below shows the value of the log-modulus in decibels for various angular frequencies as calculated from the above formula.

ω (rad/s)	$20 \log_{10} |H(j\omega)|$ (dB)
0·01	−40
0·1	−20
1·0	0
10·0	+20
100·0	+40

The phase angle $\angle H(j\omega) = 90°$ for all frequencies. The Bode diagram for this function is shown in Fig. 13.1.

330

The log-modulus graph for this function is thus a straight line of slope $+20$ dB/decade. The Bode diagram for the function $H(j\omega) = 1/j\omega$ is also simply deduced. The log-modulus graph is a straight line of slope -20 dB/decade and the phase is constant at $-90°$.

In general the function $H(j\omega) = (j\omega)^n$ has a log-modulus graph which is a straight line of slope $20n$ dB/decade where n is a positive or negative integer.

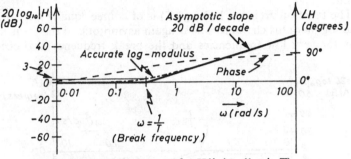

Fig. 13.2 *Bode diagram for* $H(j\omega) = (1 + j\omega T)$.

(ii) $H(j\omega) = 1 + j\omega T$

Now $\qquad 20\log_{10}|H(j\omega)| = 20\log_{10}\sqrt{(1 + \omega^2 T^2)}$

For $\omega T \ll 1$, $\quad \sqrt{(1 + \omega^2 T^2)} \simeq 1$

thus $\qquad 20\log_{10}|H(j\omega)| = 0\,\text{dB}$

For $\omega T = 1$, $\quad \sqrt{(1 + \omega^2 T^2)} = \sqrt{2}$

thus $\qquad 20\log_{10}|H(j\omega)| = +3\,\text{dB}$

For $\omega T \gg 1$, $\quad \sqrt{(1 + \omega^2 T^2)} \simeq \omega T$

thus $\qquad 20\log_{10}|H(j\omega)| = 20\log_{10}\omega T\,\text{decibels}$

Hence, for low frequencies the log-modulus characteristic is approximately a straight line lying along the axis of frequency. For high frequencies, the log-modulus is approximately a straight line of slope 20 dB/decade (this is virtually self-evident, because if we consider a high frequency ω_1, then the log-modulus is $20\log_{10}\omega_1 T$; at $10\omega_1$, the log-modulus is $20\log_{10}10\omega_1 T$, the change in the log-modulus is thus $20\log_{10}10\omega_1 T - 20\log_{10}\omega_1 T$ or $20\log_{10}(10\omega_1 T/\omega_1 T)$, i.e. 20 dB). Hence for a decade change in frequency the log-modulus changes by 20 dB.

The phase angle $\angle H(j\omega) = \tan^{-1}\omega T$ and rises from zero at zero frequency to $90°$ at infinite frequency.

The Bode diagram for this function is shown in Fig. 13.2.

The log-modulus curve is asymptotic to the frequency axis for low frequencies and is asymptotic for high frequencies to the straight line starting at $\omega = 1/T$ and having a slope of 20 dB/decade. Furthermore, the error in using the two asymptotes instead of the actual curve never exceeds 3 dB, this occurring at $\omega = 1/T$. For many practical purposes it suffices to use the asymptotes as an approximation to the curve, the saving in labour being considerable. The frequency given by $\omega = 1/T$ is termed the break frequency or break point.

The function $H(j\omega) = 1/(1 + j\omega T)$ is of course equally important. The log-modulus characteristic is again asymptotic to the frequency axis for very low frequencies and the break frequency also occurs

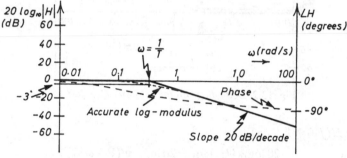

Fig. 13.3 *Bode diagram for* $H(j\omega) = 1/(1 + j\omega T)$.

when $\omega = 1/T$. For high frequencies the gain is asymptotic to a line of slope -20 dB/decade. The phase $\angle H(j\omega)$ varies from zero to $-90°$ as the frequency changes from zero to infinity. The characteristic is shown in Fig. 13.3.

For functions of the form $H(j\omega) = (1 + j\omega T)^n$, where n is a positive integer, the log-modulus is again asymptotic to the frequency axis at very low frequencies. The break again occurs at $\omega = 1/T$ and the high frequency asymptote has a slope of $+20n$ dB/decade. The phase varies from zero to $90n$ degrees as the frequency changes from zero to infinity.

When n is a negative integer, the log-modulus has a slope of $-20n$ dB/decade at very high frequencies but it is otherwise the same. The phase becomes negative tending towards $-90n$ degrees as the frequency approaches infinity.

(*iii*) $H(j\omega) = 1/\{k_1(j\omega)^2 + k_2(j\omega) + 1\}$

The quadratic factor can of course occur in both the numerator and/or the denominator of a transfer function. Only its occurrence in the denominator will be considered here.

332

The natures of the log-modulus and phase characteristics of this function are made more obvious by substituting

$$\frac{1}{\omega_o^2} = k_1$$

and

$$\frac{2\zeta}{\omega_o} = k_2$$

Thus

$$H(j\omega) = \frac{1}{\left(j\dfrac{\omega}{\omega_o}\right)^2 + 2\zeta j\dfrac{\omega}{\omega_o} + 1}$$

$$= \frac{1}{\left(1 - \dfrac{\omega^2}{\omega_o^2}\right) + j2\zeta\dfrac{\omega}{\omega_o}}$$

The log-modulus characteristic is given by

$$20\log_{10}|H(j\omega)| = -20\log_{10}\sqrt{\left\{\left(1 - \frac{\omega^2}{\omega_o^2}\right)^2 + \left(2\zeta\frac{\omega}{\omega_o}\right)^2\right\}}$$

thus when $\omega \ll \omega_o$, $20\log_{10}|H(j\omega)| \simeq 0$

and when $\omega \gg \omega_o$, $20\log_{10}|H(j\omega)| \simeq -20\log_{10}\left(\dfrac{\omega}{\omega_o}\right)^2$

Thus for very low frequencies the log-modulus is asymptotic to the frequency axis and for very high frequencies it is asymptotic to a straight line starting at $\omega = \omega_o$ and having a slope of -40 dB/decade. Between these two limiting sections the shape of the curve depends on the value of ζ. For $\zeta < 0.707$ there is a peak in the characteristic occurring at $\omega = \omega_o\sqrt{(1 - 2\zeta^2)}$. For $\zeta \geqslant 1$, the quadratic will factorize and can be dealt with as two factors of the type considered in (ii) above.

The phase is given by

$$\angle H(j\omega) = \tan^{-1}\frac{2\zeta\omega\omega_o}{\omega_o^2 - \omega^2}$$

This function varies from zero at zero frequency through $-90°$ when $\omega = \omega_o$, approaching $-180°$ as the frequency tends to infinity.

The Bode diagram for the quadratic lag is shown in Fig. 13.4 and is drawn for three values of ζ. It has been generalized by using a normalized frequency scale ω/ω_o instead of ω.

13.2.2 *Composite Functions*

The open-loop transfer function of a control system generally takes the form

$$\frac{\theta_o}{\epsilon}(j\omega) = \frac{K(1 + j\omega T_a)(1 + j\omega T_b)\ldots, \text{etc.}}{(j\omega)^n(1 + j\omega T_1)(1 + j\omega T_2)\ldots, \text{etc.}}$$

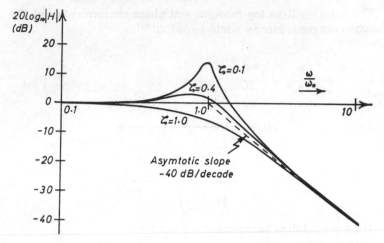

(a) Log-modulus characteristics for $H(j\omega) = 1/\{(1 - \omega^2/\omega_o^2) + j2\zeta\omega/\omega_o\}$

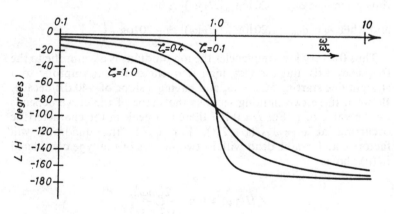

(b) Phase characteristics for $H(j\omega) = 1/\{(1 - \omega^2/\omega_o^2) + j2\zeta\omega/\omega_o\}$

Fig. 13.4 *Bode diagram for* $H(j\omega) = 1/\{(1 - \omega^2/\omega_o^2) + j2\zeta\omega/\omega_o\}$.

There may also be quadratic terms in the numerator and/or the denominator.

Taking the log-modulus first we have

$$20\log_{10}\left|\frac{\theta_o}{\epsilon}(j\omega)\right| = 20\log_{10}K + 20\log_{10}\sqrt{(1 + \omega^2 T_a^2)}$$
$$+ 20\log_{10}\sqrt{(1 + \omega^2 T_b^2)} + \text{etc.}$$
$$- 20n\log_{10}\omega - 20\log_{10}\sqrt{(1 + \omega^2 T_1^2)}$$
$$- 20\log_{10}\sqrt{(1 + \omega^2 T_2^2)} - \text{etc.}$$

The important point to note is that each term in the transfer function may be superimposed at frequencies where it becomes relevant. Thus at very low frequencies the only relevant terms are

$$20 \log_{10} K - 20n \log_{10} \omega$$

Subsequently the largest time constant (say T_1) will cause a break point to occur and the relevant terms are then

$$20 \log_{10} K - 20n \log_{10} \omega - 20 \log_{10} \sqrt{(1 + \omega^2 T_1^2)}$$

The composite characteristic for this function is simply the individual characteristics arithmetically added with due regard to sign.

Thereafter each time constant will cause a new break point and a change in the slope of the asymptotic approximation to the log-modulus characteristic.

The phase is given by

$$\angle \frac{\theta_o}{\epsilon}(j\omega) = \tan^{-1} \omega T_a + \tan^{-1} \omega T_b + \text{etc.}$$
$$- 90n \text{ degrees} - \tan^{-1} \omega T_1 - \tan^{-1} \omega T_2$$
$$- \text{etc.}$$

No simple construction is available for the phase angle but it can be calculated quite rapidly by looking up a few values in the tangent tables.

Worked Example

Draw a Bode diagram, using asymptotic approximations, for a type 1 control system having unity feedback and two exponential lags in the forward path of time constants 0·2 sec and 0·05 sec respectively. The error constant is 10.

Solution

The open-loop transfer function of the system $H(j\omega)$ is given by

$$H(j\omega) = \frac{10}{j\omega(1 + j\omega 0\cdot 2)(1 + j\omega 0\cdot 05)}$$

The log-modulus is given by

$$20 \log_{10} |H(j\omega)| = 20 \log_{10} 10 - 20 \log_{10} \omega$$
$$- 20 \log_{10} \sqrt{\{1 + (0\cdot 2\omega)^2\}}$$
$$- 20 \log_{10} \sqrt{\{1 + (0\cdot 05\omega)^2\}}$$

The first break frequency is given by

$$\omega = \frac{1}{0\cdot 2} = 5 \, \text{rad/s}$$

At $\omega = 0.01$ rad/s the log-modulus is thus approximately

$$20 \log_{10} 10 - 20 \log_{10} 0.01$$

$$= 20 + 40$$

$$= 60 \text{ dB}$$

The asymptotic log-modulus characteristic thus begins with a gain of $+60$ dB at an angular frequency of 0.01 rad/s and has a slope of -20 dB/decade due to the term $j\omega$ in the denominator until the first break frequency is reached at $\omega = 5$ rad/s. The slope then becomes -40 dB/decade until the second break is reached at $\omega = 1/0.05$, i.e. $\omega = 20$ rad/s. Thereafter the slope becomes -60 dB/decade and remains at this value.

The phase is given by

$$\angle H(j\omega) = -90° - \tan^{-1} 0.2\omega - \tan^{-1} 0.05\omega$$

The angles resulting from this expression are tabulated in the table below.

ω (rad/s)	$\angle H(j\omega)$ (degrees)
0.01	−90.1
0.1	−91.5
0.5	−97.1
1.0	−104.2
5.0	−149.0
10.0	−180.1
20.0	−210.9
50.0	−242.5
100.0	−255.9

The Bode diagram is shown in Fig. 13.5.

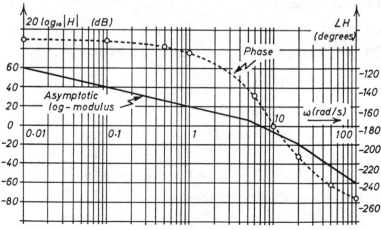

Fig. 13.5 *Bode diagram for* $10/\{j\omega(1 + j\omega 0.2)(1 + j\omega 0.05)\}$.

13.3 Interpretation of System Performance Using the Bode Diagram

13.3.1 Absolute and Relative Stability

The Nyquist stability criterion in the simple form as discussed in §10.4 may be stated in a modified form for application with the Bode diagram: *for absolute stability on closed-loop the phase lag of the open-loop frequency response at the frequency producing a log-modulus of 0 dB must be less than* 180°, i.e. the phase margin must be positive.

This is illustrated with reference to a system having an open-loop transfer function of the form:

$$\frac{\theta_o}{\epsilon}(j\omega) = \frac{K}{j\omega(1 + j\omega T_1)(1 + j\omega T_2)}$$

Fig. 13.6 shows the Nyquist and Bode diagrams for three values of *K*.

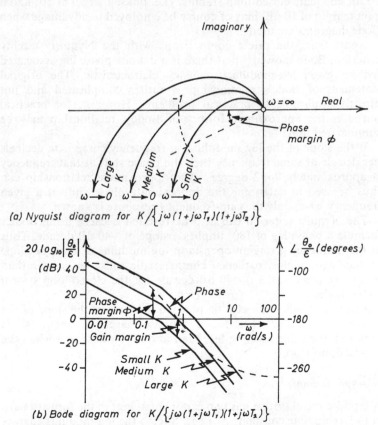

(a) Nyquist diagram for $K / \left\{ j\omega(1+j\omega T_1)(1+j\omega T_2) \right\}$

(b) Bode diagram for $K / \left\{ j\omega(1+j\omega T_1)(1+j\omega T_2) \right\}$

Fig. 13.6 *Comparison between Nyquist and Bode diagrams.*

337

The phase characteristic is given by

$$\angle\frac{\theta_o}{\epsilon} = -90° - \tan^{-1}\omega T_1 - \tan^{-1}\omega T_2$$

and is thus independent of the value of K.

The system with the large value of K is absolutely unstable, thus the phase lag is greater than 180° when the log-modulus characteristic crosses the frequency axis. The system with the medium value of K is critically stable, thus for this system the log-modulus characteristic crosses the frequency axis when the phase lag is exactly 180°.

The absolutely stable system with small K has a log-modulus characteristic which crosses the frequency axis when the phase lag is less than 180°. The relative stability of this system can be estimated from the phase margin ϕ and the gain margin which can both be read directly off the Bode diagram. The rules-of-thumb stated in chapter 10 for adequate closed-loop stability (i.e. phase margin of 50° and a gain margin of 10 dB) may of course be employed to advantage when Bode diagrams are used.

Apart from the direct comparisons with the Nyquist stability criterion, Bode showed[23] that there is a definite phase lag associated with a given log-modulus/frequency characteristic. The original statement of Bode's relationship is rather complicated and not directly applicable to practical problems. However, for practical purposes the approximate form[24] of Bode's relationship may be summarized thus:

If the slope of the log modulus-log frequency curve is m decibels per decade at some frequency then the phase shift at that frequency is approximately $9m/2$ degrees. The approximate relationship can thus be used to determine the approximate phase shift at a given frequency when only the gain-frequency response is known.

The Nyquist criterion can also be restated because using Bode's formula a phase lag of 180° implies a slope of −40 dB/decade. Thus at the frequency giving an open-loop log-modulus of zero the slope of the log-modulus/frequency characteristic must be greater than (i.e. more positive than) −40 dB/decade for the closed-loop system to be stable.

Relative stability can also be phrased in terms of the slope of the log-modulus characteristic for if a phase margin of about 50° is required, the slope must be less than about 30 dB/decade when the log-modulus is zero.

Worked Example

A type 1 control system has two exponential lags in the forward path both having time constants of 1 sec. Sketch the log-modulus characteristic and from it estimate:

(i) The value of the error constant for which the system would be just unstable on closed loop.

(ii) The value of the error constant for which the relative stability would be adequate.

Solution

For the purposes of sketching the log-modulus characteristic a value of error constant equal to unity will be used. Thus the open-loop transfer function is given by

$$H(j\omega) = \frac{1}{j\omega(1 + j\omega)^2}$$

Starting at $\omega = 0.01$ rad/s, we have $20\log_{10} H(j\omega) = 40$ dB. For very low frequencies the log-modulus will have a slope of -20

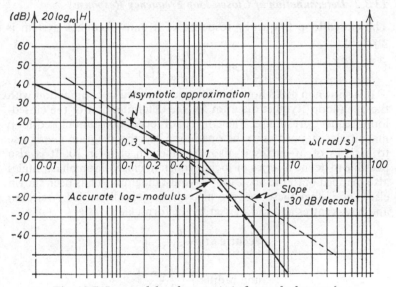

Fig. 13.7 *Log-modulus characteristic for worked example.*

dB/decade. A double break will occur at $\omega = 1.0$ rad/s and for very high frequencies the log-modulus characteristic will tend towards an asymptote having a slope of -60 dB/decade. The characteristic is sketched in Fig. 13.7, the broken line being a more accurate representation.

The slope of the broken line is 40 dB/decade when the characteristic crosses the frequency axis. This implies that the system is just unstable for the chosen value of error constant, i.e. system is just unstable on closed loop when the error constant is unity.

The broken line has a slope of 30 dB/decade when the log-modulus is about +6·5 dB. For the system to have adequate stability on closed loop the error constant must be lowered by about 6·5 dB; now 6·5 dB is a factor of about 2·11

$$\therefore \qquad \text{error constant} = \frac{1}{2\cdot 11} = 0\cdot 474$$

This value of error constant compares quite accurately with that given by Brown's construction for the same example (§10.11.2) which gives an error constant of 0·476 for $M = 1\cdot 3$.

Whilst the method cannot normally achieve the same degree of accuracy as that associated with a carefully constructed Nyquist diagram, the speed at which the work may proceed is greatly increased.

13.3.2 Determination of Closed-loop Frequency Response

The closed-loop frequency response of a unity feedback system is given by

$$\frac{\theta_o}{\theta_i}(j\omega) = \frac{\theta_o/\epsilon(j\omega)}{1 + \theta_o/\epsilon(j\omega)}$$

It is shown in §10.8 how this fact may be used in conjunction with the open-loop Nyquist diagram for the determination of the closed-loop frequency response. The concept of loci of constant closed-loop magnitudes mapped onto the open-loop Nyquist diagram giving rise to a series of M-circles is also explained in chapter 10. It is also possible to define a series of loci of constant closed-loop phase angles also mapped onto the open-loop Nyquist diagram. It has been shown elsewhere[20] that these loci are also circles (usually called N-circles) and have centres and radii given by the formulae:

$$\text{centre at} \left(-\frac{1}{2}, \frac{1}{2N} \right)$$

$$\text{and radius} \frac{\sqrt{(N^2 + 1)}}{2N}$$

where $N = \tan\left\{ \angle \frac{\theta_o}{\theta_i}(j\omega) \right\}$.

A few M- and N-circles are shown in Fig. 13.8.

If many M- and N-circles are drawn and the open-loop frequency locus of a particular system is then superimposed on the diagram it is possible to read off the closed-loop magnitude and phase of that system for the various frequencies for which the open-loop locus has been plotted.

The application of the same principles using the functions in logarithmic form as given by a Bode diagram requires the use of another diagram, known as a *Nichols chart*. This chart has rectangular coordinates with $20\log_{10}|\theta_o/\epsilon|$ plotted as ordinates versus the phase $\angle\,\theta_o/\epsilon$ plotted in degrees as abscissae. The contours of the closed-loop modulus expressed in decibels, $20\log_{10}|\theta_o/\theta_i|$, and the closed-loop phase $\angle\,\theta_o/\theta_i$ appear on the chart. The Nichols chart is shown in Fig. 13.9.

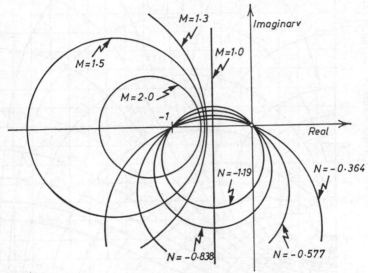

Fig. 13.8 *M- and N-circles.*

The values of $20\log_{10}|\theta_o/\epsilon|$ and $\angle\,\theta_o/\epsilon$ for a given system at a given frequency represent a single point on the Nichols chart. The position of this point may or may not lie exactly on the given contours of closed-loop magnitude and phase. If it does, then the response can be read off directly. If it does not, interpolation may be used to estimate the response. The procedure is then repeated over the range of frequencies of interest. Graphs of $|\theta_o/\theta_i|$ against frequency and/or $\angle\,\theta_o/\theta_i$ versus frequency can then be prepared if necessary. Hence the closed-loop frequency response can be deduced very rapidly from a Bode diagram of the open-loop frequency response. Nichols charts are commercially available as transparencies which fit over standard graph paper on which the open-loop frequency response has been plotted.

Worked Example

A type 0 system with unity feedback has four exponential lags of time constants 33·9 sec, 1 sec, 0·3 sec, 0·1 sec respectively and one exponential lead of time constant 1·21 sec; the error constant is

341

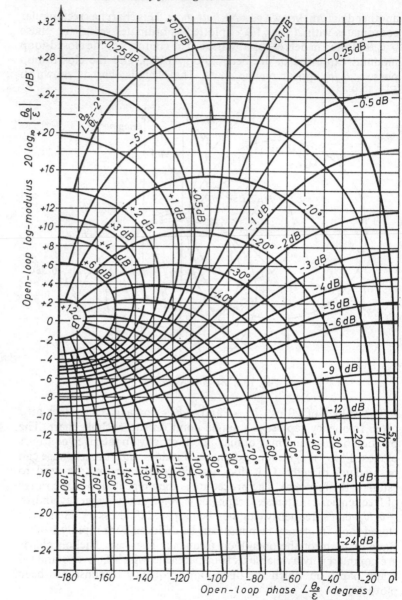

Fig. 13.9 *The Nichols chart.*

100. Draw a Bode diagram for the system and then use the Nichols chart to prepare a graph of the closed-loop magnitude $|\theta_o/\theta_i(j\omega)|$ versus angular frequency ω. Estimate the angular resonant frequency

and the resonance peak M_{pf}. Compare the results obtained with an accurate computation.

Solution

The open-loop transfer function $\theta_o/\epsilon(j\omega)$ is given by

$$\frac{\theta_o}{\epsilon}(j\omega) = \frac{100(1 + j\omega1\cdot21)}{(1 + j\omega)(1 + j\omega0\cdot3)(1 + j\omega0\cdot1)(1 + j\omega33\cdot9)}$$

The asymptotic log-modulus characteristic is horizontal at a level of 40 dB until the first break occurs at $\omega = 1/33\cdot9$ rad/s when the characteristic becomes asymptotic to a line of slope -20 dB/decade. The second break occurs at $\omega = 1/1\cdot21$ rad/s when the characteristic again becomes horizontal. Subsequent breaks at $\omega = 1$ rad/s, $\omega = 1/0\cdot3$ rad/s, and $\omega = 1/0\cdot1$ rad/s cause the slope of the asymptotic characteristic to become first -20 dB/decade then -40 dB/decade and finally -60 dB/decade.

The phase is given by

$$\angle\,\theta_o/\epsilon(j\omega) = \tan^{-1}1\cdot21\omega - \tan^{-1}\omega$$
$$- \tan^{-1}0\cdot3\omega - \tan^{-1}0\cdot1\omega - \tan^{-1}33\cdot9\omega$$

A table of phase angles for this function is given below.

Angular Frequency ω (rad/s)	Phase $\angle\,\theta_o/\epsilon(j\omega)$ (degrees)
0·1	−74·67
0·4	−90·89
0·8	−100·5
1·2	−110·0
1·6	−119·0
2·2	−131·2
2·8	−141·9
3·5	−152·5
4·5	−165·2
5·5	−175·5
6·0	−180·0
7·0	−187·9
8·0	−194·6
10·0	−205·4
14·0	−220·2
20·0	−233·4
30·0	−244·8

The Bode diagram for the open-loop transfer function is presented in Fig. 13.10. In order to achieve greater accuracy, the accurate log-modulus characteristic has been sketched (shown as a broken line).

The closeness of the accurate characteristic (which can readily be

343

sketched with the aid of an odd point or two) to the approximate asymptotic characteristic is well illustrated. The table below gives the

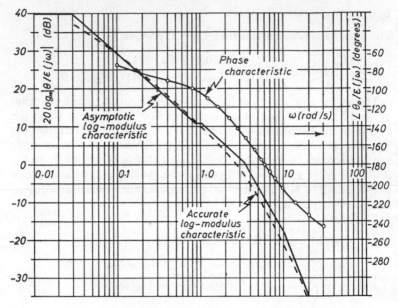

Fig. 13.10 *Bode diagram for worked example.*

values of log-modulus (in dB) for various frequencies as read off the sketched accurate log-modulus characteristic.

Angular Frequency ω (rad/s)	$20 \log_{10} \|\theta_o/\epsilon(j\omega)\|$ (dB)
0·1	29·0
0·4	17·5
0·8	11·8
1·2	8·20
1·6	5·60
2·2	2·0
2·8	−0·6
3·5	−3·6
4·0	−5·5
4·5	−7·4
5·5	−10·6
6·0	−12·1

With the aid of the open-loop phase angles, points can now be marked on the Nichols chart (Fig. 13.11). The closed-loop log-moduli ($20 \log_{10} |\theta_o/\theta_i(j\omega)|$) can now be read off from the contours. Interpolation is necessary in most cases.

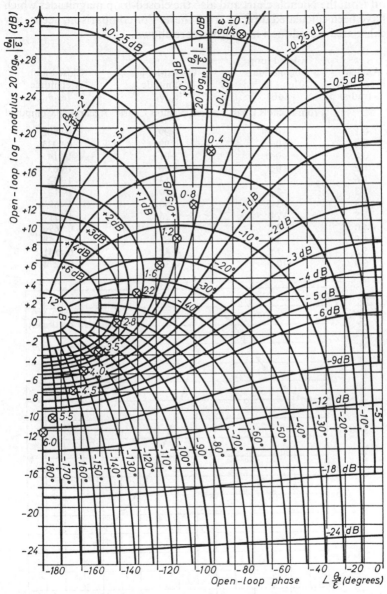

Fig. 13.11 *Nichols chart for worked example.*

The table below gives values of the closed-loop log-moduli as read off from the Nichols chart and also the closed-loop magnitudes which have been calculated directly from these. For comparison, accurately calculated closed-loop magnitudes are shown.

Angular Frequency ω (rad/s)	Closed-loop Log-modulus $20\log_{10}|\theta_o/\theta_i|$ (dB) From Nichols Chart	Closed-loop Magnitude $|\theta_o/\theta_i|$ From Nichols Chart	Closed-loop Magnitude $|\theta_o/\theta_i|$ Accurately Computed
0·1	−0·09	0·99	0·9902
0·4	−0·05	0·99	0·9933
0·8	+0·1	1·01	1·014
1·2	+0·5	1·06	1·063
1·6	+1·1	1·13	1·142
2·2	+2·2	1·29	1·313
2·8	+3·5	1·50	1·459
3·5	+2·0	1·26	1·271
4·0	−0·5	0·94	0·9696
4·5	−3·5	0·67	0·7158
5·5	−7·5	0·42	0·4141
6·0	−10·0	0·32	0·3274

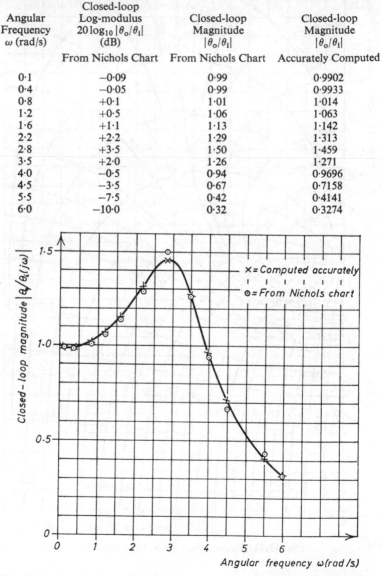

Fig. 13.12 *Graphs of closed-loop magnitudes as obtained from a Nichols chart and as accurately computed.*

Fig. 13.12 gives graphs of the closed-loop magnitude as obtained from the Nichols chart and as accurately computed.

The values of M_{pf} and ω_{rf} as obtained from the Nichols chart and as obtained by accurate computation are shown below.

	Resonant Angular Frequency ω_{rf} (rad/s)	Resonance Peak M_{pf}
From Nichols Chart	2·80	1·50
Accurately Computed	2·85*	1·459

* This figure is obtained by observing when the accurately computed magnitudes reach a maximum value. It is thus not very accurate itself. It is evident that if some care is taken in the preparation of the Bode diagram it is possible to obtain quite accurate results from the Nichols Chart.

13.3.3 Limitation of the Nichols Chart

It is important to note that the Nichols chart may only be used to compute the closed-loop frequency response *directly* when the feedback is unity.

Actually the contours form the ratio $H(j\omega)/\{1 + H(j\omega)\}$ where $H(j\omega)$ is the transfer function round the loop including the feedback path.

When the feedback is unity $H(j\omega)$ becomes the open-loop transfer function of the forward path only and the ratio $H(j\omega)/\{1 + H(j\omega)\}$ is the true closed-loop frequency response function.

When the feedback is other than unity the loop transfer function is given by

$$H(j\omega) = H_1(j\omega) \cdot H_2(j\omega)$$

where $H_1(j\omega)$ is the transfer function of the forward path and $H_2(j\omega)$ is the transfer function of the feedback path. Thus the Nichols chart will give the ratio

$$\frac{H_1(j\omega) H_2(j\omega)}{1 + H_1(j\omega) H_2(j\omega)}$$

which is *not* the closed-loop frequency response.

The true closed-loop response may, however, be computed readily from this. It is shown in §9.5.1 that the closed-loop transfer function of a non-unity feedback system is given by

$$\frac{\theta_o}{\theta_i}(j\omega) = \frac{H_1(j\omega)}{1 + H_1(j\omega) H_2(j\omega)}$$

This may be obtained from the ratio

$$\frac{H_1(j\omega) H_2(j\omega)}{1 + H_1(j\omega) H_2(j\omega)}$$

347

by multiplying by $1/H_2(j\omega)$. This multiplication may be performed rapidly on a Bode diagram by adding gains and phase angles in the normal way.

13.3.4 Estimation of the Transient Response

As is explained in §10.1, design in the frequency domain is relatively simple. The problem of translation of time domain specifications is simple so long as second-order approximations are adequate. The Nichols chart gives an accurate method of determining the closed-loop resonance peak M_{pf} and the resonant angular frequency ω_{rf}; once these are known the correlations with the second order system listed in §8.9.3 will usually yield reasonably good estimations of the transient performance of a system.

Another useful technique for estimating the angular resonant frequency ω_{rf} of an adequately damped system (i.e. one with an M_{pf} of about 1·3 or a phase margin of about 45°) should also be noted. On the Nyquist diagram, the resonant frequency occurs at the point where the open-loop frequency locus touches the M_{pf} circle. This occurs approximately (*in the case of adequately damped systems only*) when the magnitude $|\theta_o/\epsilon(j\omega)|$ is unity; that is when $20\log_{10}|\theta_o/\epsilon(j\omega)|$ is zero. Thus the angular resonant frequency ω_{rf} is approximately the frequency at which the log-modulus characteristic cuts the frequency axis (Fig. 13.13).

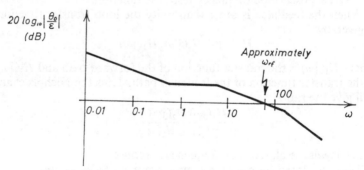

Fig. 13.13 *Determination of ω_{rf} from the Bode diagram.*

Since the method is very approximate anyway, the use of the asymptotic log-modulus approximation will scarcely worsen the accuracy. The value of ω_{rf} so determined can be related using second-order correlations to ω_{rt} the angular frequency of oscillation of the closed-loop transient response.

$$\frac{\omega_{rf}}{\omega_{rt}} = \frac{\sqrt{(1 - 2\zeta^2)}}{\sqrt{(1 - \zeta^2)}}$$

For an adequately damped system (corresponding to $M_{pf} = 1\cdot3$ or a phase margin of about $45°$) ζ is approximately $0\cdot42$. Thus $\omega_{rf}/\omega_{rt} = 0\cdot886$. The time T_p taken for the system output to rise to its first maximum in response to a step-input is approximately π/ω_{rt} (this is only exact for second-order systems). Hence

$$T_p \simeq \frac{0\cdot886\pi}{\omega_{rf}} = \frac{2\cdot8}{\omega_{rf}}$$

A better approximation is possible if we take into account the fact that ω_{rf} is slightly higher than that given by unity modulus and the following relationship is recommended:

$$T_p \simeq \frac{3}{\omega_{rf}}$$

Fig. 13.14 shows the closed-loop step-response of an adequately damped, unity feedback system.

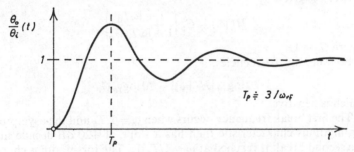

Fig. 13.14 *Closed-loop transient response.*

The approximation forms a useful basis for the design of systems requiring series compensation in which the time domain specifications are supplied.

13.4 Design of Compensating Devices using Bode Diagrams

13.4.1 General

The principles underlying compensation are discussed in detail in chapters 11 and 12. It is shown in chapter 11 how series compensation may be achieved using phase-lead or phase-lag networks and methods of designing these devices so as to bring a given system within specification are developed in that chapter. The methods described depend on obtaining a properly shaped Nyquist diagram. The Bode diagram may also be used to design series compensated systems and indeed many engineers prefer this alternative method. This section will be devoted to the development of methods of using the Bode diagram for the design of series compensating devices. In chapter 12 it is shown how the inverse Nyquist diagram can be used to design parallel compensating devices. Whilst it is not impossible to use the Bode diagram for designing parallel compensated systems, the work involved in doing so is certainly greater than that for the inverse Nyquist method. Hence no space will be devoted to a discussion of the use of the Bode diagram in parallel compensation.

The Bode diagrams for phase-lead and phase-lag networks will first be derived and methods of designing the networks will then be described.

13.4.2 Bode Diagrams for Series Compensating Devices

The Phase-lead Network

It is shown in §11.2.1 that the transfer function of a phase-lead network is given by

$$H(j\omega) = G_o \left\{ \frac{1 + j\omega T_d}{1 + j\omega T_d G_o} \right\}$$

where $G_o < 1$.

For very low frequencies,

$$20 \log_{10} |H(j\omega)| = 20 \log_{10} G_0$$

which is negative.

The first break frequency occurs when $\omega = 1/T_d$ and the asymptotic log-modulus characteristic then has a slope of $+20$ dB/decade until the second break is reached at $\omega = 1/T_d G_o$. The log-modulus characteristic then becomes asymptotic to the frequency axis. The phase angle is given by

$$\angle H(j\omega) = \tan^{-1} \omega T_d - \tan^{-1} \omega T_d G_o$$

The Bode diagram for the phase lead network is shown in Fig. 13.15.

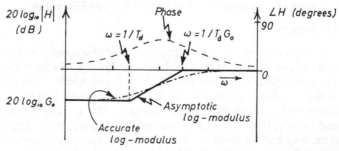

Fig. 13.15 *Bode diagram for phase-lead network.*

The Phase-lag Network

It is shown in §11.2.1 that the transfer function of a phase-lag network is given by

$$H(j\omega) = \frac{1 + j\omega T_d}{1 + j\omega T_d G_\infty}$$

where $G_\infty > 1$.

For very low frequencies

$$20\log_{10}|H(j\omega)| = 20\log_{10} 1 = 0\,dB$$

The initial asymptotic characteristic is thus the frequency axis. The first break occurs when $\omega = 1/T_d G_\infty$ and the asymptotic log-modulus characteristic then has a slope of -20 dB/decade until the second break occurs at $\omega = 1/T_d$, after which it becomes asymptotic to a horizontal line at $20\log_{10}(1/G_\infty)$.

The phase is given by

$$\angle H(j\omega) = \tan^{-1}\omega T_d - \tan^{-1}\omega T_d G_\infty$$

The Bode diagram for the phase-lag network is shown in Fig. 13.16.

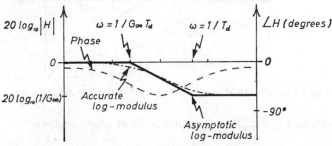

Fig. 13.16 *Bode diagram for phase-lag network.*

13.4.3 *Design of the Phase-lead Network Using the Bode Diagram*

Let us assume that it is required to design a phase-lead network for a system whose error constant and resonant frequency are too low to meet specification if adequate stability is to be maintained. The system specifications require that:

(i) The error constant must be at least K'.

(ii) The angular resonant frequency must be at least ω'_{rf}.

(iii) The damping must be adequate; a value of required phase margin ϕ or resonance peak M_{pf} may be quoted. (Note, a phase margin of 45° corresponds roughly to a value of M_{pf} of 1·3).

As with the method of design described for the Nyquist diagram given in chapter 11, the recommended philosophy of design is to

351

concentrate on achieving the specification for the resonant frequency and then see whether the error constant is large enough. If not, the resonant frequency can be arbitrarily increased and the compensating device redesigned. The following procedure will yield a design solution fairly rapidly for type 0 and type 1 systems:

1. Draw the Bode diagram for the system using an error constant of unity.

2. Adjust the error constant by inspection of the Bode diagram until the phase margin of the uncompensated system is ϕ. This is readily executed by shifting the whole log-modulus characteristic up or down.

3. Mark off the angular frequency ω'_{rf} on the frequency axis and measure off the angle α (Fig. 13.17).

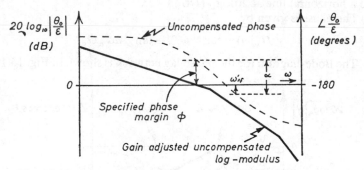

Fig. 13.17 *Design of phase-lead network using the Bode diagram.*

4. Make $\alpha = \phi_{max}$ the maximum angle of phase lead, i.e.

$$\alpha = \frac{\pi}{2} - 2\tan^{-1}\sqrt{G_o}$$

Hence calculate G_o.

5. The angular frequency at which this maximum phase lead must occur is ω'_{rf}.

Thus

$$\omega'_{rf} = \frac{1}{T_d\sqrt{G_o}}$$

Hence T_d may be found.

6. Draw the Bode diagram for the phase-lead network.

7. Combine the phase and log-modulus characteristics of the two cascaded devices by ordinary graphical addition.

8. Adjust the error constant (by shifting the composite log-modulus characteristic) until the log-modulus characteristic crosses the frequency axis at ω'_{rf}.

9. Determine the overall error constant by the method described in §13.5.3 and compare this with K'. If it is equal to or greater than

K' the error constant specification has been met. If not the value of ω'_{rf} is increased and the design repeated.

10. Use the Nichols chart to determine the overall closed-loop response and check that ω'_{rf} and M_{pf} are within specification. When the tolerances on the specifications are tight, the closed-loop response should be determined by accurate computation rather than by use of the Bode diagram and Nichols chart.

Worked Example

A type 0 system with unity feedback has three time constants in the forward path of time constants 1 sec, 0·1 sec and 0·01 sec respectively. Design, using the Bode diagram, a phase-lead series compensating device which will ensure the following overall specifications:

(i) Error constant of at least 20.
(ii) Angular resonant frequency ω'_{rf} of 20 rad/s $\pm$ 10%.
(iii) A phase margin of $45° \pm 5°$.

Solution

The open-loop transfer function of the uncompensated system is given by

$$H(j\omega) = \frac{K}{(1 + j\omega)(1 + j\omega 0·1)(1 + j\omega 0·01)}$$

Putting $K = 1$ gives a low-frequency asymptote along the frequency axis with lagging breaks occurring at $\omega = 1$ rad/s, $\omega = 10$ rad/s and $\omega = 100$ rad/s.

The phase angle is given by

$$\angle H(j\omega) = - (\tan^{-1} \omega + \tan^{-1} 0·1\omega + \tan^{-1} 0·01\omega)$$

Phase angles are given in the table below.

Angular Frequency ω (rad/s)	$\angle H(j\omega)$ (degrees)
100	−218·7
62	−201·7
46	−191·2
35	−181·7
31	−177·5
19	−160·0
15	−151·0
10	−135·0
5·6	−112·3
4·2	−101·8
3·1	−91·1

The Bode diagram is shown in Fig. 13.18.

353

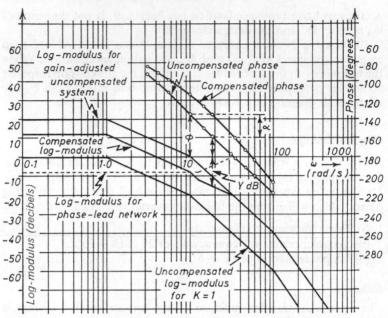

Fig. 13.18 *Bode diagram for worked example on phase-lead compensation.*

The log-modulus characteristic is first drawn for $K = 1$ and then the whole characteristic is raised to give a phase margin ϕ of 45°. The angle α is read off and in this case is given by

$$\alpha = 45° - 20°$$

i.e.

$$\alpha = 25°$$

Now

$$\alpha = \frac{\pi}{2} - 2\tan^{-1}\sqrt{G_o}$$

∴

$$25° = 90° - 2\tan^{-1}\sqrt{G_o}$$

or

$$\tan^{-1}\sqrt{G_o} = 65/2 = 32\cdot5°$$

∴

$$\sqrt{G_o} = 0\cdot636$$

∴

$$G_o = 0\cdot405$$

Also

$$\omega'_{rf} = \frac{1}{T_d\sqrt{G_o}}$$

∴

$$T_d = \frac{1}{\omega'_{rf}\sqrt{G_o}}$$

But

$$\omega'_{rf} = 20 \text{ rad/s}$$

∴

$$T_d = \frac{1}{20 \times 0\cdot636} = 0\cdot0786 \text{ sec}$$

The transfer function of the phase-lead network is thus given by

$$H_c(j\omega) = 0.405 \frac{1 + j\omega 0.0786}{1 + j\omega 0.0318}$$

The phase-lead network thus has an initial asymptote of zero slope at $20 \log_{10} 0.405$, i.e. -7.8 dB. The breaks occur at $1/0.0786$ rad/s and $1/0.0318$ rad/s, i.e. 12.7 rad/s and 31.4 rad/s.

The log-modulus characteristic for the phase-lead network (shown dotted) is also drawn on Fig. 13.18. The compensated log-modulus is then found by adding the log-modulus characteristic for the gain-adjusted, uncompensated system to that of the phase-lead network. The overall gain must now be increased by Y decibels to raise the overall log-modulus characteristic so that it crosses the frequency axis at ω'_{rf}. Now $Y \simeq 16$ dB.

$\therefore$ low-frequency log-modulus is at $12 + 16$ dB, i.e. 28 dB.

The error constant K' required is thus given by

$$20 \log_{10} K' = 28$$

$$K' = 25.2$$

The specification for the error constant is that it must be at least 20, hence that specification is satisfied. The open-loop transfer function of the compensated system is now thus

$$\frac{25.2(1 + j\omega 0.0786)}{(1 + j\omega)(1 + j\omega 0.1)(1 + j\omega 0.01)(1 + j\omega 0.0318)}$$

The angles of lead produced by the phase lead network are given in the table below, together with the resultant phase angles of the compensated system.

Angular Frequency ω (rad/s)	Phase-lead (degrees)	Resultant Phase Shift of Compensated System (degrees)
100	10.2	−208.5
62	15.3	−186.4
46	18.9	−172.3
35	22.0	−159.7
31	23.1	−154.4
19	25.1	−134.9
15	24.2	−126.8
10	20.5	−114.5
5.6	13.7	−98.7
4.2	10.7	−91.1
3.1	8.1	−83.0

The phase of the compensated system is shown in Fig. 13.18.

Bearing in mind that the axis of zero log-modulus for the compensated system is now effectively at the level −16 dB, the following

355

table gives values of phase and log-modulus for the open-loop compensated system as read directly from the Bode diagram and values of the closed-loop modulus as read from a Nichols chart (not shown).

Angular Frequency ω (rad/s)	Approximate Open-loop Response		Approximate Closed-loop Response	
	Log-modulus (dB)	Phase (degrees)	Log-modulus (dB)	Magnitude $\lvert\theta_o/\theta_i\rvert$
3·1	+18·5	−81	−0·25	0·97
5·0	+14·0	−96	0	1·0
10·0	+8·0	−115	0·80	1·1
20·0	0	−135	2·5	1·33
30·0	−4·0	−154	2·0	1·26
40·0	−8·0	−166	−4·0	0·63
56·0	−14·0	−180	−12·0	0·25

The results in the table are obtained by using the asymptotic approximation to the log-modulus characteristic and are thus very inaccurate. They do show, however, that within the limits of the accuracy of the method it is likely that the specification is satisfied. It is hence worthwhile computing the closed-loop response accurately. Such a computation shows that the angular resonant frequency is about 18 rad/s with a resonant peak of 1.26. The phase margin is 46°. The original specification is thus satisfied on all counts. Fig. 13.19 shows a graph of the closed-loop magnitude versus angular frequency (*a*) as determined using asymptotic approximations and a Nichols chart, and (*b*) as computed accurately.

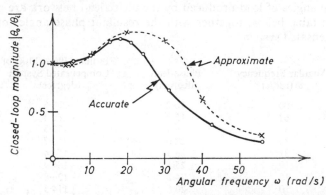

Fig. 13.19 *Closed-loop response of system with phase-lead compensation.*

The largest errors between the approximate and accurate responses occur at an angular frequency of 31 rad/s. The reason for this is that a break frequency occurs here and the asymptotic log-modulus characteristic is thus about 3 dB in error. It is possible to obtain much better approximations by sketching in a more accurate version of the log-modulus characteristic.

13.4.4 Design of the Phase-lag Network using the Bode Diagram

Let us assume that it is required to design a phase-lag network for a system whose error constant is too low but whose angular resonant frequency is too high to meet the specification if adequate stability is to be maintained. The system specifications require that:

(i) The error constant must be at least K'.

(ii) The angular resonant frequency must be at most ω'_{rf}.

(iii) The damping must be adequate; a value of required phase margin ϕ or resonance peak M_{pf} may be quoted. (Note, a phase margin of $45°$ corresponds roughly to a value of M_{pf} of 1.3.)

The following procedure will yield a design solution fairly rapidly:

(1) Plot the Bode diagram using an error constant equal to K'.

(2) Read off the Bode diagram the log-modulus at the angular frequency ω'_{rf}. If this is N decibels then the attenuation produced by the lag network must be equal to N, i.e.

$$-N = 20 \log_{10} (1/G_\infty)$$

or
$$N = 20 \log_{10} G_\infty$$

from which G_∞ may be calculated.

(3) Read off the angle α by which the phase falls short of $-180°$ at the angular frequency ω'_{rf}. Then if the required phase margin is ϕ, T_d may be determined from

$$\alpha - \phi = \tan^{-1} G_\infty \omega'_{rf} T_d - \tan^{-1} \omega'_{rf} T_d$$

The relevant solution of this equation gives

$$T_d = \frac{(G_\infty - 1) + \sqrt{\{(G_\infty - 1)^2 - 4 G_\infty \tan^2 (\alpha - \phi)\}}}{2\omega'_{rf} G_\infty \tan (\alpha - \phi)}$$

(4) Draw the Bode diagram for the phase-lag network.

(5) Combine the phase and log-modulus characteristics of the two cascaded devices by ordinary graphical addition.

(6) Use the Nichols chart to determine the overall closed-loop response and check that ω'_{rf} and M_{pf} are within the specification. Some adjustments in the values of G_∞ and T_d may be made if the first design does not quite bring the performance of the system within specification.

Worked Example

A unity feedback type 1 system has two simple lags in the forward path of time constants 0·0169 sec and 0·25 sec respectively. Design, using the Bode diagram a phase-lag series compensating device which will ensure the following overall specifications:

(i) Error constant of at least 80 sec^{-1}.
(ii) Angular resonant frequency ω'_{rf} of at most 2·0 rad/s.
(iii) A resonance peak M_{pf} lying between 1·2 and 1·4.

Solution

The open-loop transfer function of the uncompensated system is given by

$$H(j\omega) = \frac{80}{j\omega(1 + j\omega 0·25)(1 + j\omega 0·0169)}$$

The initial slope is 20 dB/decade, the first break occurring at $\omega = 1/0·25$, i.e. 4 rad/s, and the second at $\omega = 1/0·0169$, i.e. 59·2 rad/s. The phase angle is given by

$$\angle H(j\omega) = -(90° + \tan^{-1} 0·25 + \tan^{-1} 0·0169)$$

Phase angles are given in the table below.

Angular Frequency ω (rad/s)	$\angle H(j\omega)$ (degrees)
0·01	−90·1
0·1	−91·4
1·0	−104·2
2·0	−118·5
6·2	−153·2
10·0	−167·8
15·0	−179·3
31·0	−200·3
51·0	−216·3
91·0	−234·4

The Bode diagram is shown in Fig. 13.20.

Making ω'_{rf} equal to 2 rad/s, the value of N is approximately 31 dB. Hence

$$31 = 20 \log_{10} G_\infty$$

i.e.

$$G_\infty = 35·4$$

The phase angle for 2 rad/s is −118·5°. This falls short of 180° by 61·5°, i.e.

$$\alpha = 61·5°$$

The specification calls for a resonance peak of nominally 1·3 which corresponds roughly to a phase margin ϕ of 45°, i.e. angle of lag required is 61·5° − 45° = 16·5°.

Hence at an angular frequency of 2 rad/s the phase-lag device must produce a phase-lag of 16·5°; thus

$$16·5° = \tan^{-1}(T_d \times 2 \times 35·4) - \tan^{-1}(T_d \times 2)$$

Now $\quad \tan 16\cdot5° = 0\cdot296$

Hence $\quad T_{\rm d} = \dfrac{34\cdot4 + \sqrt{(34\cdot4^2 - 4 \times 35\cdot4 \times 0\cdot296^2)}}{2 \times 2 \times 35\cdot4 \times 0\cdot296}$

$$= 1\cdot64\,\text{sec}$$

The transfer function of the required phase-lag device is thus

$$\frac{1 + j\omega 1\cdot64}{1 + j\omega 58\cdot1}$$

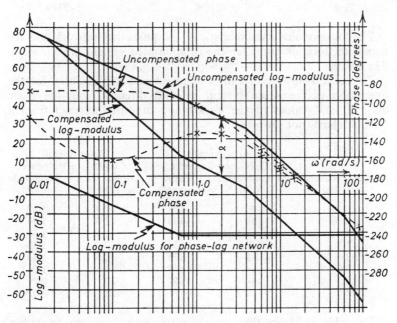

Fig. 13.20 *Bode diagram for worked example with phase-lag compensation.*

The open-loop transfer function of the compensated system is then

$$\frac{80(1 + j\omega 1\cdot64)}{j\omega(1 + j\omega 0\cdot25)(1 + j\omega 0\cdot0169)(1 + j\omega 58\cdot1)}$$

The angles of phase-lag produced by the network for various angular frequencies together with the phase angles of the compensated system are shown in the table below.

The log-modulus characteristic of the phase-lag network is initially along the frequency axis with the break at $1/58\cdot1$, i.e. $0\cdot0172$ rad/s, followed by an asymptotic slope of -20 dB/decade until the second break at $1/1\cdot64$, i.e. $0\cdot61$ rad/s when the slope again becomes zero.

359

Angular Frequency ω (rad/s)	Angle of Lag Produced by Phase-lag Network (degrees)	Phase of Compensated System (degrees)
0·01	29·2	−119·3
0·1	71·0	−162·4
1·0	31·2	−135·4
2·0	16·5	−135·0
6·2	5·4	−158·6
10·0	3·4	−171·2
15·0	2·3	−181·6
31·0	1·1	−201·1
51·0	0·7	−217·0
91·0	0·4	−234·8

The log-modulus characteristic of the phase-lag network and the complete Bode diagram for the compensated system are shown in Fig. 13.20.

The table below gives values of phase and log-modulus for the open-loop compensated system as read directly from the Bode diagram and values of the closed-loop modulus as read from a Nichols chart (not shown).

Angular Frequency ω (rad/s)	Approximate Open-loop Response Log-modulus (dB)	Phase (degrees)	Approximate Closed-loop Response Log-modulus (dB)	Magnitude $\lvert \theta_o/\theta_i \rvert$
0·19	+32	−158	0·2	1·02
0·40	+19	−144	0·8	1·09
1·0	+6·5	−135	2·5	1·33
1·5	+3·0	−134	2·6	1·35
2·0	0	−135	2·5	1·33
3·0	−4	−140	0	1·0
6·2	−14	−159	−12	0·25
10·0	−22·5	−171	−22	0·079

The table indicates that the system is now likely to be within specification and that it is worthwhile making an accurate check on the response of the system. An accurate check in fact reveals that:

(i) The angular resonant frequency is 1·6 rad/s (which is below 2 rad/s as specified).

(ii) The resonance peak M_{pf} is 1·38 (which lies between 1·2 and 1·4 as specified).

Since the error constant is 80 sec^{-1} as specified, the whole of the specification has been met.

Fig. 13.21 shows the closed-loop frequency response of the system as accurately computed and as obtained using the asymptotic log-modulus characteristic and the Nichols chart. The accuracy of the approximate response is certainly not great but could be improved substantially by sketching a more accurate log-modulus characteristic on the Bode diagram.

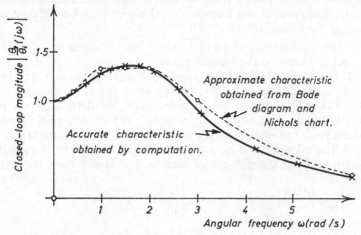

Fig. 13.21 *Closed-loop response of system with phase-lag compensation.*

13.5 Use of the Bode Diagram for the Analysis of Experimental Data

13.5.1 General

The Bode diagram provides a powerful method of determining the form of and estimating the constants of the open-loop transfer function of a system for which the frequency response has been determined experimentally. The determination is of course easy when the transfer function is simple in form but very much less so when it is complicated or contains quadratic factors.

This section will describe methods of determining the form and estimating the constants of transfer functions which contain only pure integrations, exponential lags and exponential leads.

13.5.2 Determining the Forms of a Transfer Function

For systems having an open-loop transfer function of the form:

$$H(j\omega) = \frac{K(1 + j\omega T_a)(1 + j\omega T_b) + \text{etc.}}{(j\omega)^n (1 + j\omega T_1)(1 + j\omega T_2) \dots, \text{etc.}}$$

it is possible to deduce the form (i.e. the type number n and the number of exponential leads and lags.)

The procedure is to plot the open-loop gain (as measured experimentally) expressed in decibels versus angular frequency (or frequency) plotted on a logarithmic scale. A system having a transfer function of the above form must have a log-modulus characteristic with asymptotes of slopes $\pm 20r$ dB/decade where r is a positive integer. These asymptotes can be fitted by trial to the experimental characteristic. The form of the transfer function can then be deduced by applying the following rules:

(i) The asymptotic slope for very low frequencies is $-20n$ dB/decade where n is the type number.

(ii) The number of break frequencies x is equal to the *total* number of exponential leads and lags; (note, when the slope changes by ± 40 dB/decade a 'double break' is indicated, similarly a change of ± 60 dB/decade indicates a 'triple break' and so on; such breaks indicate two or three or more leads or lags of equal time constants).

(iii) The asymptotic slope y (in decibels per decade) for very high frequencies gives the number of leads A and lags B from the relationships:

$$A = \frac{x}{2} + \frac{y}{40} + \frac{n}{2}$$

and

$$B = \frac{x}{2} - \frac{y}{40} - \frac{n}{2}$$

13.5.3 Determining the Constants in a Transfer Function

Determining the Time Constants

The angular frequencies at which the breaks occur are the reciprocals of the time constants. Where the slope changes by $+20$ dB/decade a leading time constant is implied; where it changes by -20 dB/decade a lagging time constant is implied. Fig. 13.22 shows an example of the log-modulus characteristic of a system for which the form and time constants of the transfer function are required.

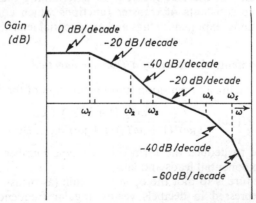

Fig. 13.22 *Example of determination of transfer function.*

The following information is obtained from the diagram:

(i) The initial slope = 0.   ∴ type number $n = 0$.

(ii) Total number of leads and lags x is 5.

(iii) Final slope y is -60 dB/decade.   ∴ number of leads

$A = \frac{5}{2} - \frac{60}{40} + 0. = 1$

Also, number of lags $B = \frac{5}{2} + \frac{60}{40} = 4$.

The transfer function is thus of the form

$$H(j\omega) = \frac{K(1 + j\omega T_3)}{(1 + j\omega T_1)(1 + j\omega T_2)(1 + j\omega T_4)(1 + j\omega T_5)}$$

The time constants can be obtained from the diagram and are as follows:

$$T_3 = 1/\omega_3$$
$$T_1 = 1/\omega_1$$
$$T_2 = 1/\omega_2$$
$$T_4 = 1/\omega_4$$
$$T_5 = 1/\omega_5$$

Determining the Error Constant

The method of determining the error constant of a system depends on the type number of the system.

(i) Type 0 System

Fig. 13.23 shows the asymptotic log-modulus characteristic of a typical type 0 system.

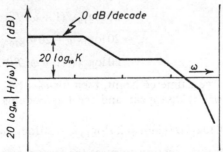

Fig. 13.23 *Asymptotic log-modulus characteristic of typical type 0 system.*

The open-loop transfer of a type 0 system is given by

$$H(j\omega) = \frac{K(1 + j\omega T_a)(1 + j\omega T_b), \text{ etc.}}{(1 + j\omega T_1)(1 + j\omega T_2), \text{ etc.}}$$

363

As ω tends to zero, $|H(j\omega)|$ tends to K and thus the low-frequency asymptote is given by

$$20\log_{10}|H(j\omega)| = 20\log_{10}K$$

The value of K can thus be determined.

(ii) Type 1 System

The asymptotic log-modulus characteristic of a typical type 1 system is shown in Fig. 13.24.

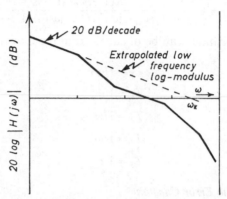

Fig. 13.24 *Asymptotic log-modulus characteristic of typical type 1 system.*

The transfer function will have the form

$$H(j\omega) = \frac{K(1 + j\omega T_a)(1 + j\omega T_b), \text{ etc.}}{j\omega(1 + j\omega T_1)(1 + j\omega T_2), \text{ etc.}}$$

Thus
$$20\log_{10}|H(j\omega)| = 20\log_{10}K + 20\log_{10}\sqrt{(1 + \omega^2 T_a^2)}$$
$$+ 20\log_{10}\sqrt{(1 + \omega^2 T_b^2)} \ldots, \text{ etc.}$$
$$- 20\log_{10}\omega - 20\log_{10}\sqrt{(1 + \omega^2 T_1^2)}$$
$$- 20\log_{10}\sqrt{(1 + \omega^2 T_2^2)} \ldots, \text{ etc.}$$

If T_x is the largest time constant, then for $\omega \ll 1/T_x$ all terms like $20\log_{10}\sqrt{(1 + \omega^2 T^2)}$ disappear and the log-modulus characteristic behaves like

$$20\log_{10}|H(j\omega)| = 20\log_{10}K - 20\log_{10}\omega$$

Extrapolating this function to meet the frequency axis at ω_k (see Fig. 13.24) makes the function equal to zero when $\omega = \omega_k$

$$\therefore \qquad 20\log_{10}K - 20\log_{10}\omega_k = 0$$

i.e. $$\log_{10}K = \log_{10}\omega_k$$

$$\therefore \qquad K = \omega_k$$

364

(iii) Type 2 System

The asymptotic log-modulus characteristic of a typical type 2 system is shown in Fig. 13.25.

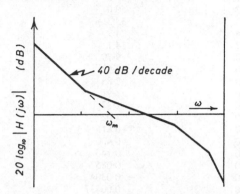

Fig. 13.25 *Asymptotic log-modulus characteristic of typical type 2 system.*

The open-loop transfer function of a type 2 system is given by

$$H(j\omega) = \frac{K(1 + j\omega T_a)(1 + j\omega T_b), \text{ etc.}}{(j\omega)^2(1 + j\omega T_1)(1 + j\omega T_2), \text{ etc.}}$$

If T_x is the largest time constant then for $\omega \ll 1/T_x$ the log-modulus characteristic behaves like

$$20\log_{10}|H(j\omega)| = 20\log_{10}K - 20\log_{10}\omega^2$$

Extrapolating this function to meet the frequency axis at ω_m (see Fig. 13.25) makes the function equal to zero when $\omega = \omega_m$

$$\therefore \quad 20\log_{10}K - 20\log_{10}\omega_m^2 = 0$$

$$\therefore \quad K = \omega_m^2$$

Worked Example

An open-loop frequency response test on a control system yielded the results shown in the table below. Use the Bode diagram to determine the form and constants of the open-loop transfer function.

The log-modulus characteristic is plotted in Fig. 13.26.

The experimental results have been joined by a broken line and the asymptotes have been fitted. Assuming that the results supplied have been taken down to a low enough frequency, the initial slope is -20 dB/decade, indicating that the system is type 1. Extrapolation of the initial asymptote gives an error constant K equal to 10 sec^{-1}. The breaks occur at angular frequencies of approximately 5 rad/s and

Feedback Control Theory for Engineers

Angular Frequency ω (rad/s)	Open-loop Magnitude $\lvert \theta_o/\epsilon \rvert$	Log-modulus $20\log_{10}\lvert \theta_o/\epsilon \rvert$ (dB)
0·1	100·0	+40·0
0·2	50·0	+34·0
0·3	33·3	+30·4
0·4	24·9	+27·8
0·7	14·1	+23·0
1·0	9·79	+19·8
2·0	4·62	+13·3
3·0	2·83	+9·04
4·0	1·91	+5·64
5·0	1·37	+2·76
6·0	1·02	+0·20
8·0	0·615	−4·20
10·0	0·400	−7·85
16·0	0·146	−16·7
20·0	0·0857	−21·3
30·0	0·0304	−30·3
60·0	0·00437	−47·2

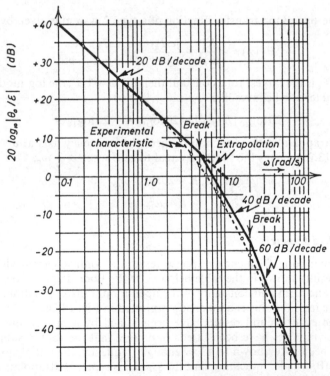

Fig. 13.26 *Log-modulus characteristic for determining transfer function in worked example.*

20 rad/s, the asymptotic slope changing by −20 dB/decade at both breaks. There are thus two lags of time constants, 0·2 sec and 0·05 sec respectively. The open-loop transfer function is thus given by

$$\frac{\theta_o}{\epsilon}(j\omega) = \frac{10}{j\omega(1 + j\omega0\cdot2)(1 + j\omega0\cdot05)}$$

13.6 Conclusion

The principles underlying the Bode diagram and some of its uses have been presented in this chapter.

The Bode diagram evidently provides a rapid method of assessing the stability and performance of a system. The Nichols chart can be used to translate open-loop data into the closed-loop frequency response and, indirectly via second-order correlations, the transient response. Rapid methods of designing and checking the design of series compensated systems are feasible. Indeed many engineers prefer such methods to those involving the Nyquist diagram.

The Bode diagram also provides a useful method of determining transfer functions from experimental frequency response data.

EXAMPLES FOR SOLUTION

1. Draw Bode diagrams, using asymptotic approximations for the log-modulus characteristics for systems having open-loop transfer functions given below. Estimate the gain margin and phase margin in each case. Also use a Nichols chart to estimate the resonant angular frequency ω_{rf} and the resonance peak M_{pf} assuming unity feedback in each case.

(i) $\dfrac{5}{j\omega(1 + j\omega0\cdot5)}$

(ii) $\dfrac{14\cdot3}{(1 + j\omega)(1 + j\omega0\cdot1)(1 + j\omega0\cdot01)}$

(iii) $\dfrac{1\cdot43}{j\omega(1 + j\omega0\cdot5)(1 + j\omega0\cdot01)}$

(iv) $\dfrac{12(1 + j\omega0\cdot245)}{j\omega(1 + j\omega0\cdot2)(1 + j\omega0\cdot05)(1 + j\omega0\cdot0294)}$

(v) $\dfrac{100(1 + j\omega1\cdot26)}{(1 + j\omega)(1 + j\omega0\cdot3)(1 + j\omega0\cdot1)(1 + j\omega33\cdot4)}$

(vi) $\dfrac{10(1 + j\omega)}{(1 + j\omega0\cdot5)(1 + j\omega0\cdot1)(1 + j\omega0\cdot01)}$

(vii) $\dfrac{(1 + j\omega0\cdot5)}{(j\omega)^2(1 + j\omega0\cdot1)(1 + j\omega0\cdot01)}$

(Note, the answers given to these problems are rather more accurate than one would expect to obtain using the Bode diagram.)

2. A unity feedback type 1 control system has two exponential lags in the forward path of time constants 0·5 sec and 0·01 sec respectively. Use Bode diagrams to:—

(i) Estimate the value of the error constant which will give a resonance peak M_{pf} of 1·3 and find the corresponding angular resonant frequency ω_{rf}.

(ii) Design a phase-lead network which will ensure the following overall specifications when connected in cascade with the main elements:

Error constant of at least 10 sec^{-1}.
Angular resonant frequency of at least 15 rad/s.
Resonance peak M_{pf} of between 1·25 and 1·35.

(iii) Design a phase-lag network which will ensure the following overall specifications when connected in cascade with the main elements:

Error constant of at least 20 sec^{-1}.
Angular resonant frequency of at most 1 rad/s.
Phase margin of 50°.

3. An open-loop frequency response test on a control system yielded the following data:

Angular Frequency ω (rad/s)	Open-loop Response	
	θ_o/ϵ	θ_o/ϵ (degrees)
11·00	0·011	−231·2
10·00	0·015	−227·8
9·10	0·019	−224·1
7·50	0·032	−215·8
6·80	0·041	−211·2
5·60	0·065	−201·5
5·10	0·081	−196·6
4·20	0·123	−186·2
3·80	0·150	−180·8
3·10	0·218	−170·2
2·60	0·293	−161·5
2·10	0·406	−152·2
1·80	0·504	−146·4
1·60	0·589	−142·5
1·20	0·843	−135·2
1·00	1·048	−132·1
0·75	1·466	−129·7
0·62	1·834	−129·6
0·51	2·321	−130·6
0·42	2·960	−132·8
0·38	3·372	−134·2
0·35	3·763	−135·5
0·29	4·891	−139·1
0·26	5·738	−141·3
0·24	6·475	−143·0
0·19	9·373	−148·2
0·16	12·50	−152·0
0·15	13·97	−153·3

Determine the form of the transfer function by drawing a Bode diagram and also estimate the constants. Use a Nichols chart to determine the closed-loop resonant angular frequency and the resonance peak assuming unity feedback.

Chapter Fourteen

Process Control Systems

14.1 Introduction

Some of the ideas associated with process control systems have already been discussed in §1.4. The majority of processes may be controlled automatically by adjusting the *rate of flow* of energy or material entering the process. In manually-controlled systems the human operator adjusts the rate of flow by means of a hand-operated valve; he will receive information regarding the state of the process from a measuring instrument giving a visual indication. Manual control has numerous disadvantages and indeed manual control of many modern plants would be virtually impossible, owing to their complexity and the speed and precision of control they require for successful operation.

The purpose of this chapter is to introduce the most important basic concepts associated with automatic process control systems and to illustrate the ways in which the general theory of feedback control systems, as presented in other chapters, can be applied to the analysis and synthesis of process control systems. The British Standard 1523: Section 2: 1960, Section 2: Process control, provides a useful glossary of terms commonly used in this field. For the sake of completeness some of the more important definitions will be included in this chapter.

14.2 The Automatic Closed-loop Process Control System

An automatic closed-loop process control system is defined as a control system in which the measured value of a controlled condition is compared with a set value and a correction dependent on their difference is applied to the correcting unit in order to adjust the

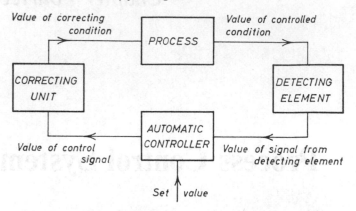

(a) <u>Simplified block diagram of single closed-loop automatic</u>
<u>process control system.</u>

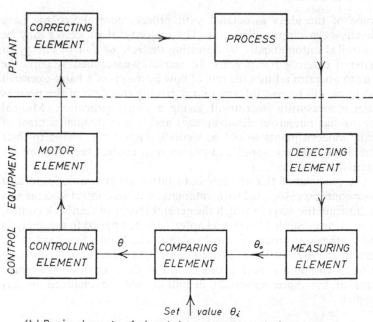

(b) <u>Basic elements of closed-loop process control system.</u>

Fig. 14.1 *The automatic closed-loop process control system.*

controlled condition, without human intervention, in the closed loop formed by the comparing and correcting chains of elements and the process (see Fig. 14.1).

The *process* may be any physical or chemical change of matter or

370

conversion of energy in the widest sense and the *plant* is the installation in which a process is carried out. The set value (θ_i) is the value of the controlled condition to which the automatic control mechanism is set whereas the measured value θ_o is the output signal from the measuring element, being a measure of the controlled condition. The deviation θ is the difference between the measured value of the controlled condition and the set value, i.e.

$$\theta = \theta_o - \theta_i$$

The automatic controller is a device in which a signal from the detecting element is compared with a signal representing the set value and which operates in such a way as to reduce the deviation. This it does by providing a control signal dependent on the deviation, for transmission to the correcting unit which adjusts the value of the correcting condition. The correcting unit comprises those elements (the motor element and correcting element) which adjusts the correcting condition, in response to a signal from the automatic controller.

The basic definitions above may be applied to a system using any control medium. Pneumatic control has, however, been firmly established for several decades and some of this chapter will be devoted to descriptions of pneumatic controllers and pneumatically-controlled systems. Pneumatic devices used at the low pressures employed in the process control industry are cheap and reliable, possess long life, are quiet in operation, give rise to no fire-risk and only a very small explosion hazard. Furthermore, air can be vented to the atmosphere and single-line working is possible, so cutting down the cost of installation. Maintenance is also simple in pneumatic systems.

An example of a typical pneumatic process control system is shown in Fig. 14.2. Here the object of the system is to provide a constant flow of hot water at a constant temperature. The process is a heat-exchange process taking place in a tank into which cold water is flowing.

The temperature of the water is raised by means of steam passing through copper pipes coiled inside the tank. The rate of flow of steam from a boiler is controlled by a steam valve operated by a pneumatic diaphragm motor (described in §7.4.4). The control signals are derived from a pneumatic proportional controller (described in §7.3.5) via a pneumatic power amplifier (sometimes called a 'relay' and described in §14.5.6).

The detecting element is an expansion-type thermometer, its output being transmitted via capillary tubing to a Bourdon tube which constitutes the measuring element and gives an output positional signal θ_o for comparison with the set value which is also a positional signal θ_i. The lever obtains a measure of the deviation θ and controls the position of the flapper of the pneumatic controller.

371

If the temperature of the emerging water tends to rise beyond the required level the mercury in the thermometer expands and the expansion is transmitted via the capillary to the Bourdon tube, which expands. This tends to open the flapper, so lowering the control pressure. A decrease in the control pressure operates the diaphragm

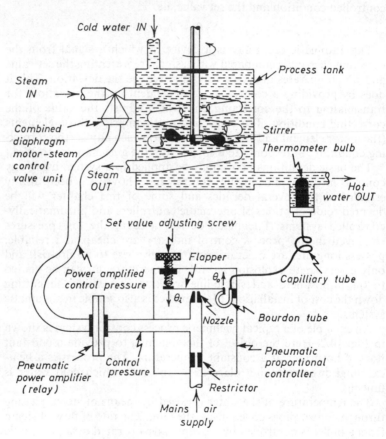

Fig. 14.2 *Typical heat-exchange process.*

motor in such a way as to tend to close the steam valve. This in turn tends to lower the temperature of the water emerging from the process tank thus counteracting the original tendency for the water temperature to rise.

A corresponding argument can be applied to the effect of a tendency for the water temperature to fall and would show that such a tendency is also counteracted.

14.3 Dynamic Characteristics of Processes

14.3.1 General

At first impression, control of the water temperature may seem quite simple. All that appears to be necessary is observation of the hot-water thermometer and correction of the steam-valve opening accordingly, so as to hold or change the water temperature to the desired value. However, processes (like the controllers and output elements of servomechanisms) have the characteristic of delaying and retarding changes in the condition of the process. There are two types of lag which normally occur in plants, namely simple exponential lags and distance/velocity lags.

14.3.2 The Simple Exponential Lag

General
The basic ideas associated with exponential 'transfer delays' have been discussed in §9.1. An exponential lag occurs when the change with time in the output signal x_o from an element or system, resulting from the application of a step change in the input signal x_i to that element or system is of the simple exponential form expressed by

$$x_o = x_f(1 - e^{-t/T})$$

where x_f is the change in the equilibrium value of x_o which will be attained if the conditions are held constant after the step change has occurred, and T is the time constant.

The transfer function relating output to input for general signals will thus be

$$\frac{x_o}{x_i}(D) = \frac{K}{1 + TD}$$

or for sinusoids, replacing D by $j\omega$,

$$\frac{x_o}{x_i}(j\omega) = \frac{K}{1 + j\omega T}$$

The time constants of most processes are usually rather long and it is more convenient to work in minutes than seconds. Thus if the time constant is expressed in minutes, the angular frequency ω must be expressed in radians per minute. Some examples of typical simple processes which give rise to exponential lags are considered below.

The Thermal Exponential Lag
Consider a vessel having a heat capacitance C joules per degree which is being heated from a source maintained at a temperature θ_i degrees

373

through a thermal resistor of resistance R degree minutes per joule.
The arrangement is shown in Fig. 14.3.

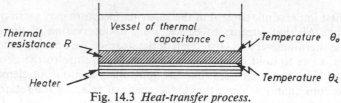

Fig. 14.3 *Heat-transfer process.*

The rate of flow of heat is proportional to the temperature difference
and inversely proportional to the resistance. Thus if I is the rate of
flow of heat in joules per minute then

$$I = \frac{\theta_i - \theta_o}{R}$$

Assuming no loss of heat this heat flow goes to raising the temperature of the vessel.

Thus
$$C\frac{d\theta_o}{dt} = \frac{\theta_i - \theta_o}{R}$$

or
$$CD\theta_o = \frac{\theta_i - \theta_o}{R}$$

Thus
$$\frac{\theta_o}{\theta_i}(D) = \frac{1}{1 + TD}$$

where $T = CR$, the thermal time constant in minutes.

The Pneumatic Exponential Lag

Consider a vessel having a pneumatic capacitance C cubic metres per
unit pressure supplied with air from a source maintained at a pressure
p_i through a pneumatic restrictor of restrictance R units of pressure
per cubic metre per minute. The arrangement is shown in Fig. 14.4.

For pressure differences below about an atmosphere, laminar flow
takes place in the connecting pipe and the rate of flow of air is pro-

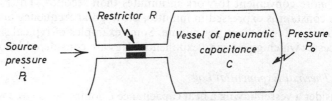

Fig. 14.4 *Air-transfer process.*

portional to the pressure difference and inversely proportional to the pipe restrictance.

Thus if I is the rate of flow of air in cubic metres per minute then

$$I = \frac{p_i - p_o}{R}$$

Assuming that no air leaks from the vessel, this flow goes to increase the pressure in the second vessel.

Thus
$$C\frac{dp_o}{dt} = \frac{p_i - p_o}{R}$$

or
$$CDp_o = \frac{p_i - p_o}{R}$$

Thus
$$\frac{p_o}{p_i}(D) = \frac{1}{1 + TD}$$

where $T = CR$, the pneumatic time constant.

Note, the units of pressure (N/m^2 in the m.k.s. system) have been omitted from the above analysis.

The Liquid Level Exponential Lag

Consider a tank having a liquid capacitance C cubic metres per metre height supplied with liquid from another tank, the level of liquid in this tank being maintained constant at h_i metres. The flow takes place through a pipe of flow resistance R metre minutes per cubic metre. The arrangement is shown in Fig. 14.5.

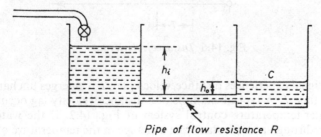

Pipe of flow resistance R

Fig. 14.5 *Liquid-transfer process.*

If the flow in the pipe is laminar flow the rate of flow of liquid into the second tank is proportional to the difference in the two levels and inversely proportional to the flow resistance of the connecting pipe. Thus if the flow rate is I cubic metres per minute

$$I = \frac{h_i - h_o}{R}$$

Increase in the level of the liquid in the second tank is due to the inflow of liquid thus

$$C\frac{dh_o}{dt} = \frac{h_i - h_o}{R}$$

or

$$CDh_o = \frac{h_i - h_o}{R}$$

$\therefore$

$$\frac{h_o}{h_i}(D) = \frac{1}{1 + TD}$$

where $T = CR$, the time constant.

14.3.3 Distance/Velocity Lag

This is the time interval between an alteration in the value of a signal and its manifestation unchanged at a later part of the system and arising solely from the finite speed of propagation of the signal (see Fig. 14.6).

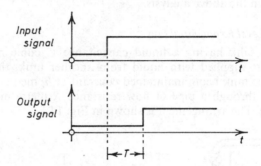

Fig. 14.6 *Distance/velocity lag.*

If a signal experiences distance/velocity lag T it emerges unchanged after a time T. A typical example of a distance/velocity lag occurs in the water-temperature control system of Fig. 14.2. If the water is flowing through at a constant rate a change in the temperature of the water in the tank does not appear at the thermometer until some time later, this time being governed entirely by the velocity v of the water flowing through the output pipe and the distance d of the thermometer from the tank. The lag $T = d/v$. Sometimes distance/velocity lag is termed 'dead time' or 'transport lag'.

The transfer function representing a distance/velocity lag can be derived quickly by consideration of the frequency response. A sinusoidal signal applied to an element possessing a distance/velocity lag will emerge unaltered in magnitude but lagging in phase by an amount directly proportional to frequency. The only transfer function which can satisfy both magnitude and phase conditions is

$$\frac{x_o}{x_i}(j\omega) = e^{-j\omega T} \tag{1}$$

The magnitude of this transfer function is unity and the angle of lag is ωT.
For general signals the operator D can be substituted for $j\omega$ and we have

$$\frac{x_o}{x_i}(D) = e^{-TD}$$

This transfer function can be regarded merely as an operator that the analyst may use to indicate a pure time delay without magnitude change.

The Nyquist diagram for the transfer function of equation (1) above is a circle of unity radius. At zero frequency the magnitude is unity and the phase lag is zero. Thereafter the lag simply increases to infinity as the frequency increases (Fig. 14.7.).

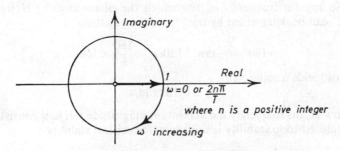

Fig. 14.7 *Nyquist diagram for distance/velocity lag.*

The problem of designing automatic controls is made more difficult by the existence of a distance/velocity lag within the plant.

Worked Example

A process control system contains a plant having a single simple exponential lag of time constant 2 min and a distance/velocity lag of 10 sec. The control equipment contains a proportional controller and the overall open-loop zero frequency gain of the plant and the control equipment is K. Determine the value of K for which the system will just be unstable on closed loop.

377

Solution

The open-loop transfer function $H(j\omega)$ of the system for sinusoidal signals is given by

$$H(j\omega) = \frac{Ke^{-j\omega\,10}}{1 + j\omega 120}$$

A sketch of the Nyquist diagram for this function is shown in Fig. 14.8.

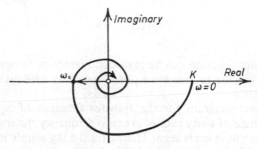

Fig. 14.8 *Nyquist diagram for worked example.*

The angular frequency ω_c for which the phase angle $\angle H(j\omega)$ is $-180°$ can be determined by trial from the equation

$$-180° = -\tan^{-1} 120\omega_c - \frac{180}{\pi} \times 10\omega_c$$

This yields a solution

$$\omega_c \simeq 0{\cdot}162\,\text{rad/s}$$

Now at this frequency the maximum magnitude $|H(j\omega)|$ consistent with closed-loop stability is unity, i.e. for critical stability

$$\frac{K}{\sqrt{\{1 + (120\omega_c)^2\}}} = 1$$

$$K = \sqrt{\{1 + (120\omega_c)^2\}} = \sqrt{\{1 + 19{\cdot}44^2\}}$$

$$= 19{\cdot}47$$

i.e. the maximum value of K consistent with closed-loop stability is 19·47.

14.4 Dynamic Characteristics of Controllers

14.4.1 General

The controlling element in an automatic process control system receives a signal proportional to the deviation θ and produces a signal

V at its output. This signal drives the motor element in direct proportion to V. The motor actuates the correcting element (Fig. 14.9).

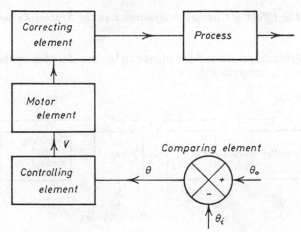

Fig. 14.9 *Position of the controlling element in a system.*

In pneumatic systems V is a controlled air-pressure signal. The motor element is usually a diaphragm motor and is normally built into a single unit with the correcting element. The correcting element is frequently a fluid flow valve; and a simplified sketch of a typical combination is shown in Fig. 14.10.

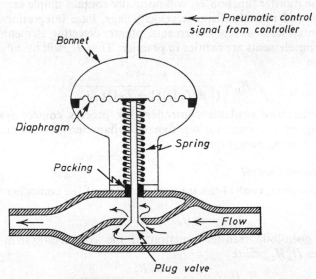

Fig. 14.10 *Combination diaphragm motor and fluid flow control valve.*

379

A great amount of work has been done in shaping the parts of the flow valve to obtain various flow-lift characteristics.

14.4.2 The Effect of Controller Dynamics on the System Response

General

The control equipment and the plant can be considered as constituting a loop as illustrated in Fig. 14.11.

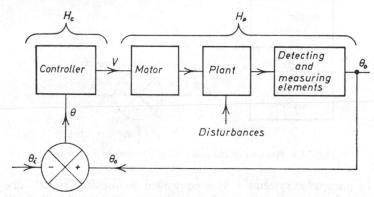

Fig. 14.11 *Alternative schematic of automatic process-control system.*

The transfer function of the controller is V/θ (termed H_c). The other elements are represented by the transfer function θ_o/V (termed H_p). The transfer function H_p will normally contain simple exponential lags and possibly distance/velocity lags. Pure integrations and exponential leads in motor elements, plants, detecting elements and measuring elements are rarities in practice. Thus H_p will usually take the form

$$H_p = \frac{K_p\, e^{-TD}}{(1 + T_1\, D)(1 + T_2\, D)}, \text{ etc.}$$

Commercially available controllers for process control systems are designed to achieve various dynamic characteristics summarized in the following paragraphs.

Proportional Control

In proportional control the transfer function of the controller takes the form

$$H_c = -K_1$$

The open-loop transfer function of the complete system thus becomes $H_p H_c$, where

$$H_p H_c = \frac{-K_1 K_p\, e^{-TD}}{(1 + T_1\, D)(1 + T_2\, D)}, \text{ etc.}$$

380

Process Control Systems

Two points emerge from a study of this transfer function. Firstly there will inevitably be a sustained deviation in response to a constant set value. This may of course be made very small if K_1 is made sufficiently high. However, the second point is that, generally, if K_1 is made high the system will become unstable on closed loop. When K_1 is set so that the system possesses adequate relative stability the speed of response to changes in the set value or to disturbances is limited entirely by the plant characteristics.

Plant disturbances will cause additional deviations, a constant disturbance producing a constant additional deviation. (Note, to apply the Nyquist stability criterion the function $-H_p(j\omega)H_c(j\omega)$ must be plotted on the Nyquist diagram.)

Commercial controllers, including the compound controllers described below, are usually calibrated in terms of the 'proportional band' which is defined as that range of values of deviation corresponding to the full operating range of output signal of the controlling unit resulting from proportional action only. The proportional band can be expressed as a percentage of the range of values of the controlled condition which the measuring unit of the controller is designed to measure (see Fig. 14.12).

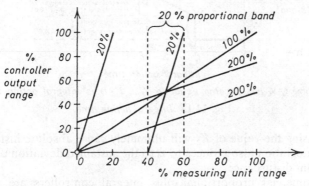

Fig. 14.12 *Proportional band.*

The proportional band P is related to K_1 by the equation

$$P = \frac{100}{K_1}$$

Proportional Plus Integral Control

In a proportional plus integral action controller the output V from the controller is given by

$$V = -K_1\left(\theta + \frac{K_2}{K_1}\int \theta\,dt\right)$$

381

The transfer function is thus

$$\frac{V}{\theta} = - K_1 \left(1 + \frac{K_2}{K_1 D}\right)$$

i.e.
$$\frac{V}{\theta} = H_c = \frac{-K_2\{1 + (K_1/K_2)D\}}{D}$$

A proportional plus integral controller thus introduces a simple lead as well as a pure integration. The overall transfer function becomes

$$H_c H_p = \frac{-K_2 K_p\{1 + (K_1/K_2)D\}e^{-TD}}{D(1 + T_1 D)(1 + T_2 D), \text{ etc.}}$$

The integration reduces the sustained deviation to zero but the response of a given plant will be slower for the same relative stability.

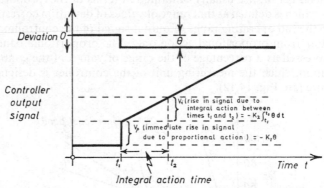

At time t_2 V_i has become equal to V_p ∴ $t_2 - t_1$ is integral action time

Fig. 14.13 *Integral action time.*

Increasing the value of K_2 will ultimately cause absolute instability. The integration also reduces to zero the sustained deviation due to a constant disturbance.

Commercial proportional plus integral controllers are usually calibrated in terms of proportional band (described previously) and 'integral action time'. This is defined as the time interval in which the part of the output signal due to integral action increases by an amount equal to the part of the output signal due to proportional action when the deviation is unchanging (see Fig. 14.13).

Integral action time has the value K_1/K_2.

Proportional Plus Derivative Control

In a proportional plus derivative controller the output V from the controller is given by

$$V = - K_1 \left(\theta + \frac{K_3}{K_1}\frac{d\theta}{dt}\right)$$

The transfer function is thus

$$\frac{V}{\theta} = H_c = -K_1 \left\{ 1 + \frac{K_3}{K_1} D \right\}$$

A proportional plus derivative controller thus introduces a simple lead. The overall transfer function becomes

$$H_c H_p = \frac{-K_1 K_p \{1 + (K_3/K_1) D\} e^{-TD}}{(1 + T_1 D)(1 + T_2 D)}, \text{ etc.}$$

The lead introduced into the transfer function allows a higher value of K_1 to be used for the same relative stability than with proportional control alone. The response to changes in set value are faster. However, a sustained deviation is still present for a constant set value; also constant disturbances will produce additive sustained deviations.

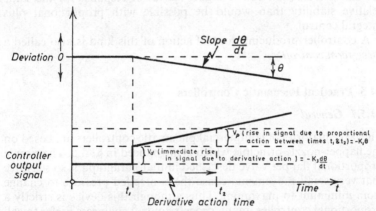

At time t_2 V_p has become equal to V_d $\therefore$ t_1-t_2 is derivative action time

Fig. 14.14 *Derivative action time.*

Commercial proportional plus derivative controllers are usually calibrated in terms of proportional band (previously described) and 'derivative action time'. This is defined as the time interval in which the part of the output signal due to proportional action increases by an amount equal to the part of the output signal due to derivative action, when the deviation is changing at a constant rate (see Fig. 14.14).

Derivative action time has the value K_3/K_1.

Proportional Plus Integral Plus Derivative Control

In a proportional plus integral plus derivative controller the output V from the controller is given by

$$V = -K_1 \left(\theta + \frac{K_2}{K_1} \int \theta \, dt + \frac{K_3}{K_1} \frac{d\theta}{dt} \right)$$

383

The transfer function is thus

$$\frac{V}{\theta} = -K_1\left(1 + \frac{K_2}{K_1 D} + \frac{K_3 D}{K_1}\right)$$

i.e.
$$\frac{V}{\theta} = H_c = \frac{-K_3\{D^2 + (K_1/K_3)D + (K_2/K_3)\}}{D}$$

The quadratic expression in the numerator normally has real roots and thus the numerator gives rise to a pair of simple exponential leads. The overall transfer function

$$H_c H_p = \frac{-K_3 K_p\{D^2 + (K_1/K_3)D + (K_2/K_3)\}e^{-TD}}{D(1 + T_1 D)(1 + T_2 D)}, \text{ etc.}$$

The integration reduces the sustained deviation to zero whereas the derivative action allows higher speeds of response for the same relative stability than would be possible with proportional plus integral control.

A controller producing control action of this kind is also called a *three-term controller*.

14.5 Practical Pneumatic Controllers

14.5.1 General

The large majority of commercial pneumatic controllers are based on the flapper-nozzle principle which is introduced in §7.3.5. The simple proportional flapper valve described in that paragraph is so sensitive that very small movements cause the controlled pressure to change from minimum to maximum. Thus although this device is strictly a proportional controller, many process control engineers prefer to call it a *two-step controller* because of its on–off action. It is the flapper valve with pneumatic feedback as described in §7.3.5 which is usually referred to as a proportional controller. This device uses the bellows as a transducer for converting pneumatic pressure to mechanical motion. Great use is made of the bellows in commercial pneumatic controllers and its mode of action will be considered next.

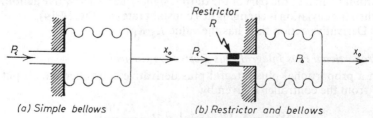

(a) Simple bellows   (b) Restrictor and bellows

Fig. 14.15 *Mode of action of the bellows.*

The simple bellows behaves in the manner of a leakage-free, spring-controlled piston. The force acting on the base is $p_i A$ where A is the effective cross-sectional area of the base. The extension of the bellows is x_o, thus if k is the spring-stiffness of the bellows the restoring force is kx_o. When the base is at rest there must be a force balance, hence

$$p_i A = kx_o$$

The transfer function of the bellows is thus

$$\frac{x_o}{p_i} = \frac{A}{k} = K$$

where K is a constant.

In the case of the restrictor-bellows arrangement [Fig. 14.15 (b)] the rate of flow of air I through the restrictance R is governed by the relationship

$$I = \frac{p_i - p_b}{R}$$

Also, if C is the pneumatic capacitance of the bellows,

$$\frac{d(Cp_b)}{dt} = \frac{p_i - p_b}{R}$$

If the change in capacitance is small compared with the total capacitance

$$\frac{d(Cp_b)}{dt} \simeq C\frac{dp_b}{dt}$$

$$\therefore \qquad C\frac{dp_b}{dt} = \frac{p_i - p_b}{R}$$

$$\therefore \qquad \frac{p_b}{p_i}(D) = \frac{1}{1 + TD}$$

where $T = CR$.

It should be noted that in practice it is found convenient to use a brass bellows with very low stiffness, additional stiffness being provided by a steel spring mounted inside the bellows. The theory, however, remains exactly the same.

14.5.2 The Proportional Controller

The pneumatic proportional controller with feedback is shown in Fig. 14.16.

The required transfer function relates the controlled pressure p_c to the displacement m. The geometry of the linkage gives the approximate relationship

$$bm + an = (a + b)x \qquad (1)$$

The bellows pressure is the same as the controlled pressure p_c, hence if K is the constant for the bellows

$$n = -Kp_c \qquad (2)$$

Now the displacement x of the flapper is very small, thus from (1) we have

$$bm + an \simeq 0 \qquad (3)$$

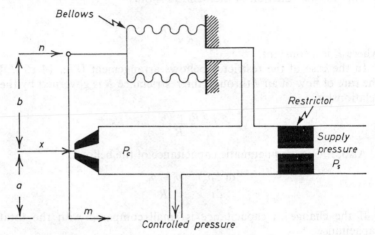

Fig. 14.16 *The proportional controller.*

Hence substituting in (3) from (2) we have

$$bm - Kap_c \simeq 0$$

∴ $$bm \simeq Kap_c$$

∴ $$\frac{p_c}{m} \simeq \frac{b}{Ka}$$

Thus b/Ka is the approximate transfer function of the controller. In practice the motion m is arranged to be directly proportional to the deviation θ.

14.5.3 The Proportional Plus Integral Controller

A simple practical arrangement for achieving proportional plus integral action is shown in Fig. 14.17.

As before, from the geometry of the linkage

$$bm + an = (a + b)x$$

But x is very small, thus

$$bm + an \simeq 0 \qquad (1)$$

The two bellows act in opposition to each other;

thus
$$n = -K(p_c - p_i) \qquad (2)$$

where K is the constant for the bellows;

and
$$C\frac{dp_i}{dt} = \frac{p_c - p_i}{R}$$

where C is the capacitance of integral bellows (assumed approximately constant) and R is the restrictance of integral restrictor.

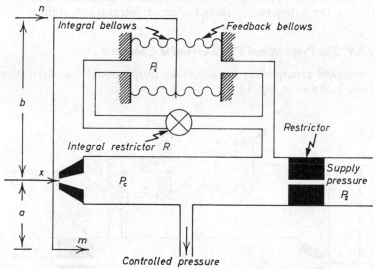

Fig. 14.17 *Proportional plus integral controller.*

Thus
$$RCDp_i = p_c - p_i$$

$$\therefore \qquad p_i = \frac{p_c}{1 + RCD} \qquad (3)$$

Substituting for p_i in (2) from (3) gives

$$n = -K\left(p_c - \frac{p_c}{1 + RCD}\right) \qquad (4)$$

Substituting for n in (1) from (4) yields

$$bm - aK\left(p_c - \frac{p_c}{1 + RCD}\right) \simeq 0$$

$$\therefore \qquad bm \simeq aK\left\{\frac{p_c(1 + RCD) - p_c}{1 + RCD}\right\}$$

$$\simeq aK\left\{\frac{RCDp_c}{1 + RCD}\right\}$$

387

$$\therefore \qquad \frac{p_c}{m}(D) \simeq \frac{b}{Ka}\frac{1 + RCD}{RCD}$$

$$\simeq \frac{b}{Ka}\left\{1 + \frac{1}{RCD}\right\}$$

In operation the controller output V would become proportional to $-p_c$ and the motion m would be made proportional to the deviation θ. Hence the integral action time, as defined in §14.4.2, becomes CR. The variable restrictor R is thus normally calibrated directly in minutes, the setting representing the actual integral action time.

14.5.4 *The Proportional Plus Derivative Controller*

A practical arrangement for achieving proportional plus derivative action is shown in Fig. 14.18.

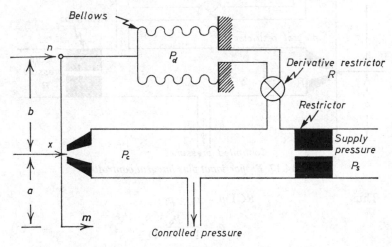

Fig. 14.18 *Proportional plus derivative controller.*

As before, from the geometry of the linkage

$$bm + an = (a + b)x$$

But x is very small, thus

$$bm + an \simeq 0 \qquad (1)$$

Also

$$n = -Kp_d \qquad (2)$$

and

$$C\frac{dp_d}{dt} = \frac{p_c - p_d}{R}$$

388

where C is the capacitance of the bellows and R is the restrictance of the derivative restrictor.

Thus
$$p_d = \frac{p_c}{1 + RCD} \qquad (3)$$

Substituting for p_d in (2) from (3) gives

$$n = -\frac{Kp_c}{1 + RCD} \qquad (4)$$

and substituting for n in (1) from (4) gives

$$bm - \frac{aKp_c}{1 + RCD} \simeq 0$$

$$\frac{p_c}{m}(D) \simeq \frac{b}{aK}(1 + RCD)$$

The derivative action time as defined in §14.4.2 thus becomes RC. The variable restrictor R is thus normally calibrated directly in minutes, the setting representing the actual derivative action time.

14.5.5 The Three-Term Controller

A three-term controller should ideally produce control action described by

$$\frac{V}{\theta} = -K_1\left(1 + \frac{K_2}{K_1 D} + \frac{K_3 D}{K_1}\right)$$

(see §14.4.2).

Now K_3/K_1 is defined as derivative action time T_d and K_1/K_2 is defined as integral action time T_i.

Hence the ideal transfer function for a three-term controller is

$$\frac{V}{\theta} = -K_1\left(1 + \frac{1}{T_i D} + T_d D\right)$$

It will be seen that the magnitudes of the integral and derivative actions can be altered independently without interacting on the remaining two terms. Such a controller is described as *non-interacting*.

The majority of commercial pneumatic controllers do not have this independency of action, an alteration of either the derivative or the integral action time has the effect of altering the proportional band though no actual change to the proportional adjustment has in fact been made. Such controllers are described as *interacting* controllers. A typical example of an interacting three-term controller is the Kent Mark 30, a simplified schematic of which is shown in Fig. 14.19.

As before, from the geometry of the linkage

$$bm + an = (a+b)x$$

But x is very small, thus

$$bm + an \simeq 0 \qquad (1)$$

The two bellows act in opposition to one another thus

$$n = -K(p_d - p_i) \qquad (2)$$

Also

$$C_i \frac{dp_i}{dt} = \frac{p_c - p_i}{R_i}$$

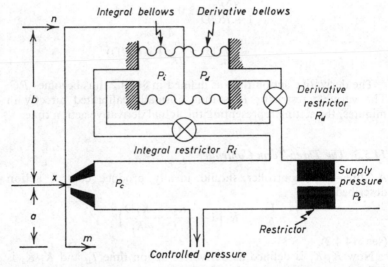

Fig. 14.19 *An interacting three-term controller.*

where C_i is the capacitance of the integral bellows (assumed approximately constant) and R_i is the restrictance of the integral restrictor.

$$\therefore \qquad p_i = \frac{p_c}{1 + R_i C_i D}$$

$$= \frac{p_c}{1 + T_i D} \qquad (3)$$

where T_i is the calibrated setting of the integral restrictor. By similar argument, for the derivative bellows we have

$$p_d = \frac{p_c}{1 + T_d D} \qquad (4)$$

where T_d is the calibrated setting of the derivative restrictor.

390

From equations (1) and (2) we have

$$bm \simeq aK(p_d - p_i) \qquad (5)$$

Substituting for p_i and p_d in (5) from (4) and (3) gives

$$bm \simeq aK\left(\frac{p_c}{1 + T_d D} - \frac{p_c}{1 + T_i D}\right)$$

$$bm \simeq aKp_c\left\{\frac{(1 + T_i D) - (1 + T_d D)}{(1 + T_d D)(1 + T_i D)}\right\}$$

$$\frac{p_c}{m} \simeq \frac{b}{aK(T_i - T_d)} \cdot \frac{(1 + T_d D)(1 + T_i D)}{D}$$

In operation the controller output V would be made directly proportional to $-p_c$ and the displacement m would be made directly proportional to the deviation θ.

Hence $\quad V = -k_1 p_c$

and $\quad m = k_2 \theta$

$$\therefore \quad \frac{V}{\theta} \simeq \frac{-k_2 k_1 b}{aK(T_i - T_d)} \cdot \frac{(1 + T_d D)(1 + T_i D)}{D}$$

$$\therefore \quad \frac{V}{\theta} \simeq \frac{-k_2 k_1 b}{aK(T_i - T_d)}\left\{\frac{1 + (T_d + T_i) D + T_d T_i D^2}{D}\right\}$$

$$\simeq \frac{-k_2 k_1 b}{aK(T_i - T_d)}\left\{(T_d + T_i) + \frac{1}{D} + T_d T_i D\right\}$$

$$\simeq \frac{-k_2 k_1 b}{aK} \cdot \frac{T_d + T_i}{T_i - T_d}\left\{1 + \frac{1}{(T_d + T_i) D} + \frac{T_d T_i D}{T_d + T_i}\right\}$$

This transfer function may be compared with the ideal transfer function

$$\frac{V}{\theta} = -K_1\left(1 + \frac{1}{T_i D} + T_d D\right)$$

In the practical arrangement it is seen by comparison that the effective proportional control factor K_1 is given by

$$K_1 = \frac{k_2 k_1 b}{aK} \times \frac{T_d + T_i}{T_i - T_d}$$

Now $k_2 k_1 b / aK$ is the nominal proportional control factor, thus

actual proportional control factor

$$= \text{nominal proportional control factor} \times \frac{T_d + T_i}{T_i - T_d}$$

Also, effective integral action time $S = T_d + T_i$, and effective derivative action time $R = T_d \times \dfrac{T_i}{T_d + T_i}$.

It can readily be shown that the ratio of effective derivative action time to effective integral action time has a theoretical maximum when $T_d = T_i$. However under these conditions the controller behaves in an undesirable manner. This can be seen physically, for if the restrictance R_d is made equal to the restrictance R_i, the proportional effect due to build up of p_d is completely neutralized by the corresponding build up of p_i so that the controller behaves as though it had no proportional feedback. George Kent Ltd. recommend that $T_d \leqslant T_i/3$ for satisfactory operation of their Mark 30 three-term controller.

Returning to the practical transfer function

$$\frac{V}{\theta} \simeq - \frac{k_2 k_1 b}{aK} \cdot \frac{1}{T_i - T_d} \cdot \frac{(1 + T_d D)(1 + T_i D)}{D}$$

it should be noted that the proportional band setting P expressed as a percentage is given by

$$\frac{k_2 k_1 b}{aK} = \frac{100}{P}$$

thus

$$\frac{V}{\theta} = - \frac{100}{P} \cdot \frac{1}{T_i - T_d} \cdot \frac{(1 + T_d D)(1 + T_i D)}{D}$$

The problem of adjusting the values of P, T_i and T_d to give optimum performance of an automatic process control system is discussed in §14.6.

14.5.6 The Pneumatic Relay

The controlled pneumatic pressure from a pneumatic controller is at a very low power level, i.e. the output restrictance of a pneumatic controller is normally high. The input capacitance of the diaphragm motor which the controller is usually required to drive would also normally be high. Thus if a pneumatic controller were used directly to control a diaphragm motor or any other high input capacitance device, the time constant of the resultant exponential lag would be excessively high. It is possible to avoid such a lag by using a pneumatic power amplifier of unity pressure gain. Such amplifiers are usually called *relays*. An example of such a device is shown in Fig. 14.20.

An increase of pressure p_c in the primary chamber A moves the block B bodily upwards by flexing the diaphragms. Thus the valve V is lifted clear of its top seating D, admitting air into the secondary chamber E from the supply pressure line. When primary and secondary chamber pressures are exactly equal the valve V closes at seating D.

Conversely a decrease of pressure in the primary chamber A will cause block B to move bodily downwards. Thus, valve V is now opened at seating F, while remaining closed at D. Excess air from the secondary chamber thus flows into the cavity in block B and away to atmosphere via ports G. When the primary and secondary pressures are exactly equal the valve V closes at F.

The pressure in the secondary chamber is thus a power-amplified version of the pressure in the primary chamber.

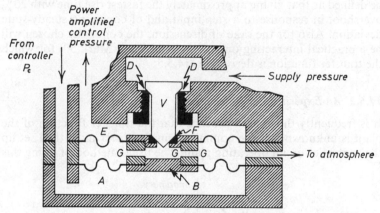

Fig. 14.20 *A pneumatic relay.*

14.6 Setting up a Controller to give Optimum System Performance

14.6.1 General

The dynamics of a plant are generally fixed; that is to say, as far as the designer is concerned the transfer function H_p of Fig. 14.21 is unalterable. The range of commercially available controllers is also limited, so that the designer's problem is really that of (i) selecting the cheapest and simplest controller which is capable of meeting the

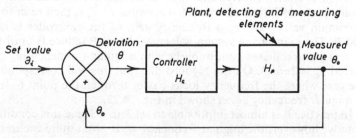

Fig. 14.21 *Simplified block diagram of process-control system.*

specification, and (ii) specifying the settings of the controller to give the 'best' performance possible with that particular controller.

The most difficult specification requires that the system shall have no steady-state deviation together with a reasonably fast response; the designer then has no alternative but to select a three-term controller. In tuning or setting up the characteristics of the controller to match the characteristics of the plant, the problem is to determine values of T_i, T_d and P which will produce the *best* response from the system on closed loop. For the sake of discussion, *best response* will be defined as that giving approximately the fastest rise time with 20% overshoot in response to a step input and of course no steady-state deviation. Also for the sake of discussion, the controller chosen will be a practical interacting one (such as the Kent Mark 30) for which the transfer function is derived in §14.5.5.

14.6.2 An Experimental Procedure

It is frequently the case in practice that the transfer function of the plant is unknown and the commissioning engineer must then set up the controller on an operating plant. The usual method of doing this

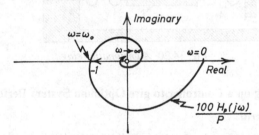

Fig. 14.22 *Nyquist condition for sustained oscillation.*

involves finding a satisfactory working point with zero steady-state deviation from the set value. To do this the derivative time setting T_d is set to minimum, the proportional band setting to 100% and the value of T_i is then slowly reduced from its maximum value until the steady-state deviation disappears. The value of T_i is then reset to its maximum value. The zero frequency gain of the controller is now $100/P$. The gain of the system is increased (i.e. P reduced) until the system just oscillates continuously with angular frequency ω_0 (i.e. period $T_o = 2\pi/\omega_0$). On the Nyquist diagram this will correspond to the case where the frequency locus passes through the point $(-1, j0)$ at angular frequency ω_0 as shown in Fig. 14.22.

In practice it is almost impossible to set P to achieve this condition exactly; however, the angular frequency ω_0 is given quite accurately by this method. When T_o has been calculated T_d is set equal to $T_o/4$

and T_i is set equal to $3T_o/4$. The proportional band setting P is then set initially to twice its original value and the system is step-response tested, adjusting P until a reasonable response is obtained.

The transfer function of the three-term controller for steady-state sinusoidal signals is given by

$$\frac{V}{\theta}(j\omega) = -\frac{100}{P(T_i - T_d)} \cdot \frac{(1 + j\omega T_i)(1 + j\omega T_d)}{j\omega}$$

The overall open-loop transfer function is thus

$$-\frac{\theta_o}{\theta}(j\omega) = \frac{100}{P(T_i - T_d)} \cdot \frac{(1 + j\omega T_i)(1 + j\omega T_d)}{j\omega} \cdot H_p(j\omega)$$

Thus, apart from introducing an integral term into the loop and so eliminating the steady-state deviations, these settings on the controller will cause a net phase-lead at an angular frequency ω_o given by

$$\angle(-V/\theta(j\omega)) = \tan^{-1}\omega_o T_i + \tan^{-1}\omega_o T_d - 90°$$

$$= \tan^{-1}(3\pi/2) + \tan^{-1}(\pi/2) - 90°$$

$$\simeq 45°$$

When the gain of the system has been adjusted to obtain a reasonable step response the peak magnitude of the closed-loop frequency response M is approximately 1·3 at an angular frequency equal to ω_o (this is equivalent to contact of the overall open-loop frequency locus with an M-circle at angular frequency ω_o for $M = 1\cdot3$). The angular frequency of oscillation ω_o of the plant thus becomes the angular frequency ω_{rf} of the overall system. Where this method is used the product $\omega_{rf}T_d$ is constant and equal to $\pi/2$ regardless of the characteristics of the plant.

Consideration of the Nyquist diagram yields a theoretical method of adjusting the proportional band setting. If P_1 is the setting of the proportional band setting for which the plant just oscillates then

$$\frac{100}{P_1}H_p(j\omega) = 1$$

In the overall system the modulus x at ω_{rf} is given by

$$x = |H_p(j\omega)| \cdot \frac{100}{P_2(T_i - T_d)} \cdot \left| \frac{(1 + j\omega_{rf}T_i)(1 + j\omega_{rf}T_d)}{j\omega_{rf}} \right|$$

Using

$$T_i = 3T_d$$

$$\omega_{rf}T_d = 1\cdot57$$

$$|H_p(j\omega)| = P_1/100$$

this gives

$$x = \frac{P_1}{P_2} \times \frac{8\cdot95}{2 \times 1\cdot57}$$

$$\therefore \qquad P_2 = \frac{2 \cdot 85 P_1}{x}$$

A reasonable choice for x is $0 \cdot 7$ which gives $P_2 \simeq 4 P_1$. In the experimental method of tuning it has been normal practice to set P_2 equal to $2P_1$ initially and this gives a rather underdamped response. The use of the above factor (4) can yield good results immediately.

14.6.3 A Theoretical Procedure

The experimental procedure for setting up a three-term controller described in §14.6.2 is frequently used in practice. It does, however, involve setting a system into oscillation on closed loop. This may be

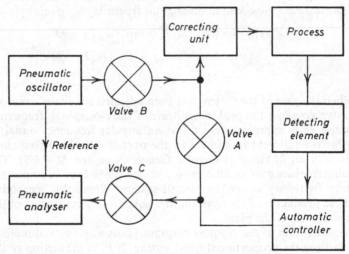

Fig. 14.23 *An arrangement for open-loop frequency response testing.*

undesirable as the possibility of a violent and dangerous build up of the magnitude of oscillation always exists. It is almost always impossible to determine analytically the transfer function of a plant because of its complexity; it is, however, normally possible to experimentally determine the open-loop frequency response of the system. This offers no severe practical difficulties nor disadvantages. A suitable arrangement for obtaining the open-loop frequency response is shown in Fig. 14.23.

To analyse the system valve A is shut and valves B and C are opened; the controller is used only as a transmitter with proportional action. The open-loop response is recorded for the range of frequencies of interest.

Once the frequency response $H_p(j\omega)$ has been determined it is possible to find the correct settings of T_i, T_d and P by a theoretical method.

The frequency response locus $H_p(j\omega)/j\omega$ is drawn on the Nyquist diagram (Fig. 14.24).

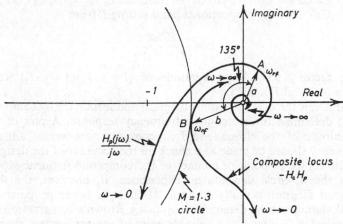

Fig. 14.24 *Nyquist diagram illustrating theoretical design of a three-term controller.*

Having already taken into account the integration by plotting the function $H_p(j\omega)/j\omega$, the effective transfer function of the controller becomes:

$$\left\{\frac{100}{P(T_i - T_d)}\right\}(1 + j\omega T_i)(1 + j\omega T_d)$$

The double exponential lead gives a positive phase shift ϕ given by

$$\phi = \tan^{-1}\omega T_i + \tan^{-1}\omega T_d$$

This phase shift moves the vector A in Fig. 14.24 round to the position of vector B. In order to obtain maximum benefit from the controller in terms of speed of response, ϕ should be as large as possible. However, the use of a phase shift of greater than 135° begins to produce undesirable side-effects and for this reason a phase shift of 135° is used in the method of design described below. The choice of T_d and T_i is limited by the condition $T_d/T_i \leqslant 1\cdot3$ and in fact $T_d/T_i = 1/3$ is used in the design because the use of smaller ratios has no practical advantages. The Nyquist design method basically shifts the vector A (length a) as shown in Fig. 14.24 round to the position of vector B which is where the composite locus should touch the $M = 1\cdot3$ circle. The procedure is as follows:

(1) Draw the Nyquist diagram for $H_p(j\omega)/j\omega$.
(2) On this diagram draw the $M = 1\cdot3$ circle (centre $-2\cdot45$, j0 and

radius 1·88) and mark on it where the compensated locus is required to touch. Measure the length *b* of the vector B.

(3) Draw a line at $-135°$ to B, measure *a* and estimate ω_{rf} from where this line cuts the original locus.

(4) Calculate T_d and T_i from the relations $T_d \omega_{rf} = \pi/2$, $T_i = 3T_d$.

(5) Calculate the proportional band setting *P* from

$$P = \frac{895a}{(T_i - T_d)\,b}$$

(The factor 8·95 is the magnitude of $(1 + j\omega T_d)(1 + j\omega T_i)$ when $\omega T_d = \pi/2$ and $T_i = 3T_d$.)

(6) Draw the overall Nyquist diagram and from it (or by computation) determine the closed-loop frequency response. A plot of the magnitude of the closed-loop frequency response versus angular frequency should be made as a check on the accuracy of the design.

The choice of point of contact of the composite frequency locus with the *M*-circle depends on experience; if, however, the final Nyquist diagram actually cuts the *M*-circle, a better proportional band setting can be determined by using Brown's construction (as described in chapter 10). A suitable point of contact is often where B has a magnitude 0·7 and is at 30° to the negative real axis.

Worked Example

An experiment on a process control system showed that the overall zero frequency gain of the motor, plant, detecting element and measuring element was unity and that these elements had five non-interacting simple exponential lags, two with time constants of 0·5 min and three with time constants of 0·2 min. Determine the best settings of a three-term controller whose action is described by the transfer function:

$$\frac{V}{\theta}(j\omega) = -\frac{100}{P(T_i - T_d)}\frac{(1 + j\omega T_i)(1 + j\omega T_d)}{j\omega}$$

Solution

Referring to a Nyquist diagram shown in Fig. 14.24, and suppose there is to be contact with the $M = 1·3$ circle when $b = 0·7$ and where B is at 30° to the negative real axis. The transfer function $H_p(j\omega)/j\omega$ is given by

$$\frac{H_p(j\omega)}{j\omega} = \frac{1}{j\omega(1 + j\omega 0·2)^3 (1 + j\omega 0·5)^2}$$

where ω is in rad/min.

Vector A is at 135° to vector B when

$$\angle H_p(j\omega)/j\omega = -285°$$

Thus ω_{rf} is given by

$$285° = 90° + 3\tan^{-1}0{\cdot}2\omega_{rf} + 2\tan^{-1}0{\cdot}5\omega_{rf}$$

i.e. when $\omega_{rf} \simeq 2{\cdot}75$ rad/min

Also
$$a = |H_p(j\omega_{rf})/j\omega_{rf}|$$
$$= 0{\cdot}085$$

Using $\omega_{rf}T_d = \pi/2$ and $T_i = 3T_d$

gives
$$T_d = 0{\cdot}572 \text{ min and } T_i = 1{\cdot}7 \text{ min}$$

The proportional band setting P is calculated from

$$P = \frac{895}{(T_i - T_d)}\frac{a}{b} = \frac{895 \times 0{\cdot}085}{1{\cdot}13 \times 0{\cdot}7}$$
$$= 96\%$$

Using these values it can be shown that the system has a maximum closed-loop frequency response magnitude M_{pf} of $1{\cdot}31$ at $\omega = 2{\cdot}78$ rad/min. (A laboratory simulation of this system gave a step-response which has a slightly slower rise time than would have been predicted using second-order correlations and an overshoot of 30%; nevertheless this was considered a very satisfactory result and well within any reasonable tolerances.)

14.7 Electronic Instrumentation for Measurement and Control

Pneumatic control systems have been firmly established for several decades and it is only during the last eight years that electronic systems have gained wide acceptance. The recent phenomenal developments in solid-state devices have secured advantages in size, performance and reliability. Some of the more important advantages of electronic systems are listed below:

(1) Solid-state devices are at least as reliable as pneumatic ones.
(2) Less maintenance is required.
(3) Installation and fault location are easier. Wires are cheaper and easier to install than pipes and are less prone to leakage.
(4) Transmission lags are eliminated.
(5) Controllers can readily be designed or adapted to give any desired form of control function.
(6) Electronic systems are extremely flexible. Units can readily be arranged in any desired lay-out and removed when required.
(7) Many measuring devices (e.g. thermocouples, magnetic flow-meters, resistance thermometers) generate electrical signals and these can be used to produce a control system directly without intermediate

conversion into force, displacement or any other different form of signal. This eliminates mechanical hysteresis and simplifies the control loop thus improving its performance and reliability.

(8) Electrical signals are more acceptable to the data-handling equipment and computers which are being used increasingly to control complex processes.

The major disadvantages are:

(1) Electrical actuators are still inadequate for many purposes.
(2) Even brief supply failures may cause serious interruption of control with most designs of electronic equipment.

An example of an electronic control system designed to control the temperature of a furnace is shown in Fig. 14.25.

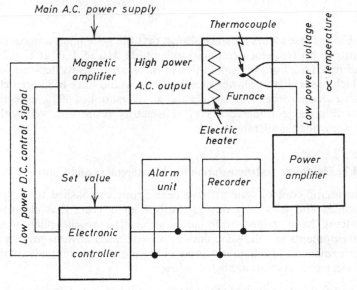

Fig. 14.25 *Electronic control system for the control of furnace temperature.*

Commercial electronic three-term controllers have been developed and Fig. 14.26 shows a typical circuit developed by George Kent Ltd.

14.8 Conclusion

Some of the theoretical and practical problems associated with the art of process control have been developed in this chapter. Many of the devices and definitions used in this field are very specialized and an attempt has been made to relate the theory to the subject matter

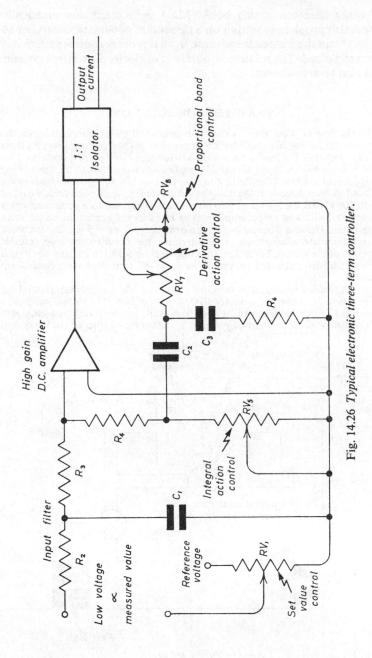

Fig. 14.26 *Typical electronic three-term controller.*

401

of other chapters in this book. Most particularly the practically important problem of setting up a three-term pneumatic controller so as to obtain the optimum response from a process control system has been explained. The relative importance of electronic control systems has also been discussed.

EXAMPLES FOR SOLUTION

1. The flow of water into a tank (1) is controlled by a diaphragm valve, the flow being from 0 to 20 m³/min for an air pressure on the diaphragm varying from 30 to 100 kN/m². The level in the tank is 1 m for each cubic metre it contains. This tank empties into an identical tank (2), the flow from one tank to the other being proportional to the level in the first tank at the rate of 0·1 m³/min for each metre of head. A level detector is fitted to the second tank giving a pneumatic signal of 30 to 100 kN/m² for a level of 0 to 4 m. This signal is fed to a controller which compares it with a set value, amplifies it by K_1 times and applies this to the valve diaphragm. The level detector has a simple exponential lag of 5 sec. Draw a block diagram for the arrangement and determine the overall open-loop transfer function of the system. Formulate the characteristic equation and use the Routh criterion to determine the maximum value of K_1 consistent with closed-loop stability.

2. A process control system contains a plant having a simple exponential lag of time constant 1 min and a distance/velocity lag of 5 sec. The control equipment contains a proportional controller and the overall open-loop zero frequency gain of the plant and the control equipment is 2. Determine whether or not the system

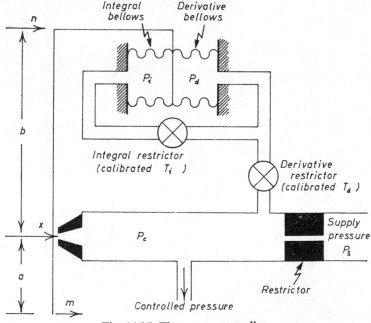

Fig. 14.27 *Three-term controller.*

will be stable on closed loop and if it is determine the phase margin and the gain margin.

3. An experiment on a process control system showed that the overall zero frequency gain of the motor, plant, detecting element and measuring element was unity and that these elements had three non-interacting simple exponential lags of time constants 0·5 min, 0·2 min and 1·0 min respectively. The controller is a proportional plus integral action device. The integral action time is set to 0·7 min. Determine the proportional band setting (as a percentage) which will just cause the system to oscillate continuously on closed loop.

4. A process control system has a motor, plant, detecting element and measuring element with an overall zero frequency gain of unity and three non-interacting simple exponential lags of time constants 0·2 min, 1·8 min and 6 min respectively. The controller is a proportional plus derivative action device. The derivative action time is set to 2·5 min. Use a Bode diagram to estimate the proportional band setting which will give a phase margin of 45°. Estimate also the angular resonant frequency of the system for this setting and the ratio of steady-state deviation to set value at zero frequency.

5. A three-term controller has a basic construction as indicated in Fig. 14.27. Determine a simplified expression for the transfer function relating the controlled pressure p_c to the movement m in terms of the lever dimensions a and b and the restrictor calibrations T_i and T_d. Also determine expressions for the effective proportional control factor, the effective integral action time and the effective derivative action time.

6. An experiment on a process control system showed that the overall zero frequency gain of the motor, plant, detecting element and measuring element was unity and that these elements had four non-interacting simple exponential lags, two with time constants of 1 min and two with time constants of 2 min. Determine the best settings of a three-term controller whose action is described by the transfer function:

$$\frac{V}{\theta}(j\omega) = -\frac{100}{P(T_i - T_d)} \cdot \frac{(1 + j\omega T_i)(1 + j\omega T_d)}{\omega j}$$

Chapter Fifteen

Analog Computing and Simulation

15.1 Introduction

Many design problems encountered in control engineering may be solved by frequency domain analysis; however it is normally essential to check the system performance in the time domain before the system is physically constructed. This is theoretically possible using a combination of operational/transform calculus and numerical analysis; the amount of tedious algebra and arithmetic involved in such methods increases rapidly with increase in the order of the system. Apart from the length of time involved in such work and the high probability of human error, the resultant analytical solution is not in a suitable form for comparison with specifications. A plot of the variables of interest as a function of time must be made; this will inevitably involve further computation. In the solution of many practical engineering problems an additional difficulty arises in that the effects of severe non-linearities such as saturation and backlash will affect the performance of the system for large and small signals in ways which are virtually unpredictable by analytical methods.

These problems have led to the very considerable use of analog, digital, and hybrid computers in the design of control systems. It is generally true to say that in the design of complex systems the use of computer-aided design techniques is essential.

Moreover computers have vast application in many other fields of scientific investigation and business systems as well as many branches of engineering.

15.2 Basic Concepts and Historic Survey

Systems which may be entirely different in physical form but which obey mathematical relationships of similar form are said to be *analogous* systems. For example, the mechanical system illustrated in Fig. 6.4 (page 89) is analogous to the torque-proportional-to-error servomechanism shown in Fig. 8.1 (page 158) because they both obey similar differential equations.

The use of electrical analogs has been very popular during the last two decades because of the relative cheapness of electrical components and the ease with which they may be connected together by means of flexible copper wire. The first analog computers, invented in the eighteenth and nineteenth century, were mechanical computers. W. Thomson (Lord Kelvin) published in 1875 his paper dealing with a mechanical analog computer using wheel-and-disc integrators. At the end of the 1914–18 War mechanical analog computers were designed for military use in gunfire control systems. In 1931, V. Bush published a paper dealing with a large-scale general-purpose differential analyzer.

At the end of the 1939–45 War electro-mechanical analog computers were widely used in military applications. The earliest use of operational amplifiers in electronic analog computers is clouded by the fog of military security but the first major article to be published describing their use in this application appeared in 1947 and was written by Tagazzini, Randall and Russell. However G. A. Philbrick is credited by some with having used high-gain d.c. amplifiers as computer components in unpublished work prior to the Second World War. Large improvements in computational accuracy were made possible by the invention of the chopper-stabilized amplifier (E. A. Goldburg, 1950).

15.3 Analog Computers

An analog computer represents the variables of a given problem by corresponding physical quantities, such as continuously variable voltages or shaft rotations. These 'machine variables' are made to obey mathematical relationships analogous to those of the original problem. The desired relationships are established by a set of 'computing elements' capable of enforcing suitable physical relationships. The conveniently measurable machine variables will then vary so that records of their values or behaviour constitute solutions of the given problem.

15.3.1 D.C. Analog Computers

The most important analog computer is the d.c. electronic analog computer. In these the machine variables are d.c. voltages which vary as functions of the machine time (which is used as the independent variable). These computers are relatively easy to construct, operate, and maintain and permit flexible interconnections by means of 'patch cords'.

405

The solution of a set of ordinary differential equations on a d.c. analog computer proceeds as follows:

(1) With the machine connected to solve the given problem, the machine variables (voltages) are set to the correct initial conditions prescribed by the problem.

(2) The computing elements are then made operative and force the voltages in the machine to vary in a manner prescribed by the given differential equations. The voltage variations with time are recorded and constitute the solutions of the given problem.

(3) The machine is stopped at a time chosen by the operator. The maximum allowable computing time is usually determined by limitations of the computing elements.

It should be noted that in many physical problems involving actual time, it is economical in time and cost to make 'machine time' a scaled down version of real time.

15.3.2 Summary of Computing Elements

General-purpose d.c. analog computers used to solve systems of equations and ordinary differential equations obtain most mathematical operations on computer voltages through combinations of a limited number of simple operations. A wide range of problems require only the following computing elements:

(1) Devices which *multiply* a machine variable by a *positive* or *negative constant coefficient*.

(2) Devices which generate the *sum* of two (or more) machine variables.

(3) Devices which generate (*a*) the time *integral* (*b*) the time *differential* of machine variable.

(4) Devices which perform *operations* on machine variables of the form $1/(1 + TD)$ or $1 + TD$.

(5) Devices which generate *functions* of machine variables.

(6) Devices which generate the *product* of machine variables.

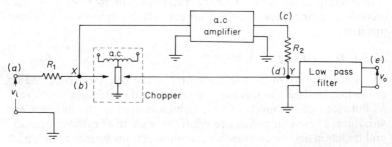

Fig. 15.1 *Chopper amplifier.*

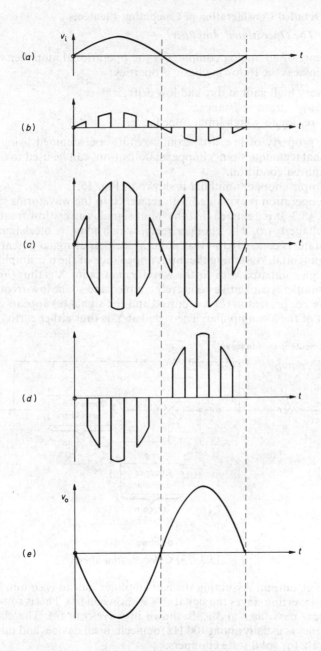

Fig. 15.2 *Waveforms.*

15.4 Detailed Consideration of Computing Elements

15.4.1 The Operational Amplifier

The heart of an analog computer is the operational amplifier which must possess the following basic properties:

  (i) very high gain at d.c. and low drift;
  (ii) low output resistance;   .
  (iii) reasonably high input impedance.

The property of low drift cannot readily be obtained using conventional techniques but 'chopper stabilization' can be used to obtain the required condition.

A simple chopper amplifier is shown in Fig. 15.1.

The operation is explained with reference to the waveforms shown in Fig. 15.2. It is assumed that the input signal is a very low frequency a.c. voltage v_i (a). The chopper relay, which may be mechanical or solid state, is connected so that point X is either at signal potential or earth potential. Assuming the input impedance of the a.c. amplifier is very high compared with R_1 the waveform at point X is thus (b). The a.c. amplifier is capacitive-resistively coupled and so the low-frequency component present in (b) is removed and the signal (c) appears at the output of the a.c. amplifier. The signal at Y is thus either earth or the

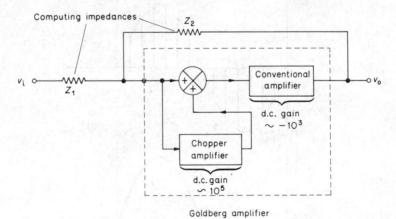

Goldberg amplifier

Fig. 15.3 *The Goldberg amplifier.*

amplifier output. Assuming the a.c. amplifier has an *even* number of phase-inverting stages the signal at Y is shown in (d). This is smoothed in a low pass filter and v_o is shown in waveform (e). The chopper frequency is usually about 100 Hz for mechanical devices and upwards of 2 kHz for solid state choppers.

The chopper amplifier is only capable of amplifying signals up to a frequency of about one-tenth of the chopper frequency. Operational amplifiers must have a gain of at least 10^3 at about 5 kHz and thus the Goldberg amplifier is usually used. In this a chopper amplifier is used in conjunction with a conventional d.c. amplifier. The series combination ensures a d.c. gain of say 10^8 to combat drift but the input signal appears at the input of the conventional amplifier as well as at the input of the chopper amplifier. The conventional amplifier will only have a d.c. gain of about 10^3 but the gain at 5 kHz will still be about the same. The arrangement is shown in Fig. 15.3.

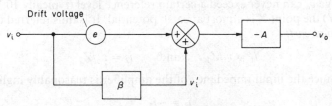

Fig. 15.4 *Drift analysis.*

The circuit of Fig. 15.4 may be used to assess the reduction in the drift. Now

$$(v_i + e + v_i')\,A = -v_o$$

But $v_i' = \beta v_i$

$\therefore$
$$(v_i + e + v_i\beta)\,A = -v_o$$

$\therefore$
$$\left(v_i + \frac{e}{1+\beta}\right)A' = -v_o$$

Here $A' = A(1 + \beta)$ which is the overall gain of the system.

The drift has thus been reduced by a factor $(1 + \beta)$ compared with the conventional amplifier having the same overall gain.

15.4.2 Uses of the Operational Amplifier

General Analysis

The operational amplifier is symbolized as shown in Fig. 15.5.

Fig. 15.5 *Symbol for the operational amplifier.*

In many computing applications the operational amplifier is connected to feed-in and feedback impedances Z_1 and Z_2 as shown in Fig. 15.6.

The point X is called the 'summing junction'. Because the gain of the amplifier is very high (typically 10^8) and because the output

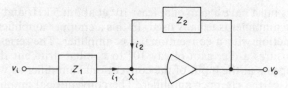

Fig. 15.6 *Operational amplifier with computing impedances.*

voltage v_o can never exceed a certain reference level (typically 10 V or 100 V) the point X is almost at earth potential. It is thus referred to as a *virtual earth*.

Thus $\qquad i_1 \doteqdot v_i/Z_1 \qquad$ and $\qquad i_2 \doteqdot v_o/Z_2$

But since the input impedance of the amplifier is reasonably high,

$$i_1 \doteqdot -i_2$$

$\therefore \qquad\qquad\qquad \dfrac{v_i}{Z_1} \doteqdot -\dfrac{v_o}{Z_2}$

or $\qquad\qquad\qquad \dfrac{v_o}{v_i} \doteqdot -\dfrac{Z_2}{Z_1}$

The accuracy of the approximation is good so long as the gain of the operational amplifier is high. In good-quality analog computers this approximation gives rise to negligible errors, and so the use of the approximation signs will be dropped in subsequent analyses.

The Amplifier and Phase Inverter

If Z_1 is made a resistance R_1 and Z_2 is made a resistance R_2 then

$$\dfrac{v_o}{v_i} = -\dfrac{R_2}{R_1}$$

or $\qquad\qquad\qquad v_o = -\left(\dfrac{R_2}{R_1}\right) v_i$

This arrangement is symbolized as shown in Fig. 15.7.

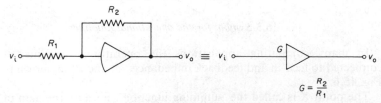

Fig. 15.7 *Basic amplifier and phase inverter.*

The arrangement can thus be used to multiply a machine voltage v_i by a constant coefficient of absolute value greater than, equal to, or less than unity. When $R_1 = R_2 = R$, then $v_o = -v_i$ and we have a *phase inverter*.

The Integrator

The Z_2 is a pure capacitor of capacitance C_2

Then

$$Z_2 = 1/C_2 \, D$$

and

$$Z_1 = R_1$$

$$\therefore \qquad \frac{v_o}{v_i} = -\frac{1}{R_1 \, C_2 \, D}$$

or

$$v_o = -\frac{1}{R_1 \, C_2} \int_0^t v_i \, dt$$

The arrangement is symbolized as shown in Fig. 15.8.

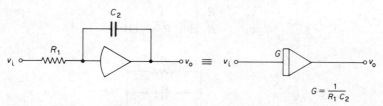

Fig. 15.8 *The integrator circuit.*

(Note: $R_1 C_2$ is sometimes called the 'time-constant' of the integrator but the author prefers to call the factor G the *sensitivity* or *gain* of the integrator.)

It is often necessary to impose an initial condition on an integrator, i.e. give it an initial output voltage at $t = 0$. This may be achieved using the arrangement shown in Fig. 15.9.

Relay K_1 is de-energized for 'pot set', 'hold' or 'compute'. Relay K_2 is de-energized for 'pot set', *'initial condition'* or 'hold'. The output voltage v_o becomes **minus** the 'initial condition voltage' when K_2 is de-energized and K_1 is energized.

The Exponential Lag

If the operational amplifier is connected as shown in Fig. 15.10 an arrangement giving an exponential lag is produced.

411

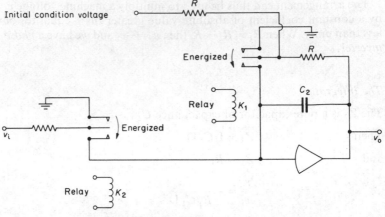

Fig. 15.9 *Use of relays to control integrator.*

Now

$$Z_2 = \frac{R_2}{1 + R_2 C_2 D}$$

and

$$Z_1 = R_1$$

∴

$$\frac{v_o}{v_i} = -\frac{R_2}{R_1}\left\{\frac{1}{1 + R_2 C_2 D}\right\}$$

Fig. 15.10 *The exponential lag.*

The time constant $C_2 R_2$ is fixed in this arrangement by the values of C and R available in the computer (e.g. the E.A.L. PACE TR 20 computer provides 10 μF capacitors and 10 kΩ and 100 kΩ resistors

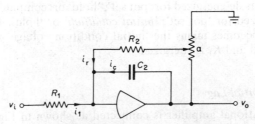

Fig. 15.11 *The long time constant.*

412

only). The time constant can be varied continuously from $C_2 R_2$ upwards to infinity by using a potentiometer (Fig. 15.11).

The potentiometer is set to give a ratio a (which is always $\leqslant 1$).

Thus
$$i_r = \frac{a v_o}{R_2}$$

and
$$i_c = C_2 D v_o$$

Thus
$$i_1 = -(i_r + i_c) = -v_o \left(\frac{a}{R_2} + C_2 D \right)$$
$$= -v_o \frac{a}{R_2} \left(1 + \frac{R_2 C_2 D}{a} \right)$$

But
$$i_1 = \frac{v_i}{R_1}$$

$\therefore$
$$\frac{v_o}{v_i} = -\frac{R_2}{a R_1} \left\{ \frac{1}{1 + R_2 C_2 D/a} \right\}$$

This circuit is very useful in simulators and is symbolized as shown in Fig. 15.12.

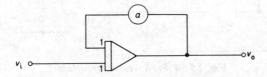

Fig. 15.12 *Symbol for exponential lag circuit.*

The Differentiating Circuit

Differentiation is always avoided where possible because the process inherently degrades the signal-to-noise ratio. The simple form of differentiating circuit is shown in Fig. 15.13.

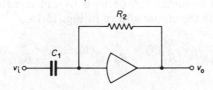

Fig. 15.13 *Differentiator.*

413

In this circuit $Z_1 = 1/C_1 D$ and $Z_2 = R_2$

$$\therefore \qquad \frac{v_o}{v_i} = -\frac{Z_2}{Z_1} = -R_2 C_1 D$$

or

$$v_o = -R_2 C_1 \frac{dv_o}{dt}$$

A further disadvantage of this circuit is that the operational amplifier will saturate on the application of signals with steeply rising or falling edges (e.g. steps and impulses). Yet another problem is that capacitor C_1 will cause the previous stage to be capacitively loaded; operational amplifiers are likely to be unstable when capacitively loaded.

In some instances the operation of differentiation is unavoidable and then it is preferable to use the circuit shown in Fig. 15.14 rather than that shown in Fig. 15.13.

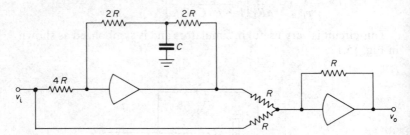

Fig. 15.14 *Preferred differentiator.*

It is left to the reader to show that:

$$\frac{v_o}{v_i} = +RCD$$

i.e.

$$v_o = RC \frac{dv_i}{dt}$$

The Adding Circuit

The operational amplifier can be used to add in equal or different proportions using the circuit shown in Fig. 15.15.

Now

$$i_1 = \frac{v_{i1}}{R_1}, \, i_2 = \frac{v_{i2}}{R_2} \ldots \text{etc.} \ldots i_n = \frac{v_{in}}{R_n}$$

and

$$i = \frac{v_o}{R}$$

414

But
$$i = -(i_1 + i_2 + \cdots \text{etc.} \cdots + i_n)$$

$$\therefore \qquad v_o = -\left\{ \frac{R}{R_1} v_{i1} + \frac{R}{R_2} v_{i2} + \cdots \text{etc.} \cdots + \frac{R}{R_n} v_{in} \right\}$$

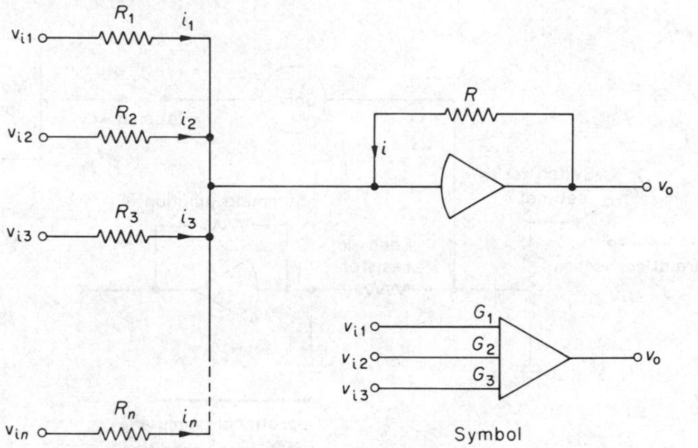

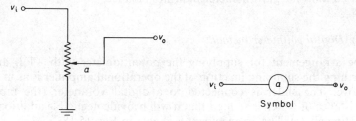

Fig. 15.15 *The adding circuit.*

15.4.3 The Coefficient Potentiometer

The potentiometers used in analog computers are usually ten-turn helical potentiometers with very accurate windings. They provide a method of multiplying a machine variable by a positive coefficient equal to or less than unity. For this device $v_o = a v_i$ (see Fig. 15.16).

Fig. 15.16 *The coefficient potentiometer.*

Normally the slider is connected to a load resistor (usually the feed-in resistor of an operational amplifier) and it will be necessary to 'set up' the potentiometer to give a certain value of *a on load*.

Most computers provide a mechanism for doing this. There are two generally used schemes:

(i) Master potentiometer method

The top of the potentiometer to be set up is automatically disconnected at the top and reconnected to the reference positive voltage $+V_{\text{ref}}$ by

415

means of a press-button or switch. At the same time the summing junctions of all amplifiers are earthed. Fig. 15.17 shows the arrangement.

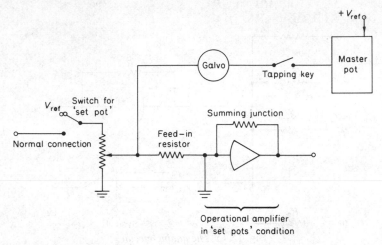

Fig. 15.17 *The master potentiometer pot set scheme.*

Automatic connection of the potentiometer slider through a galvanometer and tapping key to the master potentiometer is also normally provided. The master potentiometer is supplied from the $+V_{ref}$ line and is set to '*a*'. The potentiometer under calibration is varied until the galvanometer indicates balance.

(*ii*) *Digital voltmeter method*

The arrangement for supplying the potentiometer with $+V_{ref}$ and earthing the summing junction of the operational amplifier is as in (i) above. The slider is connected to a digital voltmeter (the input resistance of which is so high that it will provide negligible additional loading effect). The arrangement is shown in Fig. 15.18.

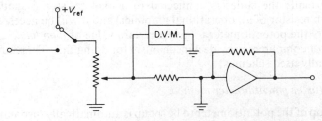

Fig. 15.18 *Digital voltmeter pot set scheme.*

416

The slider of the pot under calibration is then adjusted until the digital voltmeter reads $a \times V_{ref}$.

Note in both cases the loading effect of the feed-in resistor to *virtual* earth is approximated to by connecting the summing junction to real earth.

15.4.4 The Multiplier

General

Frequently in the solution of non-linear differential equations and in the simulation of non-linear control systems it is necessary to multiply together two machine voltages. There are a number of electronic devices capable of such a function amongst which are:

(i) the quarter-square multiplier;
(ii) the pulse-height, pulse-width multiplier (sometimes referred to as a time division multiplier);
(iii) the servo-multiplier.

The time-division multiplier is more accurate than the quarter-square multiplier but the quarter-square multiplier is capable of operation at higher speeds. The servo-multiplier is very much slower

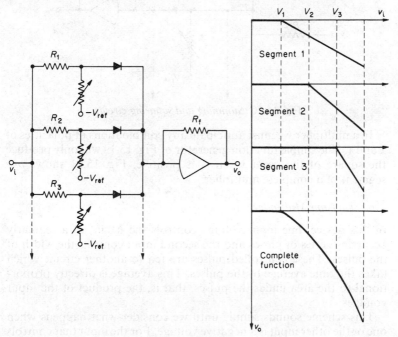

Fig. 15.19 *Simple diode function generator.*

417

Feedback Control Theory for Engineers

than either of the others but does possess the advantage that it is capable of multiplying a given voltage by a number of other voltages. All multipliers are costly.

The Quarter Square Multiplier

The operation of this device depends on the identity

$$xy = \tfrac{1}{4}\{(x + y)^2 - (x - y)^2\}$$

If this identity is to form the basis of a multiplier it is necessary to construct a device which is capable of forming the *square* of a signal voltage. This may be achieved using an arrangement of biased diodes as shown in Fig. 15.19.

The arrangement gives a piece-wise linearization of the original characteristic and its accuracy is dependent on the number of segments used and hence on the number of diodes.

In the quarter-square multiplier the squaring circuits are required to produce voltages proportional to $(x + y/2)^2$ and $(x - y/2)^2$. This can be achieved using the circuit of Fig. 15.20.

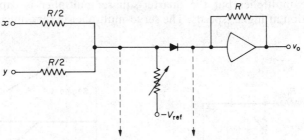

Fig. 15.20 *Summing and squaring circuit.*

In a multiplier we must anticipate any combinations of polarities of x and y. The simple function generator of Fig. 15.19 will only produce the square of the input when v_i is positive. Fig. 15.21 shows *one* segment of a complete multiplier.

Time Division Multiplier

In this device, one input voltage controls the height of a regularly occurring series of pulses and the second input controls the width of the pulses. These controlled pulses are fed to another circuit which takes the time average of the pulses. This average is directly proportional to the area under the pulses, that is, the product of the input voltages.

This scheme sounds simple until we consider what happens when one or the other input is a negative voltage. For the input that controls pulse height, this is of no concern; the pulse height will be negative

418

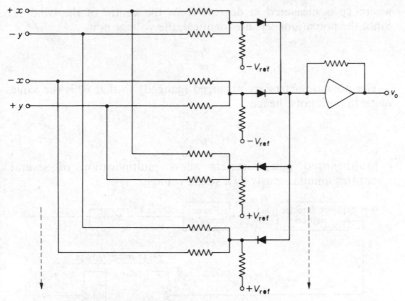

Fig. 15.21 *Single segment of quarter square multiplier.*

instead of positive. The case of a negative input voltage controlling pulse width is a problem because a negative pulse width is not physically realizable. One solution is to make zero signal input to this channel produce a pulse width of, say, one-half the repetition period. A correction term is then subtracted from the output of the averaging device, so that the output of the multiplier is zero when the input to the pulse width channel is zero.

The Servomultiplier

In the servomultiplier (Fig. 15.22) the error detector compares the voltage v_1 and the voltage v_p at the top of the left potentiometer (the follow-up potentiometer). The error signal $v_1 - v_p$ is amplified and applied to a motor which is geared to the shaft of the potentiometer. The motor will turn in such a direction as to reduce the error to a minimum.

If this servomechanism is well designed and operating within the design limits, the action will be for the voltage v_p to duplicate closely the voltage v_1. Hence $v_p = v_1$.

We can also relate v_p to the angular position of the potentiometer shaft θ_p. If there are $2m$ degrees total rotation from one end of the winding to the other, then

$$\theta_p = \frac{v_p m}{V_{ref}}$$

419

where θp is measured in degrees from the centre of the winding. Since the potentiometers are identical, the voltage v_3 is

$$v_3 = \frac{\theta_p}{m} v_2$$

The potentiometers are arranged (ganged) so that θ_p is the same angle in both pots; hence

$$v_3 = \frac{v_1 v_2}{V_{ref}}$$

Multi-ganged potentiometers allow multiplication of several quantities simultaneously by a single voltage.

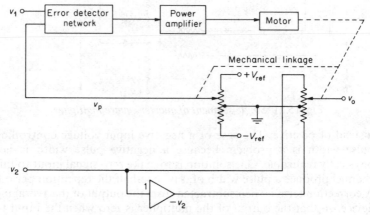

Fig. 15.22 *The servomultiplier.*

15.4.5 Function Generators

General

It has already been explained in §15.4.4 how functions may be generated using biased diodes. The squarer is one of many examples. Many commercial analog computers contain biased diode function generators which may be set up to give a variety of functions. Sometimes it is convenient to generate certain simple non-linear functions using external arrangements, as follows.

Simulation of Saturation Characteristics

Figure 15.23 shows a saturation circuit. For positive values of v_i the value of v_o will be given by

$$v_o = - \left\{ \frac{R_o}{R_i' + R_i} \right\} v_i$$

until diode $D2$ begins to conduct which will be when $v_d = E_{b2}$ for which

$$v_i = \left\{ \frac{R_i + R_i'}{R_i} \right\} E_{b2}$$

For negative values of v_i the value of v_o will be given by

$$v_o = - \left\{ \frac{R_o}{R_i' + R_i} \right\} v_i$$

until diode $D1$ begins to conduct which will be when $v_d = -E_{b1}$; then

$$v_i = \left\{ \frac{R_i + R_i'}{R_i} \right\} E_{b1}$$

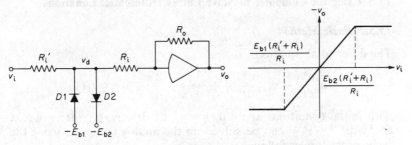

Fig. 15.23 *Saturation characteristic simulator.*

It should be noted that in practice allowance must be made for the potential drop across the diodes when they are in the conducting condition (about 0·1 V for germanium diodes and about 0·6 V for silicon diodes).

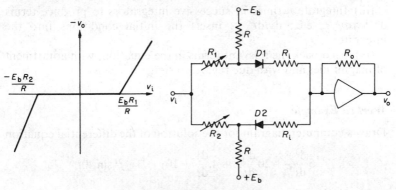

Fig. 15.24 *Dead zone simulator.*

421

Dead Zone Simulator

A dead zone simulator is shown in Fig. 15.24. D1 does not conduct until

$$v_i > E_b R_1 / R$$

D2 does not conduct until

$$v_i < -E_b R_2 / R$$

The slope of the characteristics beyond the dead zone can be found by applying Thévénin's Theorem or otherwise and its determination is left to the reader as an exercise.

15.5 Using the Computer to Solve Linear Differential Equations

15.5.1 Basic Method

The differential equation

$$a_n \frac{d^n y}{dt^n} + a_{n-1} \frac{d^{n-1} y}{dt^{n-1}} + \cdots + a_1 \frac{dy}{dt} + a_0 y = f(t)$$

with initial conditions at $t = 0$, $y = y_0$, $dy/dt = \dot{y}_0$, $d^2 y/dt^2 = \ddot{y}_0, \ldots,$ $d^{n-1} y/dt^{n-1} = y_0^{n-1}$ can be solved on the analog computer using the basic procedure as follows:

(i) Segregate the highest order differential coefficient $d^n y/dt^n$ giving

$$\frac{d^n y}{dt^n} = \frac{f(t)}{a_n} - \frac{a_{n-1}}{a_n} \frac{d^{n-1} y}{dt^{n-1}} \cdots - \frac{a_1}{a_n} \frac{dy}{dt} - \frac{a_0}{a_n} y$$

(ii) Sum all the terms on the right-hand side in a summing amplifier to give $-d^n y/dt^n$; the term $f(t)$ must be generated external to the computer.

(iii) Integrate n times in successive integrators to produce terms $d^{n-1} y/dt^{n-1}$, etc., dy/dt, y; insert the initial conditions into the integrators.

(iv) Feed back the relevant terms in the equation, with adjustment of magnitudes and with due regard to sign.

Worked Example

Draw a computer diagram for the solution of the differential equation

$$5 \frac{d^3 y}{dt^3} + 20 \frac{d^2 y}{dt^2} + 4 \frac{dy}{dt} + 10 y = 3 e^{-2t} \sin 40t$$

At $t = 0$, $d^2 y/dt^2 = 1$, $dy/dt = 0$, $y = -2$.

Solution

Segregating the highest order differential coefficient gives

$$\frac{d^3 y}{dt^3} = \frac{3}{5} e^{-2t} \sin 40t - \frac{20}{5} \frac{d^2 y}{dt^2} - \frac{4}{5} \frac{dy}{dt} - \frac{10}{5} y$$

A summation of the terms on the right-hand side can be achieved as shown in Figure 15.25.

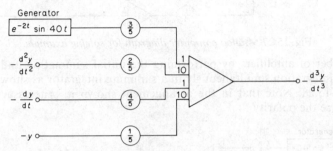

Fig. 15.25 *Summation of terms.*

A point which often leads to confusion is the fact that the output of the summing amplifier in Fig. 15.25 yields $-d^3 y/dt^3$ and *not* $+d^3 y/dt^3$. This is due to the *sign reversal produced by the operational amplifier itself.* $d^3 y/dt^3$ can now be integrated three times, as shown in Fig. 15.26.

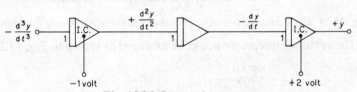

Fig. 15.26 *Integration process.*

It should be noted that, as explained in §15.4.2, the arrangement for applying initial conditions to integrators in commercial computers inevitably involves a sign reversal so that the polarity of the initial condition voltages must be chosen properly. In Fig. 15.26, the output of the first integrator is $+d^2 y/dt^2$ and it is required that this shall have an initial value of $+1$ volt, thus the initial condition voltage must be set at -1 volt. Conversely the output of the third integrator is $+y$ and the initial value of this is to be -2 volt. Thus the initial condition voltage for this integrator must be $+2$ volt.

The relevant signals must now be fed back with due regard to sign. Inverters are introduced to correct the sign where necessary. The complete diagram is shown in Fig. 15.27.

In cases where $d^3 y/dt^3$ is *not* required, it is possible to reduce the

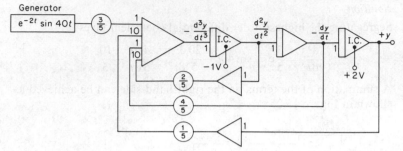

Fig. 15.27 *Analog computer diagram for solving example.*

number of amplifiers by performing the initial summation and the first integration simultaneously in a summing integrator as shown in Fig. 15.28. Note that in the arrangement shown it is necessary to reverse the polarity.

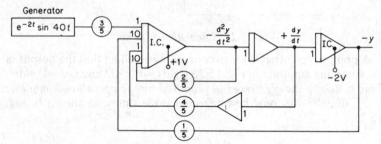

Fig. 15.28 *Elimination of summing amplifier and use of a summing integrator.*

The summing integrator might be arranged as shown in Fig. 15.29.

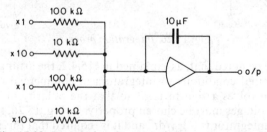

Fig. 15.29 *Practical realization of a summing integrator.*

15.5.2 Scaling

Amplitude Scaling

The computer has elements that cannot perform the mathematical operations for which they were designed if the problem voltage magnitudes are too high or too low. For the operational amplifier, an

424

upper limit on the maximum voltage is reached because it can never exceed the power supply voltage. Nor can the voltage remain below a certain level for too long an interval of computer time during the problem run. Amplifier noise and integrator voltage drift become significant compared with the voltage generated by the solution.

Worked Example

Program the equation

$$\frac{d^2 y}{dt^2} + a\frac{dy}{dt} + by = f(t)$$

where a and b are constants.

Solution

The maximum values of the problem variables are

$$|d^2 y/dt^2|_{max}, |dy/dt|_{max} \quad \text{and} \quad |y|_{max}.$$

The voltage maximum in all cases is $|V_{max}|$. Thus the scale factors are

$$k_2 = \frac{|V_{max}|}{|d^2 y/dt^2|_{max}}$$

$$k_1 = \frac{|V_{max}|}{|dy/dt|_{max}}$$

$$k_0 = \frac{|V_{max}|}{|y|_{max}}$$

The differential equation may be written without alteration to its identity as

$$\frac{1}{k_2}\left(k_2 \frac{d^2 y}{dt^2}\right) + \frac{a}{k_1}\left(k_1 \frac{dy}{dt}\right) + \frac{b}{k_0}(k_0 y) = f(t)$$

or

$$\left(k_2 \frac{d^2 y}{dt^2}\right) = k_2 f(t) - \frac{k_2}{k_1}a\left(k_1 \frac{dy}{dt}\right) - \frac{k_2}{k_0}b(k_0 y)$$

The computer diagram is shown in Fig. 15.30.

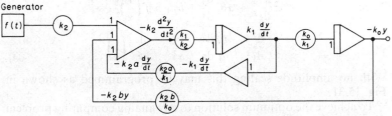

Fig. 15.30 *Amplitude scaled program.*

Note if the initial conditions are $(\mathrm{d}y/\mathrm{d}t)_0 = m$ and $(y)_0 = n$, then

$$k_1(\mathrm{d}y/\mathrm{d}t)_0 = +k_1 m$$

(implying $-k_1 m$ volts in a practical computer); and

$$-k_0 y_0 = -k_0 n$$

(implying $+k_0 n$ volts in a practical computer).

The primary and virtually insurmountable difficulty one encounters in scaling a new, unfamiliar problem is that there is almost no way of determining the maximum values of the variables. A method cited by A. S. Jackson (*Analog Computation*, McGraw-Hill Book Co. Inc., New York 1960) for a problem with *zero* initial conditions and a *step* driving function which gives approximate results is:

If the magnitude of the step input is A then the maximum values of the derivatives are as follows:

$$|D^r y|_{\max} = A/a_n \qquad 1 \leqslant r \leqslant n$$
$$|y|_{\max} = 2A/a_0$$

where a_n is the coefficient of the nth (highest) derivative of y, r is an integer lying between 1 and n, and a_0 is the coefficient of y.

Time Scaling

A problem should be 'time scaled' to achieve as rapid a run as possible consistent with accurate recording.

Let us regard the independent variable in a problem as x (x may of course be 'real time'), and let t be computer time. Then make

$$x = t/\alpha$$

When $\alpha > 1$ the problem is slowed down, and when $\alpha < 1$ the problem is speeded up.

Consider the equation

$$\frac{\mathrm{d}^2 y}{\mathrm{d}x^2} + b_1 \frac{\mathrm{d}y}{\mathrm{d}x} + b_2 y = f(x)$$

Then $\qquad \alpha^2 \dfrac{\mathrm{d}^2 y}{\mathrm{d}t^2} + \alpha b_1 \dfrac{\mathrm{d}y}{\mathrm{d}t} + b_2 y = f\left(\dfrac{t}{\alpha}\right)$

or $\qquad \dfrac{\mathrm{d}^2 y}{\mathrm{d}t^2} + \dfrac{b_1}{\alpha} \dfrac{\mathrm{d}y}{\mathrm{d}t} + \dfrac{b_2}{\alpha^2} y = \dfrac{1}{\alpha^2} f\left(\dfrac{t}{\alpha}\right)$

With no amplitude scaling this may be programmed as shown in Fig. 15.31.

To achieve the optimum solution to any analog computing problem one must normally use both amplitude and time scaling. Such scaling

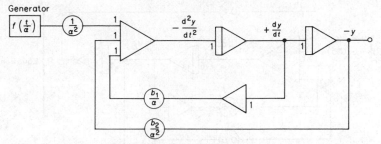

Fig. 15.31 *Time-scaled program.*

will frequently involve a certain amount of trial and error where one relies on overload indicators to show where overload is occurring.

15.5.3 *Solution of Simultaneous Linear Differential Equations*

Simultaneous linear differential equations are solved in a manner basically similar to that used for ordinary linear differential equations. A worked example will be used to illustrate the procedure.

Worked Example

Prepare a computer diagram for the solution of the following differential equations. Do not scale the problem.

$$2\frac{d^2 y}{dt^2} + \frac{dy}{dt} - \frac{dx}{dt} + 4y = f(t)$$

$$\frac{d^2 x}{dt^2} + 0\cdot 5\frac{dx}{dt} - \frac{dy}{dt} + 10x = 0$$

$$\frac{dy}{dt}(0) = \frac{dx}{dt}(0) = x(0) = y(0) = 0$$

Solution

The first equation yields

$$\frac{d^2 y}{dt^2} = \frac{f(t)}{2} - \frac{dy/dt}{2} + \frac{dx/dt}{2} - 2y \qquad (1)$$

and the second yields

$$\frac{d^2 x}{dt^2} = -0\cdot 5\frac{dx}{dt} + \frac{dy}{dt} - 10x \qquad (2)$$

The equations are programmed separately but the circuits are cross-coupled with the relevant signals, as shown in Fig. 15.32.

427

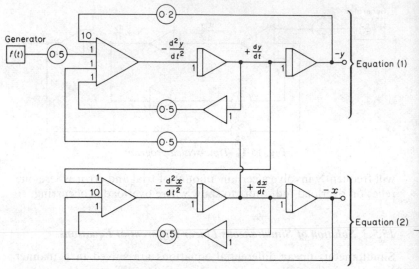

Fig. 15.32 *Solution of simultaneous differential equations.*

15.6 Using the Computer to Solve Non-Linear Differential Equations

Non-linear equations usually involve the use of multipliers for the analog computer solution. One of the classic examples of a non-linear differential equation is the Van der Pol equation which takes the form

$$\frac{d^2 y}{dt^2} + \mu(y^2 - 1)\frac{dy}{dt} + y = 0$$

when $y = y_0$ at $t = 0$; or

$$\frac{d^2 y}{dt^2} = -\mu(y^2 - 1)\frac{dy}{dt} - y$$

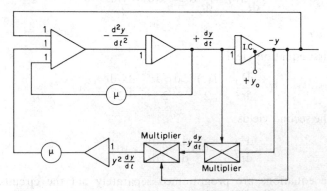

Fig. 15.33 *Program for the solution of Van der Pol equation.*

428

The terms y^2 and $y^2(\mathrm{d}y/\mathrm{d}t)$ can be obtained by the use of two multipliers connected in various ways. A typical arrangement showing the complete program is given in Fig. 15.33.

15.7 Simulation

In §§ 15.5 and 15.6 the differential equation has been regarded as the starting point for the computer study. Once the differential equation has been obtained, a block diagram is drawn which essentially gives a system of simultaneous algebraic and integral equations which have the same solution as the given differential equation.

A more usual starting point for a computer study is some physical system that requires analysis. A block diagram of the system can be drawn in which the physical equations (or 'transfer functions') governing the behaviour of each block of the system are included. Of course it is possible to derive the overall differential equation and program that for the computer, as described previously. However, simulation is a more direct and useful technique in which each block of the physical system is represented by certain computing elements. The computing elements are interconnected in exactly the same way as the system being simulated. The use of simulators is a great aid for the study of feedback control systems (particularly very complex and non-linear ones) because of the very direct relationship between the system and the simulator which allows 'one-to-one' investigation of the effects of a single parameter variation in the system by adjustment of a single potentiometer (or at most two potentiometers) in the simulator. The speed at which paper designs of both linear and non-linear systems can be checked is thus great. In some large analog computing installations some of the potentiometers are servo-controlled. The computer can be arranged to repeatedly operate for slightly different settings of a servo-controlled potentiometer until an optimum solution is reached. The variations of the potentiometer take place automatically in accordance with a pre-set instruction.

Worked Example

A position control servomechanism consists of an armature-controlled d.c. motor fed from a d.c. generator which is driven at a constant speed. The field of the generator is supplied from a d.c. amplifier, the input impedance of which is infinite. The error detector is a potentiometer bridge. The load is negligible.

System parameters are as follows:

Motor: armature resistance R_a, moment of inertia of armature plus load J, back e.m.f. per unit angular velocity K_v, torque per unit armature current K_t, coulomb and viscous friction negligible.

Generator: inductance of field winding L_f, resistance of field winding R_f, resistance of armature R_g, generated e.m.f. per unit field current K_g.
Amplifier: output resistance R_o, voltage gain into open-circuit K_a, input resistance infinite.
Potentiometer bridge: sensitivity per radian of error K_p.

Draw (i) a simplified circuit diagram, (ii) a block diagram with non-interacting transfer functions, (iii) an analog computer simulator diagram.

Solution

The solutions to parts (i) and (ii) follow the methods described in Chapter 9 (particularly the worked example given in §9.6). Figure 15.34 and Fig. 15.35 are the embodiment of the solutions.

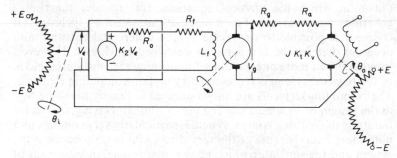

Fig. 15.34 *Simplified circuit diagram.*

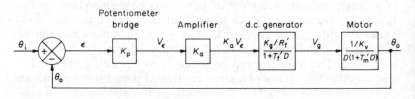

Where $T_f' = L_f / (R_f + R_o)$

$T_m' = J(R_a + R_g) / K_t K_v$

$R_f' = R_f + R_o$

Fig. 15.35 *Block diagram with transfer functions.*

The analog simulator is drawn up by use of the summing amplifier (representing the potentiometer bridge and amplifier), the exponential lag circuit (representing the d.c. generator) and the exponential lag circuit cascaded with an integrator (representing the d.c. motor). Feedback is arranged using a phase inverter, although the phase inverter is only necessary because there are an even number of operational amplifiers in the forward path so that a positive-going input signal yields a positive-going output signal. The polarity of the output must thus be changed to produce the error signal $\theta_i - \theta_o$. The complete simulator is shown in Fig. 15.36. The time constant potentiometers must be set so that

$$a_2 = 1/T'_f \quad \text{and} \quad a_3 = 1/T'_m$$

The setting a_1 of the potentiometer in the forward path must be selected so that the overall error-constant is correct, i.e.

$$\frac{a_1}{a_2 a_3} = \frac{K_p K_a K_g}{R'_f K_v}$$

or
$$a_1 = \frac{K_p K_a K_g}{R'_f K_v T'_f T'_m}$$

(iii) An analog computer simulation diagram is shown in Fig. 15.36. It should be noted that the input to the final integrator is $-d\theta_o/dt$. The effect of auxiliary velocity feedback can be observed by feeding back this signal through a potentiometer.

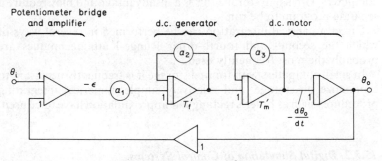

Fig. 15.36 *Servo simulator.*

The effects of non-linearities such as amplifier saturation may also readily be incorporated into a computer simulator by using arrangements such as the saturation simulator described in §15.4.5.

15.8 The use of the Digital Computer in the Simulation of Control Systems

15.8.1 Digital versus analog computation

The simulation of control systems has classically been performed using analog computers. However, now that digital computing systems with inter-active graphical displays are becoming more common, they are being used at every stage of the design process. Since this is so it would seem reasonable to use them in the final stage of the design process, i.e. time-domain check-out. There are other advantages in

431

using a digital computer compared with an analog computer. The use of an analog computer involves patching, debugging, potentiometer setting and fairly considerable maintenance. Furthermore, the accuracy available from an electronic analog computer is limited by the hardware available and the complexity of the problem. Also the simulation of distance/velocity lag on the analog machine can only be achieved at considerable expense and with very limited accuracy.

These limitations lead to the use of the digital computer for a more accurate and convenient method of performance determination. There are several methods of programming which may be used. These may be divided into two main classes:

(i) Fourier transformation of the closed-loop frequency response data (this yields the impulse response which may be numerically integrated to give the step response).

(ii) Direct numerical integration of the differential equation representing the closed-loop response.

The Fourier transform method is a satisfactory technique but does involve the extra computation of the frequency response data. In computers with small storage this is a disadvantage and may require a separate program to be run.

Direct numerical integration can be performed in several ways of which the second- and fourth-order Runge-Kutta techniques are probably the most frequently used.

In small computers with limited storage it is frequently necessary to economize on storage, and relatively simple numerical integrating procedures such as Euler's rectangular approximation have to be used.

15.8.2 Digital Simulation of Control Systems

The majority of single-loop and, with some prior manipulation, multi-loop control systems have an open-loop transfer function given by

$$\frac{\theta_o}{\epsilon}(D) = \frac{K e^{-TD}(1 + T_{e1} D + T_{ee1} D^2)(1 + T_{e2} D + T_{ee2} D^2)\dots \text{etc.}}{D^q(1 + T_{a1} D + T_{aa1} D^2)(1 + T_{a2} D + T_{aa2} D^2)\dots \text{etc.}} \quad (1)$$

where

θ_o system output;

ϵ system error;

T_{e1}, T_{ee1}, etc.   constants associated with the quadratic leads;

and T_{a1}, T_{aa1}, etc.   constants associated with the quadratic lags;

T distance/velocity lag;

K error constant;

q type number of system.

In a digital simulation the distance/velocity lag must be dealt with separately, whereas the whole of the rest of the open-loop transfer function may be simulated by means of a single basic procedure. If the term representing the distance/velocity lag in the transfer function is removed, it is then possible to represent the remaining elements by a ratio of two polynomials y/x given by

$$\frac{y}{x} = \frac{A_0 + A_1\,D + A_2\,D^2 + \cdots + A_m\,D^m}{B_0 + B_1\,D + B_2\,D^2 + \cdots + B_n\,D^n} \qquad (2)$$

where $m < n$ in physically realizable systems.

Rearrangement of this form of the transfer function yields

$$Y = (a_0\,X - b_0\,Y)\frac{1}{D^n} + (a_1\,X - b_1\,Y)\frac{1}{D^{n-1}} + \cdots$$

$$\cdots + (a_m\,X - b_m\,Y)\frac{1}{D^{n-m}} + \cdots + (a_{n-1}\,X - b_n\,Y)\frac{1}{D} \qquad (3)$$

where $a_m = A_m/B_n$, $b_m = B_m/B_n$ and $a_{m+1} = a_{m+2} = \cdots = a_{n-1} = 0$.

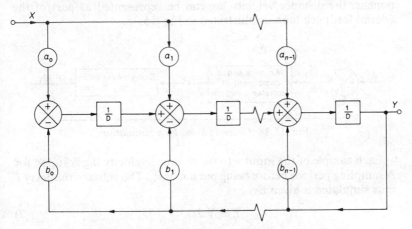

Fig. 15.37 *Flow diagram representing equation (3).*

Equation (3) can be represented by a flow diagram as shown in Fig. 15.37. From the figure it can be observed that each integrator m has three inputs:

(i) from input node X scaled by a factor a_m;
(ii) from output node Y scaled by a factor $-b_m$;
(iii) from output of previous integrator (y_{m-1}) (note $y_0 = 0$ for the first integrator).

In terms of these three inputs, the input x_m to the integrator m is given by

$$x_m(t) = y_{m-1}(t) + a_m x(t) - b_m y(t) \qquad (4)$$

where t is time.

433

The output from each integrator may be determined using one of the formulae for numerical integration. The simplest formula is the Euler rectangular approximation given in equation (5).

$$y_m(t) = y_m(t - \Delta t) + x_m \Delta t \tag{5}$$

This particular formula is well suited to application in small computers but for accurate computation it is necessary to choose Δt correctly. A useful working rule is that Δt should be *at most* one tenth of the smallest effective time constant in the open-loop transfer function.

A better approximation may be achieved using the trapezoidal method of numerical integration based on the algorithm given in equation (6).

$$y_m(t) = y_m(t - \Delta t) + [x_m(t) + x_m(t - \Delta t)] \Delta t/2 \tag{6}$$

The so-called 'minimum phase' component y/x of the transfer function can thus be satisfactorily simulated. The remaining component, the distance/velocity lag can be represented as part of the overall feedback loop as illustrated in Fig. 15.38.

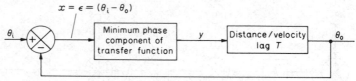

Fig. 15.38 *Overall closed-loop simulation.*

Each sample of the input y to the distance/velocity lag is stored for N sampling periods before being put out as θ_o. The value of the delay T thus simulated is given by

$$T = N \Delta t \tag{7}$$

where Δt is the time increment used in the numerical integration algorithm. The method requires a 'delay array' of N stores to hold successive values of y for the duration of the time delay.

For simulating the closed-loop response of the system to a unit step input, the signal driving the minimum phase algorithm becomes $(1 - \theta_o)$.

In a practical program the outputs of the integrators are stored in an array and there is only one integration algorithm which is used over and over again in a program loop until the required number of integrations is complete.

The output of the system may be put out as a set of numbers at suitable system time intervals on a teletype or line printer, or alternatively on a cathode-ray display following digital to analog conversion.

The cathode-ray display may be a series of bright spots or a continuous line showing the response.

15.9 Hybrid Computers

In recent years some attempt has been made to combine the best facilities available in both the digital and analog machines. The analog computer is faster than the digital computer for the same accuracy but analog computers are rarely made to achieve an accuracy of better than 0·1 per cent, indeed the cheaper commercial machines will only achieve 1 per cent overall accuracy. The digital machine possesses a memory and a decision-making capacity; it can also add and subtract and time-shift efficiently. The analog machine can integrate and multiply efficiently. Of course, interfacing is necessary and expensive A to D and D to A converters are required. Nevertheless, on certain data processing activities (e.g. cross-correlation and auto-correlation of signals recorded on magnetic tape) the hybrid machine may represent the most economic solution.

During the last few years attempts have been made to optimize the control of very complex process plants. The very expensive hybrid installation containing both a sizable digital machine and a sizable analog machine begins to prove its worth in such work. The digital computer provides a very potent method of organizing and controlling the very large number of analog computer runs which are usually required to indicate the optimum control system. It is unlikely that such hybrid installations will ever be cheap to buy or to run; at the time of writing a good, powerful system may cost in the order of a quarter of a million pounds.

15.10 Conclusions

Analog computation and simulation represents a rapid and relatively inexpensive means of checking out the design of a control system. Its accuracy is limited and under some circumstances it is better to use a digital machine for a longer period of time. Where expensive installations are possible the hybrid computer does offer a combination of speed of computation and organization which it is usually impossible to obtain using either type of computer by itself.

EXAMPLES FOR SOLUTION

1. Draw an analog computer flow diagram for the solution of the differential equation:

$$5\frac{d^2 y}{dt^2} + \frac{3\,dy}{dt} + 10y = 20$$

At $t = 0$, y and $\dot{y}$ are both zero.

2. Draw an analog computer flow diagram for the solution of the differential equation

$$6\frac{d^3 y}{dt^3} + 2\frac{d^2 y}{dt^2} + \frac{dy}{dt} + y = \sin 2t$$

Assume that at $t = 0$, $y = 0$, $\dot{y} = -1$, $\ddot{y} = +2$. Assume also that the third derivative is NOT required and thus devise your program with minimum number of amplifiers.

3. Produce a *time scaled* analog computer flow diagram for the solution of the differential equation

$$\frac{d^2 y}{dx^2} + 100\frac{dy}{dx} + 1000y = 10\sin 100x$$

Assume that computer time t is to be 10 times *slower* than real time x, i.e. $t = 10x$. Also assume *zero* initial conditions.

4. Use Jackson's method to amplitude scale the differential equation

$$250\frac{d^3 y}{dt^3} + 100\frac{d^2 y}{dt^2} + 50\frac{dy}{dt} + y = 120$$

Assume the initial conditions are zero and that the maximum machine voltage is 10 V. Draw a computer flow diagram of the scaled problem.

5. Prepare a computer flow diagram for the solution of the simultaneous differential equations:

$$5\frac{d^2 y}{dt^2} + 10\frac{dy}{dt} + \frac{dx}{dt} + x + y = e^{-t}$$

$$\frac{d^2 x}{dt^2} + 3\frac{dx}{dt} + 2\frac{dy}{dt} + 5y = 0$$

Assume that all the initial conditions are zero.

6. Prepare a computer flow diagram for solving the non-linear differential equation

$$\frac{d^2 y}{dt^2} + y\frac{dy}{dt} + y\left(\frac{dy}{dt}\right)^2 + y = 0$$

Assume that at $t = 0$, $\dot{y} = 0$ and $y = y_0$.

7. Draw a simulator flow diagram to simulate a control system having an open-loop transfer function

$$\frac{\theta_o}{\epsilon} = \frac{10}{D(1+2D)^2}$$

The system has *unity* feedback.

436

The Laplace Transforms

A.1 Introduction

There are many forms of operational calculus but the Laplace transformation is one that has been developed considerably and is well suited to the type of problems which occur in control engineering. The Laplace transformation permits a transformation from one domain to another through the use of the Laplace integral. In the analysis of linear control systems, the Laplace transform brings about a change from the time domain, in which the dynamical behaviour of the system is expressed in the differential equation, to a functional domain, in which the differential equation is expressed as an algebraic relationship. These functional expressions can be manipulated by the laws governing ordinary algebra, even though the variable is a complex quantity. After the original transformation, certain manipulations enable us to reorganize the mathematical forms and to perform an *inverse transformation* which returns the dynamical problem again to the time domain, but in such a manner that the solution to the original differential equation has been obtained.

A.2 Laplace Transform Symbolism

A distinction is made between a function of time and a function of the transform variable by the following definition or symbolism:

$$F(s) \triangleq Lf(t)$$

in which $F(s)$ is a function of the transform variable s, s is a complex variable of the form $\alpha + j\omega$, $\triangleq$ denotes equality by definition, L denotes application of transform integral, $f(t)$ is a function of time.

The transform integral, which is simply denoted above by the symbol L, in its complete form is

$$F(s) \triangleq \int_0^\infty f(t) e^{-st} dt$$

$F(s)$ is also often represented by $\bar{f}$.

The inverse transform is given by the integral

$$f(t) \triangleq \frac{1}{2\pi j} \int_{c-j\infty}^{c+j\infty} F(s) e^{ts} ds \quad \text{for} \quad t > 0$$

The process of inversion is often written as L^{-1}, i.e.

$$L^{-1} F(s) = f(t)$$

In the majority of problems encountered in control engineering $F(s)$ is a rational algebraic function, the ratio of two polynomials in s. The inverse transform can then be carried out by consulting published tables of Laplace-transform pairs.

Direct evaluation of the inverse transform is difficult.

A.3. Method of Solving Physical Problems

The routine method for solving physical problems is as follows:

(i) Use physical laws to formulate the differential equation of the system.

(ii) Use standard theorems to transform the differential equation taking into account the initial conditions; transform the driving function by reference to published tables.

(iii) Manipulate the resultant function of s using ordinary laws of algebra (particularly partial fractions) to break down the transform into a number of standard forms.

(iv) Use the published tables of transforms in the reverse direction so as to obtain a composite function of time $f(t)$; this function is the solution of the problem.

A.4 Illustrative Transforms

A.4.1 General

In order to use the method it is necessary to evolve a table of transform pairs. The method of doing this is illustrated in the examples shown below.

A.4.2 The Unit Step Function H(t)

This function has zero value for all negative values of time and is equal to unity for all positive values of time. It is sometimes represented by the symbol 1 or $H(t)$.

Now
$$Lf(t) \triangleq \int_0^\infty f(t)\,e^{-st}\,dt$$

$$\therefore \qquad LH(t) = \int_0^\infty 1 \cdot e^{-st}\,dt$$

$$= \left[-\frac{e^{-st}}{s} \right]_0^\infty$$

$$= \frac{1}{s}(-e^{-s\infty} + e^0)$$

$$= \frac{1}{s}$$

Thus
$$LH(t) = \frac{1}{s}$$

A.4.3 The Exponential Decay $f(t) = e^{-\alpha t}$

Here α may be real or complex

$$F(s) = \int_0^\infty e^{-\alpha t} e^{-st}\,dt = \int_0^\infty e^{-(s+\alpha)t}\,dt = \frac{1}{s+\alpha}$$

Thus
$$L(e^{-\alpha t}) = \frac{1}{s+\alpha}$$

A.4.4 Sinusoid $f(t) = \sin \omega t$

$$F(s) = \int_0^\infty \sin \omega t\, e^{-st}\,dt$$

$$= \frac{1}{2j} \int_0^\infty (e^{j\omega t} - e^{-j\omega t}) e^{-st}\,dt$$

$$= \frac{1}{2j} \int_0^\infty [e^{-(s-j\omega)t} - e^{-(s+j\omega)t}]\,dt$$

$$= \frac{1}{2j} \left(\frac{1}{s-j\omega} - \frac{1}{s+j\omega} \right)$$

$$= \frac{\omega}{s^2 + \omega^2}$$

Thus
$$L[\sin \omega t] = \frac{\omega}{s^2 + \omega^2}$$

A.5 Commonly Used Transform Theorems

A.5.1 General

In order to use the Laplace transform most successfully and economically it is necessary to apply certain theorems, the most important of which are given below.

A.5.2 Linearity Theorem

(1) If $Af(t)$ is a transformable function in which A is a constant, then,

$$L[Af(t)] = AL[f(t)] = AF(s)$$

(2) If $f_1(t)$ and $f_2(t)$ are transformable time functions, then

$$L[f_1(t) + f_2(t)] = F_1(s) + F_2(s)$$

A.5.3 Real Differentiation Theorem

If $f(t)$ is a transformable time function, then

$$L\left[\frac{d}{dt}f(t)\right] = sF(s) - f(0+)$$

The term 'real' in this case refers to the real domain or untransformed state. Also $f(0+)$ is the value of $f(t)$ at the instant immediately after $t = 0$.

Now

$$\int_0^\infty f(t)\,e^{-st}\,dt = F(s)$$

thus using the method of integration by parts, let $u = f(t)$ and $dv = e^{-st}dt$ in

$$\int u\,dv = uv - \int v\,du$$

This gives

$$\int_0^\infty f(t)\,e^{-st}\,dt = \left[-\frac{1}{s}f(t)\,e^{-st}\right]_0^\infty + \frac{1}{s}\int_0^\infty \left[\frac{df(t)}{dt}\right]e^{-st}\,dt$$

$$= \frac{f(0+)}{s} + \frac{1}{s}\int_0^\infty \left[\frac{df(t)}{dt}\right]e^{-st}\,dt$$

Rearranging terms and multiplying by s gives

$$\int_0^\infty \left[\frac{df(t)}{dt}\right]e^{-st}\,dt = s\int_0^\infty f(t)\,e^{-st}\,dt - f(0+)$$

Thus

$$L\left[\frac{d}{dt}f(t)\right] = sF(s) - f(0+)$$

Second derivatives may be treated as two first derivatives taken successively, hence

$$L\left[\frac{d^2 f(t)}{dt^2}\right] = L\left[\frac{d}{dt}\left(\frac{df(t)}{dt}\right)\right] = s^2 F(s) - sf(0+) - \frac{df}{dt}(0+)$$

In general

$$L\left[\frac{d^n}{dt^n}f(t)\right] = s^n F(s) - s^{n-1}f(0)$$
$$- s^{n-2}f'(0) - \ldots - f^{(n-1)}(0)$$

A.5.4 Real Integration Theorem

If $f(t)$ is a transformable time function, its time integral is also transformable and has the following form:

$$L\left[\int f(t)\,dt\right] = \frac{F(s)}{s} + \frac{1}{s}\left[\int f(t)\,dt\right]\Big|_{t=0+}$$

where

$$\left[\int f(t)\,dt\right]\Big|_{t=0+}$$

is the initial value of the integral [sometimes abbreviated to $f^{-1}(0+)$].

A.5.5 Final Value Theorem

If as t tends to infinity the $f(t)$ approaches some fixed value then the final value theorem will give that value:

$$\operatorname*{Limit}_{s\to0} sF(s) = \operatorname*{Limit}_{t\to\infty} f(t)$$

A.5.6 Initial Value Theorem

If as t tends to zero the $f(t)$ approaches some fixed value, than the initial value theorem will give that value:

$$\operatorname*{Limit}_{s\to\infty} sF(s) = \operatorname*{Limit}_{t\to0} f(t)$$

A.5.7 The Time Shift Theorem

In certain instances the transform of some function $f(t)$ is known and it is required to determine the transform of a function $f(t - \tau)$ which is simply a *time-delayed* version of the original function.

The time shift theorem allows direct determination of the transform of the time-delayed function:

if
$$Lf(t) = F(s)$$

then
$$Lf(t - \tau) = e^{-s\tau} F(s)$$

A.6 Table of Laplace Transforms

The table below summarizes some of the most useful theorems and transforms.

$L[f(t)]$ is defined by

$$\int_0^\infty f(t)\,e^{-st}\,dt$$

and is written as $F(s)$.

$f(t)$ from $t = 0$	$F(s) = L[f(t)]$
$\dfrac{d}{dt} f(t)$	$sF(s) - f(0)$
$\dfrac{d^n}{dt^n} f(t)$	$s^n F(s) - s^{n-1} f(0)$ $-s^{n-2} f'(0) \ldots -f^{(n-1)}(0)$
$\displaystyle\int_0^t f(t)\, dt$	$\dfrac{1}{s} F(s) + \dfrac{f^{-1}(0+)}{s}$
$f(t - \tau)$	$e^{-s\tau} F(s)$
$e^{-at} f(t)$	$F(s + \alpha)$
Unit impulse δ	1
Unit function 1 or $H(t)$	$\dfrac{1}{s}$
Ramp function t	$\dfrac{1}{s^2}$
$t^{n-1}/(n-1)!$	$\dfrac{1}{s^n}$
$\dfrac{t^{n-1}}{(n-1)!} e^{-at}$	$\dfrac{1}{(s + \alpha)^n}$
e^{-at}	$\dfrac{1}{(s + \alpha)}$
$1 - e^{-at}$	$\dfrac{\alpha}{s(s + \alpha)}$
$t e^{-at}$	$\dfrac{1}{(s + \alpha)^2}$
$e^{-at} - e^{-\beta t}$	$\dfrac{\beta - \alpha}{(s + \alpha)(s + \beta)}$
$\sin \omega t$	$\dfrac{\omega}{s^2 + \omega^2}$
$\cos \omega t$	$\dfrac{s}{s^2 + \omega^2}$
$1 - \cos \omega t$	$\dfrac{\omega^2}{s(s^2 + \omega^2)}$
$\omega t \sin \omega t$	$\dfrac{2\omega^2 s}{(s^2 + \omega^2)^2}$
$\sin \omega t - \omega t \cos \omega t$	$\dfrac{2\omega^2}{(s^2 + \omega^2)^2}$
$e^{-at} \sin \omega t$	$\dfrac{\omega}{(s + \alpha)^2 + \omega^2}$
$e^{-at} \cos \omega t$	$\dfrac{s + \alpha}{(s + \alpha)^2 + \omega^2}$
$e^{-at} \left(\cos \omega t - \dfrac{\alpha}{\omega} \sin \omega t \right)$	$\dfrac{s}{(s + \alpha)^2 + \omega^2}$
$\sin (\omega t + \phi)$	$\dfrac{s \sin \phi + \omega \cos \phi}{s^2 + \omega^2}$

$e^{-at} + (\alpha/\omega)\sin\omega t - \cos\omega t$	$\dfrac{\alpha^2 + \omega^2}{(s + \alpha)(s^2 + \omega^2)}$
$\sinh\beta t$	$\dfrac{\beta}{s^2 - \beta^2}$
$\cosh\beta t$	$\dfrac{s}{s^2 - \beta^2}$

A.7 Illustrative Example

Suppose it is required to find the solution to the differential equation

$$\frac{d^2 y}{dt^2} + 5\frac{dy}{dt} + 6y = 3t$$

for which at $t = 0$, $y = 2$, $\dfrac{dy}{dt} = -1$.

The left-hand side is transformed by rule according to the real differentiation theorem (as given in §A.5.3) and the linearity theorem (§A.5.2). Letting $\bar{y}$ be the Laplace transform of y we have:

$$L\left[\frac{d^2 y}{dt^2}\right] = (s^2\bar{y} - 2s + 1)$$

$$L\left[5\frac{dy}{dt}\right] = 5(s\bar{y} - 2)$$

and
$$L[6y] = 6\bar{y}$$

Then

$$(s^2\bar{y} - 2s + 1) + 5(s\bar{y} - 2) + 6\bar{y}$$

which simplifies to

$$\bar{y}(s^2 + 5s + 6) - (2s + 9)$$

The right-hand side or driving function may be transformed by using the table of §A.6 combined with the linearity theorem of §A.5.2. Thus the driving function transforms to $3/s^2$. We now equate the transform of the left-hand side to that of the right-hand side, hence

$$\bar{y}(s^2 + 5s + 6) - (2s + 9) = \frac{3}{s^2}$$

Thus
$$\bar{y}(s^2 + 5s + 6) = \frac{3}{s^2} + 2s + 9$$

or
$$\bar{y} = \frac{3 + 2s^3 + 9s^2}{s^2(s^2 + 5s + 6)}$$

In order to find the solution for y the inverse transform of the function of s must be found. Unless one happens to possess a very comprehensive table of transforms this function must be expanded into partial fractions for which the transform pairs are available. Thus

$$\bar{y} = \frac{A}{s^2} + \frac{B}{s} + \frac{C}{s+3} + \frac{D}{s+2}$$

The coefficients A, C and D are given directly by the 'cover-up rule', such that

$$A = \tfrac{1}{2}$$

$$C = -\tfrac{10}{3}$$

$$D = \tfrac{23}{4}$$

B may now be found by a variety of procedures; for instance putting s equal to 1 and equating the original function of s to the expanded version gives

$$B = -5/12$$

$$\therefore \qquad \bar{y} = \frac{1/2}{s^2} - \frac{5/12}{s} - \frac{10/3}{s+3} + \frac{23/4}{s+2}$$

The inverse transform is now found by using the table of transforms in reverse in combination with the linearity theorem. Thus

$$y = \frac{t}{2} - \frac{5}{12} - \frac{10\,e^{-3t}}{3} + \frac{23\,e^{-2t}}{4}$$

A.8 Application of the Laplace Transform to Control Engineering

A.8.1 The Proportional-to-error Servomechanism

The Laplace transform will be used to deduce the step response of the servomechanism with torque proportional to error which is described in chapter 8. As shown in §8.2 the differential equation for the system is given by

$$J\frac{d^2\theta_o}{dt^2} + F\frac{d\theta_o}{dt} + K\theta_o = K\theta_i$$

Assuming the system to be initially at rest, the initial conditions are at $t = 0$, $\theta_o = 0$ and $d\theta_o/dt = 0$. Suppose the input is a step of magnitude θ_i and that the system is underdamped [i.e. $F < 2\sqrt{(JK)}$]. Then transformation yields

$$Js^2\,\bar{\theta}_o + Fs\bar{\theta}_o + K\bar{\theta}_o = \frac{K\theta_i}{s}$$

where $\bar{\theta}_o$ is the Laplace transform of θ_o, i.e.

$$\bar{\theta}_o = \frac{K\theta_i}{s(Js^2 + Fs + K)}$$

$$= \frac{(K/J)\,\theta_i}{s\left(s^2 + \dfrac{F}{J}s + \dfrac{K}{J}\right)}$$

Since $F < 2\sqrt{(JK)}$ the quadratic term in the denominator cannot be factorized with real roots. It is therefore necessary to complete the square for this term, i.e.

$$\bar{\theta}_o = \frac{(K/J)\,\theta_i}{s\left\{\left(s + \dfrac{F}{2J}\right)^2 + \dfrac{K}{J} - \dfrac{F^2}{4J^2}\right\}}$$

Now let $\quad F/2J = \alpha \quad$ and $\quad \sqrt{\left\{\dfrac{K}{J} - \dfrac{F^2}{4J^2}\right\}} = \omega_r$

as in the nomenclature of chapter 8.

Thus $\qquad \bar{\theta}_o = \dfrac{(K/J)\,\theta_i}{s\{(s + \alpha)^2 + \omega_r^2\}}$

Expanding into partial fractions we have

$$\bar{\theta}_o = \frac{A}{s} + \frac{Bs + C}{(s + \alpha)^2 + \omega_r^2}$$

Using the 'cover-up rule' gives

$$A = \theta_i$$

Recombining the partial fractions we have

$$\bar{\theta}_o = \frac{\theta_i\{(s + \alpha)^2 + \omega_r^2\} + Bs^2 + Cs}{s\{(s + \alpha)^2 + \omega_r^2\}}$$

Equating the numerator of this fraction to the numerator of the original fraction yields

$$\theta_i\{(s + \alpha)^2 + \omega_r^2\} + Bs^2 + Cs = \frac{K\theta_i}{J}$$

$$\therefore \qquad \theta_i\{s^2 + 2\alpha s + \alpha^2 + \omega_r^2\} + Bs^2 + Cs = \frac{K\theta_i}{J}$$

Equating coefficients of s^2 yields

$$\theta_i + B = 0$$

$$\therefore \qquad B = -\theta_i$$

Equating coefficients of s yields

$$2\alpha\theta_i + C = 0$$

$$\therefore \qquad C = -2\alpha\theta_i$$

Returning to the original expansion we now have

$$\bar{\theta}_o = \frac{\theta_i}{s} - \frac{\theta_i s + 2\alpha\theta_i}{(s+\alpha)^2 + \omega_r^2}$$

$$= \frac{\theta_i}{s} - \frac{\alpha\theta_i}{(s+\alpha)^2 + \omega_r^2} - \frac{\theta_i s + \alpha\theta_i}{(s+\alpha)^2 + \omega_r^2}$$

$$= \frac{\theta_i}{s} - \frac{\alpha\theta_i}{\omega_r} \frac{\omega_r}{(s+\alpha)^2 + \omega_r^2} - \theta_i \frac{s+\alpha}{(s+\alpha)^2 + \omega_r^2}$$

Each fraction has been manipulated into a form for which the inverse is immediately recognizable from the table of §A.6.

Thus $$\theta_o = \theta_i - \frac{\alpha\theta_i}{\omega_r} e^{-\alpha t} \sin \omega_r t - \theta_i e^{-\alpha t} \cos \omega_r t$$

Further simplification using a trigonometric identity gives

$$\theta_o = \theta_i \left[1 - e^{-\alpha t} \sqrt{\left\{ 1 + \left(\frac{\alpha}{\omega_r} \right)^2 \right\}} \sin \left(\omega_r t + \tan^{-1} \frac{\omega_r}{\alpha} \right) \right]$$

This result is identical to that obtained in §8.3 in which the D-operator was used. The amount of algebra involved in using the Laplace transform is greater than that used for the identical problem solved by D-operator methods. The advantage of the Laplace method is in its mathematical rigour, and the simplicity with which the initial conditions are inserted. The Laplace method, unlike the D-operator method, is routine and is always the same regardless of the nature of the driving function. Its disadvantage is that the algebra becomes laborious unless a really comprehensive table of transforms is available.

A.8.2 Determination of Velocity lag using the Final Value Theorem

In §8.4, the steady-state error is determined which results from the application of a ramp input to the proportional-to-error servomechanism. The method used involves the D-operator. If, however, the Laplace transform is used it is advantageous to employ the final value theorem quoted in §A.5.5. It is shown in §8.4 that the proportional-to-error servomechanism can be described by the differential equation

$$J \frac{d^2 \epsilon}{dt^2} + F \frac{d\epsilon}{dt} + K\epsilon = J \frac{d^2 \theta_i}{dt^2} + F \frac{d\theta_i}{dt}$$

Let the input ramp be given by $d\theta_i/dt = \omega_i$.

The initial conditions at $t = 0$ will thus be $\epsilon = 0$ and $d\epsilon/dt = \omega_i$. Since $d^2 \theta_i/dt^2$ is always zero with this input the differential equation reduces to

$$J \frac{d^2 \epsilon}{dt^2} + F \frac{d\epsilon}{dt} + K\epsilon = F\omega$$

Transformation yields

$$J(s^2 \bar{\epsilon} - \omega_i) + Fs\bar{\epsilon} + K\bar{\epsilon} = \frac{F\omega_i}{s}$$

or

$$Js^2 \bar{\epsilon} + Fs\bar{\epsilon} + K\bar{\epsilon} = \frac{F\omega_i + sJ\omega_i}{s}$$

$\therefore$

$$\bar{\epsilon} = \frac{F\omega_i + sJ\omega_i}{s(Js^2 + Fs + K)}$$

The final value theorem gives

$$\underset{t\to\infty}{\text{Limit}}\,\epsilon = \underset{s\to 0}{\text{Limit}}\,s\bar{\epsilon}$$

i.e.

$$\underset{t\to\infty}{\text{Limit}}\,\bar{\epsilon} = \underset{s\to 0}{\text{Limit}}\left\{ \frac{s(F\omega_i + sJ\omega_i)}{s(Js^2 + Fs + K)} \right\}$$

$$= \frac{F\omega_i}{K}$$

But

$$\underset{t\to\infty}{\text{Limit}}\,\epsilon = \text{Steady-state error } \epsilon_{ss}$$

i.e.

$$\epsilon_{ss} = F\omega_i/K$$

This result agrees with that obtained in §8.4.

A.8.3 The Transfer Function

If a linear system has an output signal θ_o for which the Laplace transform is $\bar{\theta}_o$ in response to some input signal θ_i for which the Laplace transform is $\bar{\theta}_i$, then if *all* the initial conditions of the *system* are zero, the ratio $\bar{\theta}_o/\bar{\theta}_i$ is the *transfer function* of the system (see §9.1). The transfer function $\bar{\theta}_o/\bar{\theta}_i$ is often written as $\bar{\theta}_o/\bar{\theta}_i(s)$ to distinguish it from the other operator forms $\theta_o/\theta_i(D)$, $\theta_o/\theta_i(p)$ and $\theta_o/\theta_i(j\omega)$ and also to distinguish it from the time domain response $\theta_o/\theta_i(t)$ which is of course $L^{-1}\theta_o/\theta_i(s)$. In §9.2.4 it is shown that a field-controlled d.c. motor has a transfer function

$$\frac{\theta_o}{\theta_i}(D) = \frac{K/FR_f}{D(T_m D + 1)(T_f D + 1)}$$

To obtain $\theta_o/\theta_i(s)$ we can always simply replace D by s,

thus

$$\frac{\theta_o}{\theta_i}(s) = \frac{K/FR_f}{s(T_m s + 1)(T_f s + 1)}$$

The various methods of determining the overall open- and closed-loop transfer functions of multiloop systems as described in §9.7 are equally applicable when the Laplace variable s is used in place of the operator D. The substitution $j\omega = s$ for steady-state sinusoids is equally valid.

A.8.4 The Dirac Impulse and the Impulse Response

The Laplace Transform of a Dirac Impulse

A 'perfect' impulse has an infinite height and zero duration. A practical impulse (called a Dirac impulse function δ) is a pulse of height A and duration T such that the area TA is unity and T is very small [see Fig. 2.4 (a)] compared with the response time of the system to which the impulse is applied.

$$L[\delta] = \int_0^T A \, e^{-st} \, dt$$

$$= -\frac{A}{s} [e^{-st}]_0^T$$

$$= -\frac{A}{s} (e^{-sT} - 1)$$

The exponential term may be expanded as a power series in sT, thus

$$L[\delta] = -\frac{A}{s} \left(1 - sT + \frac{(sT)^2}{2} - \text{etc.} - 1 \right)$$

$\therefore$ as $T \to 0$, $L[\delta] \to 1$.

Impulse Response of a System

If a system has a transfer function

$$\frac{\theta_o}{\theta_i}(s) = H(s)$$

Then $$\bar{\theta}_o = H(s) . \bar{\theta}_i$$

But if θ_i is a δ function, $\bar{\theta}_i = 1$,

$\therefore$ $$\bar{\theta}_o = H(s)$$

This is an important concept which may be stated in words as follows:

The transfer function of a system expressed as a function of the Laplace variable s is the Laplace transform of its impulse response.

A.9 Convolution

The Laplace transform of the output of a linear system is the product of the system transfer function and the transform of the input time function, i.e.

$$\theta_o(s) = H(s) \times \theta(s)$$

where $H(s)$ is the transfer function of the system.

Whereas in systems for which the function $H(s)$ is known and rational it is possible by inversion to find $\theta_o(t)$ for a transformable input $\theta_i(t)$, there are many occasions in practice where only the impulse response of the system in the time domain is known (possibly in numerical rather than analytical form). In such instances it is not usually possible to apply the Laplace transform method; however, the convolution integral may then be used. This integral is sometimes stated as

$$\theta_o(t) = \int_0^\infty h(x)\,\theta_i(t-x)\,\mathrm{d}x$$

Here x is a time delay and $h(x)$ is the impulse response of the system as a function of the time delay.

The alternative form of the convolution integral

$$\theta_o(t) = \int_0^\infty \theta_i(x)\,h(t-x)\,\mathrm{d}x$$

The use of the infinite upper limit can lead to errors when one is dealing with a function of time $\theta_i(t)$ which is zero for $t < 0$. Thus when using the convolution integral to solve problems in which such signals occur it is advisable to incorporate the implied limit by redefining the upper limit as $x = t$.

The two forms of the convolution integral then become

$$\theta_o(t) = \int_0^t h(x)\,\theta_i(t-x)\,\mathrm{d}x$$

or

$$\theta_o(t) = \int_0^t \theta_i(x)\,h(t-x)\,\mathrm{d}x$$

Worked Example

A linear device having an impulse response e^{-t} is supplied with a ramp input signal θ_i given by

$$\theta_i = 3t$$

where t is time.

Use the convolution integral to determine the output θ_o of the device assuming that no input signal is applied before the instant $t = 0$.

Solution

The impulse response $h(t)$ of the device is given by

$$h(t) = e^{-t}$$

$\therefore$ $\qquad\qquad h(x) = e^{-x}$

Also $\qquad\qquad \theta_i(t) = 3t$

$\therefore$ $\qquad\qquad \theta_i(t-x) = 3(t-x) \text{ for } t > 0$

449

Now using convolution we have

$$\theta_o = \int_0^\infty \theta_i(t - x)\, h(x)\, dx$$

$\therefore$ since $\theta_i = 0$ for $t < 0$,

$$\theta_o = \int_0^t 3(t - x)\, e^{-x}\, dx$$

Integrating by parts we have

$$\theta_o = [-3(t - x)\, e^{-x}]_0^t - \int_0^t 3\, e^{-x}\, dx$$

$$= [-3(t - x)\, e^{-x}]_0^t + [3\, e^{-x}]_0^t$$

$$= 3t + 3\, e^{-t} - 3$$

A.10 Conclusion

This appendix contains an introduction to the method of Laplace transforms together with a brief survey of the more important theorems. A few elementary problems are solved for comparison with the D-operator method used in the main text of this book. In the elementary study of control systems the Laplace transform has little to offer when compared with the D-operator method owing to the laboriousness of the algebra involved in the inversion. The use of the Laplace variable s as an algebraic quantity in transfer function analysis is identical to the use of the D-operator. In the more advanced work on control systems the Laplace transform begins to show its advantages (see for example Truxal, J. G. *Control System Synthesis*, McGraw-Hill, New York, 1955).

Although the important and fundamental concept of *convolution* is quite independent of the theory of the Laplace transform it is included in this appendix for the sake of completeness.

References

1. MAXWELL, J. CLARK. 'On Governers', *Proceedings of the Royal Society* (London, 16 (1868), pp. 270–283).
2. TRINKS, W. *Governers and the Governing of Prime Movers* (Princeton, New Jersey: D. Van Nostrand Co., 1868).
3. DRAPER, C. S. and LI, Y. T. 'Principles of Optimalizing Control Systems and an Application to the Internal Combustion Engine', *Transactions of the American Society of Marine Engineers* (U.S.A., Sept. 1951).
4. MISHKIN, E. and BRAUN, L., JR. (Editors). *Adaptive Control Systems* (New York: McGraw Hill, 1961).
5. GEARY, A., LOWRY, H. V. and HAYDEN, H. A. *Advanced Mathematics for Technical Students, Part 1* (London: Longmans, Green and Co., 1945).
6. HUMPHREY, D. *Intermediate Mechanics–Dynamics* (London: Longmans, Green and Co., 1930).
7. RAMSEY, A. S. *Dynamics, Part 1* (Cambridge: Cambridge University Press, 1933).
8. PIAGGIO, H. T. H. *Differential Equations* (London: G. Bell and Sons Ltd., 1952).
9. GARDNER, M. F. and BARNES, J. L. *Transients in Linear Systems* (New York: J. Wiley & Sons, Inc., 1942).
10. GOLDMAN, S. *Transformation Calculus and Electrical Transients* (New Jersey: Prentice-Hall Inc., 1949).
11. THALER, G. J. and BROWN, R. G. *Analysis and Design of Feedback Control Systems, Second Edition* (New York: McGraw Hill, 1960).
12. GIBSON, J. E. and TUTEUR, F. B. *Control System Components* (New York: McGraw Hill, 1958).
13. DAVIS, S. A. and LEDGERWOOD, B. K. *Electromechanical Components for Servomechanisms* (New York: McGraw Hill, 1961).
14. INGLIS, C. E. *Applied Mechanics for Engineers* (Cambridge: Cambridge University Press, 1951).
15. FROST-SMITH, E. H. *Theory and Design of Magnetic Amplifiers* (London: Chapman and Hall, 1958).
16. TUSTIN, A. *Direct Current Machines for Control Systems* (London: Spon, 1952).
17. DUNCAN, J. *Applied Mechanics for Engineers* (London: Macmillan and Co. Ltd., 1926).
18. CLAYTON, A. E. and SHELLEY, H. J. *Elementary Electrical Engineering* (London: Longmans, Green & Co., 1953).
19. EVANS, W. R. *Control System Dynamics* (New York: McGraw Hill Book Co. Inc., 1954).
20. BROWN, G. S. and CAMPBELL, D. P. *Principles of Servomechanisms* (New York: J. Wiley & Sons, Inc., 1948).
21. NYQUIST, H. 'Regeneration Theory', *Bell System Tech. Journal* (Vol. 11, pp. 126–147 Jan., 1932).
22. BOWER, J. L. and SCHULTHEISS, P. M. *Introduction to the Design of Servomechanisms* (New York; J. Wiley & Sons, Inc., 1958).
23. BODE, H. W. *Network Analysis and Feedback Amplifier Design* (Princeton, New Jersey: D. Van Nostrand Co., 1945).
24. DOUCE, J. L. *An Introduction to the Mathematics of Servomechanisms* (London: E.U.P., 1963).

451

Answers to Examples for Solution

CHAPTER 2

2. Half cycle mean value $\frac{\theta}{2}$; r.m.s. value $\frac{\theta}{\sqrt{3}}$

3. $\theta = A_1 + A_2(1 - e^{-t/T})$

4. Instantaneous value $= 14 \cdot 14 \sin 628t$. (a) 10 units; (b) $13 \cdot 07$ units

5. $\theta_R = 5 \cdot 44 \sin(\omega t + 1 \cdot 32)$; r.m.s. value $= 3 \cdot 85$

6. $4 \cdot 44 \sin(\omega t + 2 \cdot 7)$

CHAPTER 3

1. (i) $-9 - j5$
    (ii) $11 - j3$
    (iii) $4 + j3$
    (iv) $-17 - j7$
    (v) $5 \cdot 5 \, e^{j2 \cdot 65}$

2. (i) $21 - j17$
    (ii) $21 - j17$
    (iii) $-50 + j30$
    (iv) $\dfrac{-9 - j37}{29}$
    (v) $0 \cdot 9 + j1 \cdot 7$
    (vi) $\dfrac{18 + j11}{89}$
    (vii) $\dfrac{30 - j6}{72}$
    (viii) $0 - j30$
    (ix) $2 \cdot 43 \, e^{-j1 \cdot 375}$
    (x) $\dfrac{23 - 11j}{50}$

3. $20 \cdot 8 \text{p}$

452

4. (a) $(8\cdot42 + j4\cdot5)\,e^{j\omega t}$ or $9\cdot5\cos(\omega t + 0\cdot492) + j9\cdot5(\sin\omega t + 0\cdot492)$
   (b) $9\cdot5\,e^{j(\omega t + 0\cdot492)}$.
   (c) $9\cdot5\sin(\omega t + 0\cdot492)$

5. (a) $40\cdot88\,e^{j(\omega t + 1\cdot47)}$
   (b) $40\cdot88\sin(\omega t + 1\cdot47)$

6. (i) $\pm(-4\cdot25 + j2\cdot47)$
   (ii) $\pm(0\cdot494 + j0\cdot381)$
   (iii) $\pm(1\cdot6 - j2\cdot21)$

CHAPTER 4

1. (i) 39 m/s
   (ii) 16 m/s²

2. (i) 20 m/s
   (ii) 8·67 m

3. 12 m/s²

4. 5000 N

5. (i) 40 m/s
   (ii) −800 m/s²

6. Velocity = 47·8 m/s
   Acceleration = 5·01 m/s²

7. 20·45 kW

8. 26·6 MW

9. 19·7 kW, 157 sec

10. Radius of gyration = 4·57 m
    $\omega = 5\cdot64$ rad/s

11. 31·4 kW

12. $27\cdot8 \times 10^5$ J

13. (a) 0·3 A
    (b) 36 C

14. 625 Ω

15. 36×10^6 C

16. (i) 1·82 A
    (ii) 9·1 V

17. (i) 1·5 kΩ
    (ii) 1·6 W
    (iii) 40 V

18. 100 μWb

19. 0·18 V

20. 0·166 H

21. 20 kA/s

22. $5i + 2\dfrac{di}{dt} = 100$

23. Sensitivity $= 4\cdot 8$ degrees/mA

24. 1×10^{-3} C

25. $10\dfrac{di}{dt} + i = 0$

CHAPTER 5

1.   (i) $\theta_t = e^{3t}(A\cos 2t + B\sin 2t)$
   (ii) $\theta_t = Ae^t + Be^{2t} + Ce^{3t}$
  (iii) $\theta_t = Ae^{-0\cdot 5t} + Be^{-2t}$
  (iv) $\theta_t = A\cos 2t + B\sin 2t$
   (v) $\theta_t = A + Be^{-4t}$
  (vi) $\theta_t = (A + Bt)e^{-3t}$

2.   (i) $\theta_{ss} = 0$
   (ii) $\theta_{ss} = 2$
  (iii) $\theta_{ss} = 2t + A$
  (iv) $\theta_{ss} = \frac{1}{2}$
   (v) $\theta_{ss} = 6t^2 - 6t + 3$
  (vi) $\theta_{ss} = t^2 - \frac{1}{2}$
 (vii) $\theta_{ss} = 2e^{2t}$
(viii) $\theta_{ss} = \frac{50}{6}e^{2t}$
  (ix) $\theta_{ss} = 4\cdot 48\sin(2t - 1\cdot 108)$
   (x) $\theta_{ss} = 7\cdot 07\sin(4t - 3\cdot 925)$

3.   (i) $\theta = \frac{2}{3}e^{-t} - \frac{2}{3}e^{-4t}$
   (ii) $\theta = \cos 3t - 0\cdot 467\sin 3t + 0\cdot 2\sin 2t$
  (iii) $\theta = 3e^{-3t} + e^{-2t}$
  (iv) $\theta = \frac{3}{8}\sin 2t + \dfrac{t}{4}$
   (v) $\theta = e^{-2t} + e^{-t} - e^{-3t}$
  (vi) $\theta = \frac{1}{2}e^{-5t} - \frac{5}{2}e^{-t} + 2$

CHAPTER 6

1.   (i) $m\dfrac{d^2 x_o}{dt^2} + f\dfrac{dx_o}{dt} + kx = kx_1$

  (ii) $x_o = x_1\left[1 - \left\{1 + \sqrt{\left(\dfrac{k}{m}\right)}t\right\}e^{-\sqrt{(k/m)t}}\right]$

2. 3·23 Nm per rad/s

3. $\sqrt{\dfrac{J_1}{J_m}}$

4. (i) $2\dfrac{d^2\theta_o}{dt^2} + 4\cdot9\dfrac{d\theta_o}{dt} + 3\theta_o = 3\sin 0\cdot1\pi t$

    (ii) $\theta_{o\,ss} = 0\cdot938\sin(0\cdot314t - 0\cdot5026)$

5. (i) $i = \dfrac{2}{10^6}(1 - e^{-t/2})\,\text{A}$

    (ii) $v_r = 4(1 - e^{-t/2})\,\text{V}$

    (iii) $v_c = 2t + 4(e^{-t/2} - 1)\,\text{V}$

6. $i = 1\cdot155\,e^{-500t}\sin 866t\,\text{mA}$

7. $39\cdot1$ sec

8. (i) $1 - 0\cdot200024\dfrac{d\theta_m}{dt} = 0\cdot10001\dfrac{d^2\theta_m}{dt^2}$

    (ii) $4\cdot9994/500$ rad/s

    (iii) $2\cdot5$ sec

CHAPTER 7

1. (b) $0\cdot027$ rad

2. (ii) $n = \dfrac{V_1}{3\cdot5} - \dfrac{T}{14}$

    (iii) $28\cdot6$ rev/s, $0\cdot374\%$

    (iv) None

3. (ii) $\omega = \dfrac{200V_1}{101} - \dfrac{2T}{101}$

    (iii) 200 rad/s

    (iv) $0\cdot099\%$

4. (i) $V_o = \dfrac{1000}{1007}V_i - \dfrac{21}{1007}I_o$

    (ii) $99\cdot3$ V

    (iii) $0\cdot42\%$

    (iv) $0\cdot691\%$

5. (b) (i) $0\cdot0293$ rad/s

    (ii) $0\cdot0224$ rad/s

6. 211 Nm/rad

CHAPTER 8

1. $8° 12'$

2. $0\cdot0143$ rad

3. $2\cdot76$ c/s

4. (i) The transient response is oscillatory

    (ii) $34° 57'$

5. $\theta_o = 2\cdot1t - 0\cdot61\left\{1 + 1\cdot41\,e^{-t}\sin\left(2\cdot42t - \dfrac{\pi}{4}\right)\right\}$

6. $\epsilon_{ss} = 0\cdot132$ rad

7. $K = 12 \cdot 4$ Nm/rad
   $F = 3 \cdot 22$ Nm per rad/s

8. (iii) $2 \cdot 34 \times 10^{-3} \sec^2$
   (iv) $3°$

9. (i) $\epsilon_{ss} = \dfrac{(F + k_t k_v) \, \omega_i}{k_t}$
   (ii) $k_v = \dfrac{2\sqrt{(Jk_t)} - F}{k_t}$

10. (ii) $6°$

11. $\omega_n = 25 \cdot 1$ rad/s
    $\zeta = 1 \cdot 414$

12. $\zeta = 0 \cdot 592$
    $M_{pf} = 1 \cdot 05$
    $\omega_n = 21 \cdot 7$ rad/s
    $\omega_{rf} = 11 \cdot 8$ rad/s

13. (i) $(JD + K)\omega_o = K\omega_i$
    (ii) $\omega_o = \omega_i(1 - e^{-Kt/J})$
    (iii) $3 \cdot 912$ sec, $2 \cdot 932$ rad

CHAPTER 9

1. (i) $\dfrac{\theta_o}{\epsilon}(D) = \dfrac{K}{D(D + 1)^2}$
   (ii) $0 < K < 2$

2. (a) $\dfrac{V_o}{V_i}(D) = \dfrac{K}{1 + DT}$
   (b) $-\dfrac{1}{K^3} < \mu < \dfrac{8}{K^3}$

3. $Fk_1 > Jk_2$

4. $0 < K < 100$

5. (ii) Open loop $\dfrac{\theta_o}{\epsilon}(D) = \dfrac{500}{D(1 + D)(1 + 0 \cdot 0005D)}$
   Closed loop $\dfrac{\theta_o}{\theta_i}(D) = \dfrac{500}{D(1 + D)(1 + 0 \cdot 0005D) + 500}$
   (iii) System is stable
   (iv) $0 \cdot 00209$ rad

6. $\dfrac{\theta_o}{\theta_i}(D) = \dfrac{K_1(1 + T_3 D)}{D(1 + T_1 D)(1 + T_2 D)(1 + T_3 D) + k_1 k_2 D^2 + k_1(1 + T_3 D)}$

7. $\dfrac{\theta_o}{\theta_i} = [(H_1^{-1} + H_6)\{H_2^{-1} H_3^{-1}(H_4^{-1} + H_5)\} + 1]^{-1}$

CHAPTER 10

1. (i) Absolutely stable
   (ii) Absolutely stable
   (iii) Absolutely stable
   (iv) Absolutely stable
   (v) Unstable on closed loop
   (vi) Absolutely stable
   (vii) Unstable on closed loop
   (viii) Unstable on closed loop

3. Gain margin 6·02 dB
   Phase margin 21·4°

4. Gain margin 12·8 dB
   Phase margin 26·8°

5. (b) $H(j\omega) = \dfrac{5}{j\omega(1 + j\omega)(1 + 0·1j\omega)}$

6. Absolutely stable on closed loop
   Phase margin 3·5°
   Gain margin 1·96 dB
   This system is relatively unstable

7. (ii) $H(j\omega) = \dfrac{40·5}{(j\omega)(1 + 0·0169j\omega)(1 + 0·25j\omega)}$
   (iii) Phase margin 6·3°
   Gain margin 3·87 dB

8. (i) 14·3
   (ii) 2·74
   (iii) 0·27

CHAPTER 11

1. $H(j\omega) = \dfrac{12(1 + j\omega0·245)}{j\omega(1 + j\omega0·2)(1 + j\omega0·05)(1 + j\omega0·0294)}$
   ($K' = 12$ sec^{-1}, $T_d = 0·245$ sec, $G_o = 0·12$)

2. $H(j\omega) = \dfrac{0·0415(1 + j\omega13·7)}{(j\omega)^2(1 + j\omega)(1 + j\omega0·1)(1 + j\omega0·288)}$
   ($K' = 0·0415$ sec^{-2}, $T_d = 13·7$ sec, $G_o = 0·0209$)

3. $H(j\omega) = \dfrac{100(1 + j1·25\omega)}{(1 + j\omega)(1 + j\omega0·3)(1 + j\omega0·1)(1 + j\omega41·9)}$
   ($K' = 100$, $T_d = 1·25$ sec, $G_\infty = 33·6$)

CHAPTER 12

1. $K = 235$ sec^{-1}, $k_s = 0·0208$ sec

2. $T = 0·371$ sec, $k_s = 0·317$ sec

3. $K = 0·438$ sec^{-1}, $k_a = 2·37$ sec^{-2}

CHAPTER 13

1. (i) Infinity, 35°, 2·9 rad/s, 1·66
    (ii) 19·2 dB, 45°, 10·0 rad/s, 1·31
    (iii) 34·4 dB, 51°, 1·5 rad/s, 1·17
    (iv) 12 dB, 45·4°, 13 rad/s, 1·34
    (v) 12 dB, 40°, 2·9 rad/s, 1·5
    (vi) Infinity, 44°, 120 rad/s, 1·34
    (vii) Infinity, 21°, 1·0 rad/s, 2·87

2. (i) 2.7 sec^{-1}, 1·8 rad/s
    (ii) $G_o = 0·163$, $T_d = 0·165$ sec, $K' = 55$ sec^{-1}
    (iii) $G_\infty = 20$, $T_d = 4·37$ sec, $K' = 20$ sec^{-1}

3. $\dfrac{\theta_o}{\epsilon}(j\omega) = \dfrac{0·27(1 + j\omega4)}{(j\omega)^2(1 + j\omega0·25)^2}$

    $\omega_{rf} = 0·75$ rad/s
    $M_{pf} = 1·3$

CHAPTER 14

1. $\dfrac{5K_1}{D(1 + 10D)(1 + D/12)}$ (time constants in minutes)

    $D(1 + 10D)(1 + D/12) + 5K_1 = 0$

    $0 < K_1 < 2·42$

2. Stable on closed loop
    Gain margin 19·8 dB
    Phase margin 111·8°

3. 20%

4. 2·78%
    5·65 rad/min
    0·027

5. $\dfrac{p_c}{m} = \dfrac{b}{aKT_i} \cdot \dfrac{(1 + T_d D)(1 + T_i D)}{D}$

    where K is the stiffness of the bellows

    Effective proportional control factor $= \dfrac{b(T_d + T_i)}{aKT_i}$

    Effective integral action time $= T_d + T_i$

    Effective derivative action time $= \dfrac{T_d T_i}{T_d + T}$

6. $T_d = 1·94$ min
    $T_i = 5·82$ min
    P = 66%

Index

465